MY YEAR OF SAYING NO

MAXINE MORREY

Boldwood

First published in Great Britain in 2020 by Boldwood Books Ltd.

I

A CIP catalogue record for this book is available from the British Library.

Paperback ISBN: 978-1-80048-142-8

Ebook ISBN: 978-1-83889-038-4

Kindle ISBN: 978-1-83889-034-6

Audio CD ISBN: 978-1-83889-035-3

Digital audio download ISBN: 978-1-83889-036-0

Large Print ISBN: 978-1-83889-732-1

Boldwood Books Ltd.

23 Bowerdean Street, London, SW6 3TN

www.boldwoodbooks.com

For Jo P
Your support and enthusiasm for the books means so much, and your
wonderful friendship means even more. Love and hugs.

1

I inhaled deeply, sucking in a big lungful of grimy London air as I finally squeezed myself out of the rowdy, celebratory throng who were now linking arms with each other and making up random words to 'Auld Lang Syne'. The air was sharply cold and dry and I shivered as it cooled me from both outside and within. Slumping down on to a garden bench, I let out a breath in a long, slow release, watching it cool and cloud in front of me. It was over.

'Fancy starting the new year off with a bang?' My questioner let out a braying laugh, amused by his own clever repartee before punctuating the question with a loud belch.

I looked up at the man, his tie askew, expensive suit quite possibly ruined by whatever that was he'd spilt down it, and tilted my chin up.

'That would absolutely, most definitely, be a no.'

I stood and walked past him back into the party, found my coat and left, closing the door behind me. Thank god. The Year of Saying Yes was finally over.

* * *

Admittedly, on paper, it had seemed like a good idea. Jess, my best friend, certainly seemed to think so. After seven years with the man I had assumed I would one day marry, we'd both realised that that would, in reality, probably be a very bad idea. It wasn't that we didn't care for each other any more, but something had changed. Neither of us could put our finger on what, or when, but there was no denying it had happened. Being together had turned into more of a habit than a passion and that was not a strong enough foundation to build a marriage on.

Of course, just because we both felt the same way, and there hadn't been any dramatic bust-up or throwing of dishes, didn't mean it wasn't sad. We'd had dreams and plans and realising that those hadn't come to fruition, and now never would, was still heart-breaking.

Jess had tried to encourage me to get out and meet new people, but I was in no mood for company. I'd had to say goodbye to something that had been a big part of my life and I needed time to grieve. Once again, I'd been thankful for my job as an online virtual assistant. I still did all the tasks I'd done before when employed as a Personal Assistant to an Executive – skills I'd honed over the years and was good at. But striking out on my own and going 'virtual' had been the best thing I could have done. The thought of having to go into an office, with everyone knowing your business, and gossiping about it behind your back, still made me shiver. But for the last couple of years I hadn't had to deal with any of that office-politics rubbish and I couldn't have been happier about it. Also, I got to wear pyjamas to work. I mean, if that isn't a major perk, I don't know what is.

Setting up my own business had been a bit scary, of course, but I'd started small and on my own time, working in an office in the day and on my own company in the evenings and weekends. It was exhausting at times, but I kept my goal in sight and that magical day when I was able to hand in my notice and hang up my suits was utter bliss. Life was good! And then it wasn't.

Jess had let me mope for a couple of weeks and then got bored. Which sums Jess up. Her attention span is not the longest, but it's a quirk that makes her fun and spontaneous and I wouldn't change her for anything.

'OK,' she'd begun with a mouthful of the spaghetti carbonara I'd cooked for us both one Friday night a little while after I'd moved into my own flat, and my newly single life. 'Time to move on. God, that's so good. You need to give me the recipe.'

'You don't cook anything, apart from cakes.'

'I might start one day.'

I couldn't argue with that, so I nodded and hoped the carbonara had been enough to distract her from whatever it was she'd been planning on saying. It wasn't. I was good, but not that good.

'Agreed?'

'Huh?'

'That it's time to move on.'

'I'm not stuck.'

'You kind of are.'

'No, I'm just... here. And I'm OK with that. I'm not mooning over Tom and what might have been. I'm fine, really.'

Despite what Jess thought, I truly was content with my current situation.

'You're bored.'

'No, I'm not.'

'OK. Let me put it another way. You're being boring.'

'Thanks.'

'It's said with love!' She grinned at me as she forked up some more dinner.

My mouth full, I responded by arching an eyebrow.

'I know what!' Jess said, her fork suddenly clattering against the side of the pasta bowl. 'Oh my god, this is totally brilliant!'

I had my reservations and I hadn't even heard the idea yet. I had, however, known my friend a very long time, so against my better judgement I let her continue.

'I've had nothing but bad dates this year, and you're suddenly single after, like, forever.'

'Not exactly forever.'

She waved a perfectly manicured hand at me, dismissing my protest. 'So, next year – basically in two weeks' time, on the first of January, we begin the year that's going to change our lives!'

I gave a mental eye roll. 'Change our lives?' I asked, not too worried. Jess had gone to drama school and although she ran a PR firm now, the training, and her natural inclination towards the dramatic, had never disappeared.

'Yes! Next year is going to be The Year of Saying Yes!' She threw her hands out and her head back like she'd just finished a West End show and was, apparently, waiting for the applause to begin.

I chased the last of the spaghetti around my bowl instead.

'Well?' Jess asked, looking slightly annoyed.

'Well, what?'

'What do you think about my plan?'

'Go for it, if you want. Sounds like something you'd enjoy.'

'It's a joint plan. For me. And you.'

It definitely didn't sound like something I'd enjoy. Quite the opposite in fact. I enjoyed the quiet life. I worked in my pyjamas for goodness' sake, and it suited me perfectly. The Year of Saying Yes, I knew, would not.

'Oh. I'm not sure it's something I'm ready to embark on just yet. But you should totally go for it.' I hoped that encouraging Jess to pursue her latest idea would distract her from remembering that I was supposed to be a part of it. It was a tactic I had employed in the past on several occasions to good effect. Unfortunately, she seemed to have cottoned on.

'Oh no, you don't! Not this time! This is something we're doing together!'

'Jess. I really don't want to.'

'That's because you've forgotten how to have fun!'

'I have not! I just have a different concept of what's fun than you do! Bars and dating apps are not my idea of fun. You know that.'

'I didn't say it was only going to be bars and dating apps.'

Which clearly meant they were definitely still included. This was not good.

'Look,' Jess said, calming down a little and taking my hand. 'You've had a rough time, and you were in the same relationship for a long while. Let's take the opportunity to do some fun things together. It's not necessarily about meeting someone else. It's more about adventure, getting out there, grabbing hold of life and saying "OK, show me what you've got!"'

What I had was indigestion.

* * *

'How bad can it be?' Seb asked when I told him the day after New Year's Day as we had a catch-up Skype meeting.

'Bad,' I said, laying my head on the desk so that he was left looking at the top of my head. 'Very, very bad.'

'Things often seem worse than they really are at first.'

I made a noise that could have been agreement but most definitely wasn't.

'What's the scar from?'

'Huh?' I asked, pulling my head back up to look at the screen.

Seb tapped the top of his head. 'Little scar. There.'

'Oh,' I put my hand over it automatically. 'I was playing tug of war at primary school and hadn't quite learned all the laws of physics yet. When I let go, I went flying back into some railings and cut my head open.'

'Whoops.'

'Yeah. Jess had a right meltdown!' I laughed, remembering back to those playground days. 'She's always been a bit of a drama queen, in a good way though. But I think I properly traumatised her, with blood pouring down my face. She was screaming her head off.'

'And what were you doing?'

'Asking her to shoosh because I had a headache!' I grinned at him and, as he returned it, my tummy did a little flip. OK, a big flip. It really was inconvenient to have quite such a huge crush on my biggest client, but I couldn't help it. It was just there. And I'd been dealing with it just fine. After all, lots of people have crushes. An incredibly happily married friend of ours admitted to a huge crush on one of their kid's teachers. Her husband knows and isn't worried. It's just one of those things that happen in life, and Seb is my secret crush. Even Jess doesn't know about it. I am professionalism personi-fied with my work, except with Seb, with whom it is a little more relaxed. The veterans' charity he ran had been my first full time client and was still a major part of my workload. Most clients I caught up with over email, by message, or occasionally the phone, but Seb had asked from the start if we could catch up face to face, as it were. I'd agreed and prepared for the first meeting as I would have done for one in my old job – smartly dressed, with make-up and hair all done. But the moment Seb had come up on the screen, given me a wave and smiled that smile, all the formality seemed unnecessary. Don't get me wrong, we got the work done, but there had never been any awkwardness, and there was a lot of laughter which, after my last job, I was both surprised at and very glad about. Today, though, even Seb's smile couldn't unknot the tangle in my tummy at the thought of Jess' plan.

'So, explain to me again. What exactly does this Year of Saying Yes entail? You have to say yes to everything?'

'Pretty much.'

He paused. 'Even if you don't want to?'

'Especially if I don't want to, which, bearing in mind it's me, is going to be pretty much all the time!'

He frowned, then nodded. 'You know you don't have to do this, don't you? You have a choice.'

'I have already agreed now. After the third glass of wine, it didn't seem like such a bad idea. Now I've had time to think about it in the cold and sober light of day, it seems like a terrible one!'

'So, cancel.'

'I gave Jess my word I wouldn't.'

'She'll understand.'

'You don't know Jess. Also, when you give someone your word, I'd bet my eleven o'clock doughnut you don't go back on it.'

'You have doughnuts?'

I leant over and then waggled the bag of Sainsbury's jam doughnuts at him.

'Lottie. That's not one, that's a bag of five!'

'Well, they do say it's important to have your five a day.'

'Yeah, I'm pretty sure they're not referring to doughnuts.'

I shrugged. 'You wouldn't though, would you?'

'OK, no. But I'd also probably not have agreed to something whilst half cut either.'

I snorted into my mug of tea. 'Must be hard work being so angelic.'

His eyes sparkled with amusement. 'It's got nothing to do with being angelic.'

I flicked a glance at the screen. Seb's dark eyes and cropped hair were complemented by him being broad and well-built and, although the T-shirt he wore wasn't close fitting, there was no hiding the fact there was a pretty damn good body beneath it. It wasn't exactly hard to imagine that angelic was quite the opposite of what he might be. If ever a body was made for sin, I was pretty sure I was looking at it right now.

I hid my face in the huge mug for a moment. Imagining anything with regards to Seb was probably not a good idea. The last thing I needed was for him to find out I thought he was almost as delicious as those doughnuts. Possibly more so.

'Anyway. I've agreed, so I've just got to get on with it now.'

Seb gave me a considered look and nodded. 'I guess so.'

* * *

'Well, you look happier than you did this time last year.' Seb grinned at me when I answered the video call, pulling my knees up to my chest as I hugged a mug of ginger tea. 'Happy New Year, again, by the way.'

'And to you, and thanks for the message on New Year's Eve. I'd just had the most awful proposition. I can't tell you how glad I was to be reminded that that hideous year was over!'

'What was the proposition?'

I told him and he shook his head.

'Would you have said yes if it had been a few minutes earlier?'

'Actually, no. Not in a million years. It might have been a year to say yes, but I still have standards. Thankfully, though, I could say no with absolute certainty and belief, because I, my friend, have come up with my own plan for this year.'

'Is that so?' Seb looked amused, settling back in his chair and crossing his arms across his broad chest, the scar on his forearm tracing a pale line through the dark hair, a silvery trail that ended just past his elbow.

'Yep!'

'Do I get to hear this magnificent plan?'

'You do! In fact, you are the very first person I'm telling, so I hope you're feeling suitably honoured.'

'Of course. Come on then, don't keep me in suspense. Out with it.'

'After a year of going on dates I didn't want to, terrifying myself doing adventure activities I wouldn't ordinarily have done if you'd paid me, and shelling out to go on a holiday to see a level of drunkenness and behaviour I couldn't quite believe instead of a nice, relaxing hotel in some quiet corner of the Med, I am drawing a huge, thick line under it all.'

'And how exactly are you planning to do that?'

'Because I am declaring this to be The Year of Saying No!' Having now put my mug down, I threw my hands out in a dramatic gesture that even Jess would have been proud of.

2

When I looked back at the screen, Seb had an inscrutable expression on his face.

'What?' I asked.

'What?'

'Your face. Don't you think it's a good idea? You've spent the last year hearing about every awful date, knee-wobble inducing activity and never ending round of parties when you know that, for the most part, I'd have happily been sat on my sofa in my pyjamas with a good book. Surely you don't disagree that this is a much, much better idea?'

He made the slightest of gestures with his head, which, frankly, could have meant anything.

'I take it you do disagree then.'

'I didn't say that.'

'You didn't say anything, but your lack of enthusiasm speaks volumes.'

He shrugged.

'Right. That makes all the difference.'

He glanced at something out of my vision, then looked back. 'It just seems like a bit of an extreme reaction. I mean, I know you didn't enjoy a lot of the things you tried last year, but at least you tried them. You do spend a lot of time on your own. Sometimes it's good to open yourself up to opportunities, no matter how uncomfortable they might feel to start with.'

'I'm hardly a hermit.'

Seb gave me a look that suggested he had his doubts about that.

'I'm not!'

'You do like staying in.'

'So?'

'A lot.'

'So, I'm not a party animal. There's nothing wrong with that. Everybody's different.'

'Except that now you're planning to do nothing but work and sit and read for the entire year. I'm just not sure it's the best plan for you, going forward.'

'Now you sound like one of your reports.'

A ripple of humour showed in his eyes. 'I do know a thing or two about mental health. And shutting yourself away doesn't seem like the best option. That's all I'm saying.'

'Who said I was shutting myself away?'

'You did.'

'No, I didn't.' I shook my head. 'I just said I was going to say no.'

'To everything.'

'No. Only to the things I don't want to do. I refuse to feel obliged to say yes to things I'd rather not, just because someone else wants to do it, or someone else wants *me* to do it. I am giving myself permission to say no.'

'Well, that's a good thing.'

'So now you agree? Talk about fickle.'

The serious expression he'd been wearing evaporated and he

laughed, deep and melodic, and my treacherous tummy did the flip again. I mentally told it to behave and tried to ignore the wave of newly released butterflies.

'I've been called a lot of things in my time—'

'That doesn't surprise me.'

Seb gave me a look that I imagined had silenced many a lower ranked soldier in his time, but I could see the softness around those chocolate brown eyes and gave him a grin in response.

'So why the change of heart?'

'I was just concerned you had planned to shut yourself away entirely, that's all.'

'Nope. Just no more bloody bungee jumping, rampant, runaway Segways or hideous dates with men who look nothing like their profile picture and then leave me to pick up the bill.'

'You know not every guy is like that, don't you?'

'Once upon a time I might have believed you, but if my experience over the past year is anything to go by, then I'm sorry, but I'd have to disagree.'

'You do seem to have had some... fun experiences.'

'Fun isn't exactly the word I'd use for most of them.'

'No. I guess not.'

'And you should have seen some of the messages from the blokes that I didn't agree to meet up with!'

'It's probably better that I didn't,' he replied, that unreadable expression settling back on his features once again.

I shrugged and kind of got it. Seb was one of those men who couldn't help feeling protective towards women, however outdated some people felt that was. Personally, I thought it was sweet. I knew from all he'd done with the charity, the men and women he'd helped via that and the effort he put in, that he had an incredibly caring nature. If that spilled over into what I considered a nice touch of old-fashioned chivalry, I wasn't about to complain. And I'd certainly take that over the behaviour of most of the dates I'd had in the past year. Honestly, the fact that there were single men out there like Seb, who were nice and normal, gave me the slightest sliver of hope for the future. It was just kind of a shame that he lived over two hours away and was, more importantly, a client. My biggest and best client. This was my livelihood and as much as I liked Seb, he'd had to be put firmly in the fantasy pile. But what a fantasy that would be! Oh. My. God. With a capital O!

Making a concerted effort to push those unhelpful thoughts out of my mind, I focused back on the moment.

'I kind of thought you'd be behind me on this.'

'I am.'

I gave him a look similar to the one he'd given me earlier.

'I am!' he laughed. 'I just don't want you sitting in your house for a year in your pyjamas, picking Wotsits out of your hair after three months.'

The mouthful of tea I'd just taken nearly came out of my nose as I flapped and struggled to force it back down the right tube. 'Oh my god! Is that how you think of me?'

'Not always.'

'But sometimes?' I wailed, my voice pitching higher. 'Oh god.'

At least I didn't have to worry about ever being in the quandary of Seb having asked me out and not knowing what to do. In his eyes, I was the epitome of the word spinster, complete with added stale Wotsits tangled in my unkempt tresses. Excellent.

'Only since you announced this plan.'

'Like I said. I'm not planning to be a hermit. I'm just going to take time for me. Get me some of that self-care everyone is always banging on about. I've ordered a bunch of books on it.'

'Oh. OK. Well, that sounds a lot better.'

'Than me in stinky pyjamas with three month old cheesy snacks in my hair? I hope so!'

He let out that laugh again. 'I never said anything about stinky.'

'You didn't have to. It was there by inference.'

Seb's grin was wide and my own followed. 'I'm all for the idea though, but I'm not sure you need a tonne of books on the subject. A lot of it is just common sense and listening to your body. Plus, as you know, it's part of our programme, so if you want any advice or to talk about it, I'm more than happy to help.'

'No, of course. I did think about that, to be honest, but I know your schedule,' I said, waving a piece of paper in front of the screen, 'and all the things already on your plate. The last thing you need to do is add another task.'

'You wouldn't be a task. That's not how I'd see it. You've done so much for me and the charity, it'd be the least I could do.'

'You pay me to do those things.'

'Not everything. We both know you go above and beyond on the work you do for me and the veterans.'

'I enjoy the work and it's worth doing.'

'And so are you.'

A moment of silence descended slowly and awkwardly.

'That came out so entirely wrong,' Seb said eventually, one large hand now covering his eyes.

I was trying to keep a straight face, but it was a battle I was quickly losing. Even through the screen, I could feel the mortification radiating off him in waves, and there was a spot of high colour on each cheek. In all of the time I'd known him, I'd never seen Seb flummoxed or stuck for words.

'I can't believe I just said that,' he said, his eyes still covered, elbow resting on the pale wood of his desk.

'Don't worry about it, honestly.' I suddenly wished, not for the first time, I was in the same room as him so that I could gently remove that hand and smile into those eyes that always made me think of melting milk chocolate and reassure him. 'I know you didn't mean it how it sounded and, frankly, even that's pretty polite compared to some of the stuff I've heard over the past year.'

He peeked out between two fingers. 'Then it's definitely a good job you refrained from telling me about those.'

I gave a nod of agreement.

'Am I forgiven?' he asked.

'For saying I'm doable?' I grinned.

He gave me a look that was part embarrassment at himself, part exasperation at me, and altogether way too attractive for ten o'clock in the morning on my first day back at work in a new year. 'Accidentally.'

'Yes. You are.'

'Thank you. And what I meant to say is that you are worth all the effort in helping you find whatever it is that you need to make yourself happy.'

'I'm not unhappy. Honestly. I'm just... well, after last year I'm just exhausted. I know Jess meant well with her plans and, after a while, she did convince me that it could be a good thing. And we did have some fun times. But, on the whole, it was just too full on for me. That much activity could have been happily spread over three years and been enough. And, obviously, with Jess finding the love of her life rather unexpectedly partway through, I felt a bit of gooseberry at times.'

'So why did you carry on?'

'Because if I hadn't it would have felt like giving up.'

One corner of his mouth rose in amusement. 'And you call me stubborn.'

'You are.'

'And you're not?'

'Not in general, no.'

'I think you've got more of that trait than you think.'

I opened my mouth to protest, but Seb held up a hand. 'It's not a bad thing. Sometimes we need a bit of determination. Look at how far it's brought you with running your own business, sticking out a year of challenges just to prove to yourself you can do it, and now having the gumption to turn round and start saying no to people.'

'Gumption. That's a good word.'

'It is a good word. Sometimes it feels like there's not a lot of it about these days and then someone like you comes along and surprises me.'

'Especially when I have Wotsits in my hair.'

'I reckon you could pull it off.'

'Maybe.'

'So, what's the actual plan with this year?'

'Basically saying no to stuff I don't want to do, and just taking time for myself and doing the things I want to, rather than letting all my free time get sucked into stuff I feel obliged to do. I really only came up with the idea last night, so I haven't quite figured all the details out yet.'

'But you already have a tonne of books on order?'

'Arriving later today. I don't hang around.'

'No, I've learned that. It's why the charity has only become more and more efficient and effective since I hired you as my virtual assistant.'

I laughed. 'As flattering as that is, I don't think I can take that credit.'

'Nope. It's true. Before I found you, I knew what I wanted to do, and I was doing it, but I was also drowning in paperwork, real and virtual, and getting more and more frustrated because I knew if the charity was run more efficiently, we could be helping more people. And then there you were. The rest is history.'

'Well, I'm glad you took a chance on me too. As for what else is on the list, I'll have to come back to you on that.'

'If you need a hand, then just give me a shout. I'd love to be able to help.'

'I will. I promise. Although I have decided on one thing. It's something I've been thinking about for ages, actually, but then Jess came up with that crazy idea for last year and I knew it wouldn't work, but now I think it's perfect.'

'And what's that?'

'I'm getting a dog!'

3

The following Saturday morning I was sat in the waiting room of the local rescue centre, glancing nervously at a connecting door every few seconds. If only I'd had the same level of excitement on any of the dates I'd had in the past year as I did now. And then he was there, trotting along on the lead and heading straight for me, his fuzzy body wiggling and wriggling as he rested his paws up on my leg and pressed his little head into my hand as I gave him all the rubs and cuddles I could. He was mostly toy poodle, a little miniature schnauzer, and a dash of mystery, but clearly all heart and cuddles.

'I think we can say he definitely likes you,' the kennel assistant laughed as I picked the little dog up and snuggled him into me, whereupon he nuzzled into the crook of my arm and made himself comfortable, surveying the waiting room and looking for all the world as if he was right where he was supposed to be. And that was exactly how it felt. My year of saying no was beginning with most definitely saying yes to this little boy.

* * *

'You really called him Humphrey?' Seb asked, grinning at the little fuzzy face now peering at him through the screen. 'Is that even legal?'

I covered Humph's soft ears with my hands. 'Don't listen to the big mean man. He's just jealous.'

'You're not wrong, there. He looks like he's being thoroughly spoiled.'

'In a good way.'

'Of course. We all need a bit of spoiling from time to time.'

I glanced up from popping Humphrey back in his soft bed down by my feet, where he was now busy walking round in circles to find the exact point which would be the comfiest. From observation, this usually took him three or four turns. Right on cue, he plopped down with a contented sigh and within moments was snoring gently. 'I guess we do.'

'So, he's settling in OK?'

Seb had been travelling on business quite a lot over the last few weeks, raising the profile of the charity and taking on a keynote speech at a conference in America. We'd spoken by message on and off, but this was our first proper catch-up for work in three weeks.

'He is. I was a bit worried how he'd be as the rescue place thinks he'd been abandoned and had lived on the streets for a short while before some kind soul brought him in to them. But he's so chilled. It's brilliant. He loves his toys and walks but seems happy to just sit curled up with me when I'm reading or working.'

'Sounds like this was definitely one of your better dates then?'

'This,' I said, 'was the perfect date.'

* * *

'So, how's work?' Jess asked, handing me a glass of chilled white wine as I sat, legs curled under me, on her sofa. Half-packed boxes surrounded us, as Jess began to pack up her little flat, ready for the next step.

When we'd both embarked on the year of saying yes, neither of us had envisioned it involving Jess saying a very big yes to the huge, sparkling rock she now wore on her left hand. Moments into New Year's Day, as I was being propositioned by a belching city type, Jess was receiving a far more romantic proposal from a far more evolved city type. I'd never seen her so happy and they'd decided that her moving in to Harry's larger apartment was the logical next step. She'd already begun turning his once sleek and shiny bachelor pad into a much more homely place, filled with scented candles and scatter cushions. She practically lived there anyway, so paying rent on a place she hardly used didn't seem the most financially wise decision.

Jess stepped over a box and plopped down next to me.

'Good thanks. I've got a couple of new clients and I'm just helping finalise the guest list for the charity's summer gala so we can get the invitations printed and sent.'

'Don't forget to make sure Harry and I are on it.'

'Already done. Thanks, Jess. We both really appreciate you supporting it.'

Jess smiled. 'And how is the delectable Major Marshall?'

I rolled my eyes at her.

'He's fine.'

'Still single?'

'I've no idea,' I said.

Jess gave me a look.

'What?'

'Why don't you just ask him out?'

'Because I don't want to!'

She gave a snort of disbelief. 'We've known each other since we were four. You're going to have to try harder than that.'

OK, so maybe she did know about my crush then. That still didn't mean I had any intention of actually admitting it.

'I don't! He's a client, that's all.'

'A client you talk to every day. A client you remotely watch Eurovision together with. A client who—'

'Yes, all right. I get your point. OK, he's a friend, as well as a client.'

Jess opened her mouth to speak, but I headed her off.

'But he's still a client. Besides which, he's never suggested anything, and he's not exactly the shy and retiring type. If he had any interest in me, he would have said something by now. I think he probably prefers women whose wardrobes don't largely comprise of pyjamas.'

'You don't know until you ask.'

'I do. And I'm not asking. Can you imagine how awkward that would be? I have to work with this guy. He's my biggest client. I can't afford to lose him just because I have a little crush on him.'

Jess gave another very unladylike snort. 'Little?'

'Oh pffft!' I said, blowing a raspberry, before grinning and taking a large swig of wine. That was the trouble with your best friend having known you for decades. It was kind of hard to get anything past her. 'So, let's talk about you. What's with the box explosion going on here?'

Jess looked around. 'I'm struggling. I start one, and then I find something else and that feels like it should be in a different box and when I look up, I have like twenty-five boxes on the go, get overwhelmed and go and do something else. Rinse and repeat.' Her normally wide, gap-toothed smile was hidden as she leant down to call Humphrey over from where he'd stuck his nose in a box and was so enthralled by the possibility of what might be in it that he was now two paws in and lifting one back leg up in the effort to explore further.

At her call, he popped his head back out, his ears pricked. His sensitive nose twitched as his long-lashed eyes focused in on what was in her hand. Reversing at speed out of the box, Humph scooted over to us and sat with a bump in front of Jess. She held out the little square of cheese and he took it gently, swallowing it, before nudging her hand for the possibility of more. She opened them both to show him that was it. He gave a little hard-done-by sigh before toddling over to me. I reached down and lifted him up, plopping him on my lap, where he proceeded to make himself comfy. Jess leant across the sofa, placing her hand on Humph's soft fur and stroked his head.

'Everything all right?' I asked.

Jess nodded but didn't meet my eyes.

'Jess. If you're not ready for this step, you need to say so. There's no rush. Harry's bonkers about you. He'll wait.'

She sat up suddenly. Humphrey opened one eye, looked at her curiously for a moment, assessed her for cheese and then went back to sleep.

'No! It's not that. I'm totally ready for this. Even more than I thought I was. I'm... I'm just a bit worried that I'm not going to be... good at it.'

'Good at what?'

'Living with someone. Marriage.'

'What on earth are you talking about? There's nothing to be good at. It just... is. Besides, we lived together for years and you were fine.'

'That's not the same. And you told me I was the messiest person you'd ever known.'

'I said that once because I had a hangover and had just stepped on plate of cold baked beans on toast.'

'It's kind of true though, isn't it?'

I took her hand. 'Jess. We're all different. I like things tidy and neat and you are more free-flowing and take it as it comes. That doesn't mean either is wrong. They're just different. Although maybe not leaving a plate of cold baked beans on the floor wouldn't hurt?' I gave her a wink.

She let out a sigh. 'I can't even pack a box!'

'But you can run a brilliant PR firm, cook the best cakes in the world and bring light to a room just by walking in.'

She looked up at me.

'True,' I assured her.

'I really am sure about this, I promise.'

'OK,' I said, hearing the sincerity in her voice and seeing it in her eyes. She was.

'I guess all the packing started to get a bit overwhelming and then everything takes a knock, doesn't it?'

'It certainly can do. But you're fine, and this is going to be wonderful. Just think, in a couple of weeks' time, you're going to get to wake up every morning to a beautiful view of the Thames and look out over the twinkling lights of London every evening. And share all that with the man you love. Plus, you get to cut out the crappy commute for a brief tube hop.'

'There are definitely benefits. Although the view here of next door's bins was one that was hard to beat.'

'I hope the estate agent listed that as a feature.'

'Why do you think I've had such a stream of viewings?' Her grin widened and she leant over and hugged me. 'Thanks, Lots.'

'You're welcome,' I said, my voice slightly muffled by her shoulder. Sitting her back, I tilted my head. 'Do you want some help with this?' I nodded at the boxes surrounding us.

'I'd say yes, but I know it's your year of saying no, so I'm thinking this might be a trick question.'

I grinned. 'No tricks, I promise. The saying no thing doesn't mean saying no to everything—'

'I feel like this is information I really ought to pass on to Seb Marshall.'

'Oh shoosh. Look, do you want me to come round with my incredible organisational skills tomorrow and help you whip this lot into shape so you can stop tying yourself up in knots about it all?'

'I do.'

'OK. Good. We'll be round at ten.'

'We?' Her eyes lit up expectantly.

I rolled my own. 'If you're thinking what I think you're thinking, I'm pretty sure the way to Seb's heart is not to ask him to come and pack up my best friend's house as a first date.'

Jess shrugged. 'He's ex-military. They're usually really organised and like things just so. Who knows? That might be a dream date for him!'

'He's been on quite a few dates since I've known him and, as far as I can remember, none of them have veered in the direction of moving someone's stuff. It's been more candlelit dinners and walks in the great outdoors.'

'And yet he's still single. Perhaps because none of those dates were the perfect one?' My friend was nothing if not persistent.

'I really don't know. I know one girl got funny about his prosthetic when it came to... getting intimate.'

'Getting intimate? You all right, grandma?' Jess laughed. 'What do you mean, anyway? She didn't know?'

'Oh, she knew. He's upfront about that and lives in shorts half the time anyway, but... I don't know. I guess she hadn't clicked that he takes it off at night or something.'

'How did he seem after that?' Jess' forehead wrinkled with concern and I loved her for it.

'OK. Just took it in his stride – no pun intended. He said it's not the first time someone's been uncomfortable about it, and it won't be the last. He wasn't bitter about it and didn't hold it against her. Said it just showed she wasn't the one for him and that was OK.'

'Sounds like he has a pretty healthy attitude.'

'He does. Although he'll be the first to admit he struggled with that when he was first injured. I think that's why he's so good at what he does with the charity. He's been there, literally.'

Jess went quiet.

'I can practically hear the cogs turning. What?'

'Does it bother you?'

'Does what bother me?'

'His injury.'

'Of course not. Why would it?'

'I don't mean now. I meant if something happened. You know, between you two.'

'Nothing's going to happen, but it would still be the same answer. Why should it bother me? He's still Seb. I'm just grateful that he survived and came out the other side of it.'

'I agree. I have a soft spot for him, being your first client. I still remember how excited you were when you signed him up. Of course, that had nothing to do with you having seen his profile picture on his website...' Jess arched a perfect brow.

'It didn't.' *Much.* 'I was just thrilled, and a little scared, that things were starting to happen.'

'Of course.' She nodded in a way that suggested she disagreed with the words coming from both our mouths.

'Whatever. Do you want me to help you with this tomorrow or not?'

'Yes.'

'Then I suggest you stop giving me grief about my love life.'

'Or lack thereof.'

'Which is just the way I like it. I have Humphrey and that's all the men I need in my life right now.'

'Humphrey is wonderful, of course.' At this, my little mutt woke up, basked for a moment in the praise, and then went straight back to sleep. 'But I just worry about you. Especially once I move.'

'You won't be that far away.'

'I won't be round the corner any more.'

'Jess, I'm fine. You're not getting rid of me that easily.'

She flung her arms out. 'I never want to get rid of you. I'm just worried you will hibernate even more without me living on top of you.'

'Hibernation is very underrated, I find.'

'This is not helping my concern.'

'Oh, will you stop worrying? I'm fine. You're supposed to be getting excited about this new step in your own life, not fretting about me.'

'So, go out with Seb and I won't.'

'Jess, he lives two hours away. It's not even practical. And that's without the small point of the fact he's never even hinted that he'd be interested. We're just friends, and right now, that's actually really good for me. We get on really well but I honestly don't think we'd be all that compatible as anything more.'

'What makes you say that?' Jess asked, topping up my wine.

'You know what he's like. He's missing part of a leg and he can, quite literally, still run rings around me when it comes to fitness and stuff like that.'

Jess paused, thoughtful for a moment. 'You do have an affinity for your pyjamas, I will give you that. But you're not entirely potato.'

'Always good to hear.'

'And you're out every day now with Humphs.'

'That's true. It's not been that long since I got him, although I can hardly remember how I got by without him in my life—'

'We're still talking about the dog, right?'

'Yes. We are.'

'OK. Just checking.'

'Harry is aware how you're like a dog with a bone sometimes, and how entirely annoying it is, right?'

'Oh yeah. Absolutely.'

'Good. Just checking.' I echoed.

She grinned.

'Anyway. As I was saying, I've already noticed some benefits to having him. Even just getting up to let him out for a tinkle gets me moving away from the computer, whereas I'd probably have sat there – correction, did sit there – for hours at a time before. And then, obviously, we have our walk every day, rain or shine. I'd never have just gone out for a random walk in the rain, but now I don't even think about it. We just go.'

'And they say it's sociable, walking a dog.'

'It can be. You start seeing some familiar faces and we've met a few dogs that Humphrey loves to see now.'

'Anyone interesting?'

I looked up and immediately became suspicious at the far too innocent expression Jess was wearing. 'Oh, for goodness' sake! Just because you're hooked up doesn't mean I have to be!' I said, half laughing, half exasperated. 'Two minutes ago you were trying to set me up with Seb Marshall, and now we're already on to the other dog walkers!'

'I'm just giving you options!'

'I choose the option of none of the above, thanks!'

Jess gave a dramatic roll of her eyes. 'Fiiiiine.'

I leant over, chinked my glass against hers and smiled. 'Perfect.'

4

'You look knackered.'

'Thanks. Remind me to write to Yves St Laurent later.'

'OK. Any particular reason?'

'Only because when I caught a glance of myself in the mirror late yesterday afternoon after stacking up the last of Jess' boxes, I made a detour to the local department store and forked out on a tube of Touche Éclat. It claims to make "signs of fatigue virtually disappear". And, judging by your immediate reaction upon seeing me, it would appear I have been diddled.'

He grinned and, tired as I was, bits of me definitely perked up.

'Rubbish. You still look great. You always do. I just know you pretty well by now.'

I made a derisive noise. 'It's a bit late to start sucking up now. I've already worked out where I'm sticking the fee for that comment.'

'Damn. Worth a try.'

I smiled and shook my head.

'You do look tired though, and,' he held up his hands, palms towards the screen, 'I mean that in a concerned friend kind of way, not in a critical one.'

I waved my hand. 'I know. I am. Turns out Jess has waaaay more stuff than even I anticipated.'

'Did you have to get it all done this weekend?' Seb had rung for a video chat with a cup of tea around eleven on Saturday morning, as he quite often did, but I'd had to quickly explain that I was taking part in Operation How The Hell Has Jess Accumulated All This Crap and couldn't really talk.

'Kind of. They both can't wait to live together and she was only working herself up about getting everything done. It wasn't good for her.'

'I'm not sure it was that good for you. Why don't you take the day off?'

'No, I'm fine. It's done now anyway, so she can stop worrying. Harry's arranged for a firm to move all her stuff and put it in his spare room and she can just unpack at her leisure.'

'You still look shattered.'

'I'll get an early night tonight. And it's looking a bit breezy out there,' I said, leaning back in my chair to peer out of the window, 'so that'll wake me up when I take Humphs out in a bit.'

'Don't overdo it.'

'Says the man who probably went on a ten mile walk with his own dog this morning before dawn.'

His laugh reverberated around me, warm and deep. 'Only five and definitely after dawn.' He moved his screen to take in Scooby, sprawled out on the floor behind him, legs up, family jewels on display to the world, snoring softly as the tips of his paws moved in his dream. 'Classy, eh?'

'Must take after his master.'

Seb glanced back at me, then back at the dog, before returning his attention to me. 'You know, I think you might have a point. Maybe that's why we bonded so quickly.'

'Kindred spirits.'

At this, Scooby let out an audible, and judging by Seb's face, pungent parp. 'Jesus, Scoobs,' Seb grumbled, pulling his hoody sleeve down and burrowing his nose into it. 'In the interest of accuracy, I'd like to point out that we're not kindred in everything,' he said, his voice now muffled somewhat.

'If you say so.'

Above his hand, his brown eyes twinkled with amusement.

'How did your meeting with Lady Carstairs go on Friday?' I gave a little eyebrow wiggle. Rumour had it that the Lady Genevieve had the hots for Seb – gossip Jess had been more than eager to find out more about from Harry, whose family knew hers in the way that aristocratic families often knew each other's business. Apparently, the rumours were entirely true. And, from what Jess could find out, this was a woman who tended to get what she wanted.

'OK.' Seb nodded, not quite meeting my eye. If I'd had antennae, they'd be on high alert right now.

'Anything I should know?' I asked, casually.

Seb lifted his gaze, meeting my apparently nonchalant one. 'You're enjoying this far too much for someone who professes to be a nice person.'

'I am a nice person. And what exactly am I enjoying?'

'My discomfort.'

I made a sympathetic face. 'Yes. It must be awful to be pursued by a very attractive, intelligent and insanely rich woman. If I said "there, there" would it help?' I tried not to grin, but with the way Seb was looking at me, it was an impossible feat.

'You're hilarious. You know that, don't you?'

'It's one of my best qualities.'

He shook his head, still smiling. 'The meeting went fine. She's still keen on supporting the charity but wants to discuss things further.'

'I bet she does,' I mumbled.

'You know I can hear you, right?'

I coughed. 'Sorry? Frog.' I coughed again for effect.

Seb gave me a patient look and I returned an innocent smile.

'Yeah, right. Anyway, I mentioned that we're hoping to arrange this summer gala thing and she immediately said she'll take a table, so that's a good start.'

He glanced away for a moment. I narrowed my eyes.

'Was there a caveat to that?'

'What?'

'You've gone all shifty.'

He straightened up, laughter creasing his face. 'I am not shifty!'

I gave him a look that suggested I disagreed with that.

'Fine. She laughingly said it was on the proviso that she danced with me.'

'There are far worse catches to a deal.'

Seb dismissed it. 'I'm pretty sure she was joking. She'd had a couple of glasses of champagne by that point anyway.'

I was pretty sure Lady Carstairs was deadly serious, and from what Jess had found out, a dance was just the beginning of what she really wanted. I pushed the thought to the back of my mind and straightened my notes.

'So, agenda?' I said, pulling it up on my screen so that it was now split between our video chat and the document he'd sent over last week.

'Yes, ma'am,' he grinned and I tried not to think about Seb Marshall in a uniform.

I cleared my throat. 'Item one. Funnily enough, the summer gala. I've had some more thoughts on this.'

* * *

By the end of the following week, I was shattered. Jess had moved in and Harry had very sweetly held a welcome home dinner party for her, which, of course, I'd wanted to go to. It had just coincided with a super busy week at work, including a new client, on top of the busy weekend we'd had getting Jess' life into boxes ready for the move.

'How's that year of saying no working out for you?' Seb teased me over the top of his coffee mug.

'It's fine.'

'Looks it. Are you not saying no enough?'

'I am, to things I don't want to do. I said no to signing up to a mailing list when I got caught by a chugger on the street the other day. Plus, just last week I turned down a week's hen do in Ibiza for someone I haven't even seen in nearly ten years, as well as a candle party from someone at my previous office. Both of which I probably would have said yes to out of a sense of obligation before. It just so happens that this week has involved quite a lot I actually have wanted to do.'

'You look like you could do with a rest.'

'You know what I really fancy?'

'Enlighten me.'

'A spa weekend.'

'Right now?'

'No. Just to look forward to. This weekend, I want to just veg with Humphs in front of the telly, watch old films and eat crumpets.'

'Crumpets? That's very specific.'

'I bloody love crumpets. And you'd better not say you don't like them because I'm not sure we can be friends any more if you don't.'

'Then I most certainly do.'

'Is that a fib?'

'Nope. I like a bit of crumpet as much as the next man.'

'You're such a cliché.'

'You say the nicest things.'

I toasted him with my tea cup and nodded.

'I'm not sure crumpets are going to cover all the major food groups though.'

'No. I suppose not. I will eat other stuff too. But mostly crumpets.'

Seb's laugh took me by surprise and sent a warming thrill throughout my body. I really hated, and loved, when it did that.

'What?' I asked.

'You.'

'What about me?'

'You just make me laugh. And, before you analyse it, that's a good thing.'

I nodded in acceptance.

'So. This spa thing? I take it you've done one before.'

'No. I haven't actually,' I admitted.

'Really?'

'I know. Everyone and their dog seems to have done one but me. But that's the other thing.'

'What is?'

'Humphrey.'

'I still can't believe you called him that.'

'Oh shoosh. He likes it, and so do I.'

Seb shook his head and made a motion with his hand for me to continue.

'Well, I don't want to leave Humphs out. My parents are off on one of their jaunts. Jess would take him, but I don't really want to ask her. She's still settling in and it seems a bit cheeky.'

'Shame you don't live closer.'

Wasn't it just?

'I'd take him otherwise.'

'Even though you have a hang-up about his name.'

'Even though. That just goes to show what a good guy I am.'

'A good guy wouldn't make fun of his name in the first place.'

'I said I was good, not perfect.'

'That is true. Anyway, I don't live closer, so, unfortunately, that's not an option either.'

'Do you have any preference as to where you go for this spa weekend?' Seb asked.

'No, not especially. Why?' I squinted at him. 'You have your "I might have a plan" face on. Which is both worrying and exciting in equal parts.'

'I wasn't aware I had one of those faces, but it's a good thing to know. And yes, I might just have a plan.'

'Which is?'

'An ex of mine is the manager of a small chain of boutique hotels and I'm pretty sure some of them do spa days. I've also got a feeling at least a couple of them are dog friendly because we talked about going to one once and obviously Scoobs would have had to come. I can ask her if you like.'

'Ooooooo... K.'

He folded his arms, giving me a front row view of perfectly muscled forearms. Perhaps I should send him a couple of long-sleeve T-shirts for days I really needed to concentrate... 'What's up?'

'You're still in touch then?'

'Yeah.'

'Right.'

'Spit it out, Lots.'

'Well, I'm just a little concerned that if you enquire for me, that, depending on what you did, once she finds out I'm anything remotely connected to you, the rates they charge might suddenly double!'

His brows rose. 'Who said I did anything?'

'Did you?'

He furrowed his brow. 'I don't think so.'

'Oh god, you totally did something.'

'I did not,' he laughed. 'It was just one of those things that didn't work out. Not enough spark, chemistry, whatever you want to call it. We still chat though. She's a nice woman.'

'OK.'

'Want me to see what I can find out?'

'Do you mind?'

'Of course not. It'd be my pleasure. Especially if I know you're actually going to get some proper rest and pampering, then it's definitely my pleasure.'

'Don't worry. I won't let my work slide.'

His face was serious. 'That's not what I meant.'

'No, I know. I'm just messing about.'

He nodded.

'I promise. I know you look out for people. For me. And I do appreciate that. It's very kind.'

'I just want you to practise some of that self-care you spoke about earlier in the year. The last couple of weeks seem to have been about everyone but you.'

'Which is why I'm looking into spa weekends.'

'And why I'm going to get on that right now. Talk to you in a bit.'

5

I may have to give you a few days free for arranging this

I pressed send and put my phone down next to me on the table, exchanging it for a delicious juice full of organic goodness and a bunch of ingredients I'd never even heard of.

Good then?

My phone lit up as Seb's reply came in. I'd turned the ringer off so that it didn't disturb me or anyone else in the relaxing surroundings as various guests lay on loungers, some in swimsuits, some, like me, snuggled in the softest of fluffy white dressing gowns with a subtle logo embroidered on the right chest. The area was warm but not stuffy and an assortment of greenery, from small ferns to large palms, was interspersed around it, providing both privacy as well as that sense of relaxation that comes from being surrounded by plants.

Gorgeous! I'm still convinced they're going to come and ask for the rest of the money! I can't believe the deal you got me

I couldn't help but wonder if perhaps something had reignited with Seb and his ex because I was pretty sure what I'd paid for this weekend was a fraction of what it should be. And that feeling caused a little ripple in my stomach. Which was ridiculous because Seb had dated plenty of people during the time I'd known him and it had never bothered me. So why did it send a quiver of curiosity through me now? I knew the answer, of course. Before, I hadn't been single, so what Seb did and who he saw had no impact on me. But now that I was... I gave my towelled head a gentle boink back against the top of the lounger. Now that I was – it made no difference. I just needed my body to start listening to my brain.

A laughing face emoticon bounced in on to the screen and I could see that he was still typing.

Don't worry about it. They won't. Secret? They had someone cancel a package last minute. With you there, they know they're getting some money on top of the other person's deposit they lost, but they'd have been unlikely to fill it this late otherwise. You're doing them a favour

Winky face.

Ha! I'm not sure about that, but thanks again to you and your friend for arranging this.

You're more than welcome. I'm glad you're having a nice time. Humphrey all right? (I can't believe I have to write that name...)

A rolly-eyed emoticon winged its way to him.

Get over it. It's a good name. And yes, he's having a wonderful time! He's having a doggy massage at the moment.

Shocked face quickly followed by laughing one.

He's so chilled anyway, I don't know what this will result in. He may just sleep for the entire next week!

Hope you're having one too. I think you're probably more in need than the dog, to be honest.

Don't worry. I am. I've just had a lovely hair treatment and I've got a massage booked at 2

Sounds good. Also, why is your phone not turned off? You're supposed to be decompressing

Funny face.

Ha ha! It's only on because I wanted to speak to you…

I reread the message and deleted some of the words. Try again.

It's only on because I wanted to thank you for setting this up. I'm not looking at emails, messages, social media or anything else. Jess is offline at some romantic retreat Harry's whisked her off to this weekend, so it's fine, really

He sent a smile.

I'm torn between being happy to hear you're having a good time and wanting you to switch off entirely.
I will. Stop worrying about me so much

Winky face.

He sent back a shrug.

Can't help it. This is just what I do when it comes to people I care about

I didn't know how to reply. The words were so simple, but they meant such a lot. That was one of the things I'd liked about Seb from the beginning. He was straightforward. Said what he meant, but without being overly blunt or rude. He took people's feelings into consideration and I always knew where I stood with him. I imagined he'd been a good and respected officer in the army. I'd said something to that effect once and he'd shrugged it off, saying something non-committal like he'd hoped so, which made me think he definitely had been.

There was no question of him being a complete angel – he certainly still got wound up about things, but he always tried to see things from all perspectives before leaping in and making a decision or comment. I admired this trait, although I'd been less admiring of it when someone had pranged my car in a line of traffic and he'd begun to question it. I'd told him in no uncertain terms I'd been sat there in a queue minding my own business and that the only perspective he needed to see on this occasion was that I was annoyed, sore and now the owner of a car with its boot smashed in and that I'd rung for sympathy, not a balanced view of things. Seb had laughed and the next day I'd received flowers and a box of biscuits, as well as a tube of muscle rub. The card had read 'Some people just shouldn't have a licence!!!' Apparently he'd been very specific about the three exclamation marks required, just to ensure I could tell exactly how outraged he was on my behalf.

I looked back down at my phone. There was really only one way to reply...

Thank you

A hugging emoji appeared, bringing a smile to my face as I put the phone down on the table and glanced at the clock on the wall across from me. Time for a little nap before going off to collect Humph from his treatment and get him settled in the room before heading back down for my own massage. Perfect.

* * *

The hotel Seb's connections had wangled for me was close to a National Trust property, the grounds of which were open to the general public for free from dawn to dusk and this had proved to be a beautiful place to take Humphrey for a long walk each day, as I absorbed the atmosphere and listened to the birds chatter, hidden from sight in the branches of the trees above. The relaxing natural landscape built on the calm feeling the whole weekend was instilling in me.

As I returned from a walk with the dog, stepping into the elegant foyer that merged modernity with a nod to the grace of Art Deco, I heard my name called.

'Ms Wentworth?'

I looked up to see a tall brunette striding towards me on heels so beautiful, I had trouble pulling my eyes away from them for a second or two. The beauty of the shoes matched that of their owner, and as she approached me, a wide and perfect smile broke on her face at the same time as she held out her hand.

Quickly, I jiggled Humphrey's lead to the other hand and took the woman's, accepting the firm but friendly shake.

'I just wanted to check that everything was OK for you?'

I nodded. 'It's absolutely lovely, thank you.'

She smiled again, and gave a little laugh. 'I'm sorry. I should have introduced myself. I'm Carla.' At the lack of any sign of recognition on my part, she continued, 'I'm the manager of the chain. Seb Marshall's... friend.' She hesitated on the last word and I wasn't quite sure if I should make something of that.

'Oh! Right. Thank you for arranging all this for us.' I nodded down at Humphrey as I spoke and Carla smiled and briefly dipped to give Humph a little head rub.

'You're more than welcome. Seb was very insistent that you only got the best.' She gave me a little smile and the merest hint of enquiring eyebrow.

'Ha!' I laughed, a little awkwardly. 'Oh. Oh dear. I hope it wasn't any trouble. It really was something I just mentioned in passing and then he said he knew someone and that he might be able to have a chat with you and...' I tailed off, aware that I was beginning to ramble out of control.

Carla laid a hand on my arm briefly. 'Don't worry about it. It really was my pleasure. Seb's a great guy.'

'He is. Yes. And, um, a great client too.'

'Client?' she frowned a little.

'Yes. I'm a virtual personal assistant. Seb was my first client. Well, I suppose technically the charity is, but... so yes.' Again with the rambling.

'Oh. I see. I thought maybe he'd finally found someone who was right for him. And the way he talked about you...'

I felt myself blush and flapped my hand. 'You know what he's like.'

'I do.' Those two words seemed loaded and I felt the blush deepen. 'And, frankly, this was such a pleasure to arrange as he obviously cares about you and I'll never be able to repay him for introducing me to my fiancé.'

'He did?'

She smiled and glanced down at her left hand. A huge sparkling solitaire diamond set in a platinum band caught the light as she moved it. 'He did. Seb and I went out a few times, but it never came to anything. Just not the right chemistry for something to happen, I guess, but we had a fun time, so it was lovely to stay friends with him.'

'He is a good friend,' I replied, relieved to be back on more solid ground.

'So then he calls me up and tells me he's just had a meeting with this guy who's planning on sponsoring the charity for something and thinks he'd be perfect for me and that he'd set up a dinner date for that evening.'

'He didn't?'

'I know, right? I kind of wanted to be cross with him for barrelling ahead without asking me first, but there's something about Seb. He's a pretty good assessor of people. And, frankly, I had nothing better to do that night, so I went.'

I pointed at her left hand, grinning. 'I guess it worked out.'

'Perfectly. Of course, Seb did his best not to be smug about it when I told him, but he didn't quite pull that off.'

'No, well, he is a man.'

Carla laughed and glanced at the expensive watch on her wrist. 'I'd better get on, but I just wanted to meet you and check everything was OK.'

'And check out who Seb had pulled strings for?' I grinned.

She wrinkled her nose. 'Was I that obvious?'

I shook my head, still smiling. 'Not at all. It was really nice to meet you. I wanted to thank you anyway. And I'd totally have done the same thing. It's obvious that Seb means a lot to you, which is understandable. But don't worry, we're just friends. There's absolutely no romance there, so I'm not about to break his heart or anything. I think I'd be just as upset as you if someone did that to him, so I totally get it.'

'There was some aristocrat after him when we were going out. He didn't seem interested at the time, but I did wonder...'

I nodded. 'Yes. She's still interested apparently.'

Carla pulled a face. 'I know he's Mr Tough Guy, but she's already been through three husbands.' She made a palms-up gesture. 'I'd just hate for Seb to get hurt.'

'I know. Me too.'

Carla touched my arm again. 'I'm so glad he sent you here. It was lovely to meet you. I really hope you enjoy the rest of your stay, and don't forget,' she handed over her card, 'anything you want, just let me know.'

'Thanks, Carla. For everything.'

'My pleasure. Keep an eye on that boy for me, won't you?'

'Will do.'

She gave me another full-wattage smile and then strode off across the foyer, heading for a door marked 'Staff Only.'

'Come on, Humph. Time to go upstairs and see what we might fancy from room service tonight.'

Humphrey looked up from where he'd flopped over on to his side and was now sprawled out like a very small, shaggy rug.

'Come on, lazybones. There might even be a charcoal biccie in it for you.'

At this, his ears perked up and he scrabbled up onto all fours.

'Thought that might help,' I said, laughing at his antics as we headed towards the stairs. As we climbed, one sentence from my conversation with Carla kept twirling around in my head... *the way he talked about you.*

Back in the room, I settled Humphrey in his bed with his promised treat and switched on the mini kettle as I laid a turmeric teabag in the bone china mug. I'd turned my nose up at these when I first saw them, but, actually, they were surprisingly enjoyable.

It doesn't mean anything, I told myself as I gave the teabag a few dunks. As Carla had said, and as he himself had admitted, that's just how Seb was with people he cared about. And there was no reading into that caring any further than needed either. We were friends. That was it. He cared about me as a friend. Just as he did Carla. Which was great. Lovely, in fact.

I squished the pillows up behind me as I flicked on the telly with the remote control. With a bit of luck, he might be able to find someone to present me with a rock the size of my dog too.

* * *

'I'm thinking you could do with another weekend at that spa,' Seb said, frowning at me as I answered his call distractedly while in the middle of ensuring my last emails of the day had all been sent and I could close my computer down for the weekend.

'Hi. No, I'm fine. Just been a busy day. I'm very ready for the weekend. Did you need something doing?'

'I'm hardly likely to ask that at gone five on a Friday night, especially after seeing you looking like you need to go and put your feet up with a big mug of tea.'

'One sugar, lots of milk if you're making.'

He grinned and gave me a salute. 'Get your arse over here and I will.'

'You say the nicest things.'

'Yep. They always say I'm a charmer.'

I gave him an eye roll. 'Did you really want something doing? You know I don't mind.'

He shook his head and yawned. 'Nope. I just shut stuff down myself and thought I'd see what you were up to.'

'Well, I'm about to go and make that tea.'

'OK, ring me back when you've got it.'

Ten minutes later, I was ensconced on my sofa with a soft snuggly blanket, a warm snuggly dog, a huge mug of tea and three chocolate digestives.

'You look like you're all ready to hit the town this evening,' Seb stated upon popping back up on my phone screen's video call.

'Oh yeah,' I replied through a mouthful of biscuit. My mother would not be impressed by my manners, but I was tired and it was only Seb. I'd apologised for speaking with my mouth full once before, at which he'd given a deep rumbling laugh, telling me that he wished that was the worst manners he'd ever seen. Army life was enlightening, he'd said. Deployment was another whole step again. After that, I hadn't worried.

'What you up to tonight?' he asked, sliding down his own sofa into a slouch and taking a sip of what I knew would be black coffee.

'Pretty much this,' I replied.

'Fair enough.'

'You?'

Seb gave a slow wave over himself to indicate his own plans involved about as much movement as my own. I smiled, enjoying the fact that my friend, who was, in general, a pretty active guy, didn't judge me for my choices and wasn't averse to the pleasures of an evening's sofa-vegging himself.

'Did you see that new comedy has just come onto Netflix?' I asked.

'Oh yeah. I saw the email. Have you watched it yet?'

'Nope,' I said through a yawn.

'Want to watch it later?'

This was something we'd begun to do around six months or so ago. Watching the same thing at the same time, messaging comments to and fro while we watched. It was nice. Silly but fun. Like having company even though you were on your own – four pawed friends excepted.

6

Having now freed up some time thanks to my new saying no policy, I decided to go ahead with some things I actually did want to do. At the time, this had seemed like a good idea. Peeking into the room now, I wasn't so sure.

'Ooh, are you here for dance classes too?' A vivacious looking woman with Hollywood curves and a mass of auburn curls which she'd piled messily, but sexily, on top of her head kind of ushered me in the door along with her and I lost my last chance of scooting out of there before anyone noticed.

'There you are!' Jess rushed forward, Harry being propelled along behind as he held onto her hand. I don't think Harry had been entirely prepared for the amount of energy my friend kept balled up inside her at any given moment, but he seemed to be coping admirably and, from the look on his face, thoroughly enjoying it.

'Here I am,' I replied, attempting to inject the same level of enthusiasm, but feeling like I somehow fell short. Hopefully no one else noticed.

'What's the matter?' Jess asked, not fooled in the slightest. 'I thought you wanted to do this? It was your idea, remember?' she said, softly.

'Yeah. I know,' I smiled, trying not to be put off by the fact that everyone around the room already seemed to have partnered up. 'I'm just not sure it was one of my better ones.'

'Oh, nonsense,' Jess said. 'You've wanted to learn to dance for years. I'm thrilled you're finally doing something about it. I can't believe I didn't think about putting this on the list for last year.'

'I'm glad you didn't. I barely survived as it was.'

'Oh, pffft,' Jess batted me on the arm. 'You loved it.'

I stared at her for a moment.

'OK. Maybe not loved it exactly.'

'Definitely not.'

'But you did it!'

'Because I love you. No other reason.'

'And I love you! Which is why we're here now.'

I returned her hug. I wasn't entirely convinced that was the only reason Jess and Harry were here now, although it was a good start. Jess had always loved the drama of Latin dance and had toyed with doing something about learning on and off for years, but she was always too busy doing something else. But when I'd mentioned I'd found some classes and had signed up, Jess' enthusiasm was fired again. Even more so when Harry agreed to come with her and learn so that they could dance together.

I was thrilled he was so supportive and up for doing it, I really was. But I couldn't help feeling like a large, green, slightly fuzzy piece of fruit as I stood next to them and they practised gazing meaningfully deep into each other's eyes.

In my pocket, my phone buzzed. I pulled it out and saw the light flashing. Pressing the messages, one from Seb showed unread. I glanced up, but it didn't seem like we were starting, so I quickly opened it.

Just to say hope it goes well tonight. Enjoy yourself!

I replied.

Just got here. Can we all say 'gooseberry'?

I added a fruit emoji, that might have been a gooseberry, for extra emphasis.

The message showed read almost immediately and the words 'typing' appeared at the top of the screen.

Don't worry about it. You won't be the only one not paired up already. Just remember to enjoy it

Easy for you to say

Want me to zoom down? You might have to stall them for a bit, but I still have contacts. I'm sure I can rustle up a helicopter from somewhere

Would you? That'd be great

He sent a laughing emoji before following it up.

At least I can't be accused of being a cliché and having two left feet

He added a wink.
I sent him a rolling eyes one back in response.

I'm pretty sure you'd still be better than me

The fact that Seb could now make light of the devastating injury that had ended his career and upended his life was something I truly admired about him. It illustrated to him, and others, just how far he

had come. As our business relationship began to merge into friendship, we'd opened up about ourselves more. His bio for the charity
stated that he'd lost his lower right leg on deployment in
Afghanistan when the vehicle he'd been travelling in had hit an IED,
but I knew I'd never be able to understand all the things that had
crashed through his mind at that moment, as the dust began to clear
and reality, in all its horrific colour, dawned. He'd lost a good friend
and his own life had changed for ever – all in one split second. For a
while it had beaten him, become bigger than him – but then he'd
begun to fight back and had truly won.

I doubt that

Get your arse down here, and I'll prove it

The voluptuous redhead who'd propelled me through the doors
earlier clapped her hands.

'Hello, hello, darling members of my new class! Are you ready to
begin to learn the dances of love?' She gave a sensuous sway. My
stomach was currently performing a similar movement, but it most
definitely wasn't sensuous.

Oh god. It's starting. Have to go

He replied quickly with a phone emoticon and I got the message.

Seb was right. I wasn't the only one who hadn't paired up. Thankfully, there was Mario.

'Thank god for you!' he said, laughter in his eyes as he took the
stance Beth, our instructor, was currently demonstrating with Harry.
'I thought I was going to be twirling around on my own!'

I grinned back. 'I know the feeling.'

Mario leant his head closer. 'I think this is going to be a lot of
fun.' His dark eyebrows wriggled above mischievous eyes.

I grinned. He might just be right.

An hour later and I wasn't sure I'd got any of the moves right, but I'd certainly laughed more than I had in ages. Mario was the perfect dance partner, with a wicked sense of humour and an even more wicked eye for mimicry.

One couple were clearly in the wrong class as they already seemed to have a pretty good grasp of everything and swanned around the room, serious expressions on their faces, as they absorbed the music and concentrated on their moves. Even Beth mentioned they might be better suited to her later class which was more advanced. At this they showed surprise and humility, the woman's impressively long false eyelashes fluttering madly as she waved away the suggestion.

'Oh, please,' Mario whispered under his breath so that it was audible only to me.

I looked round. He stepped closer.

'They know exactly what they're doing. I've been at classes like this before. People who know they're pretty good still go so they can show off just how wonderful they are to others who are trying to learn. They don't want to move on because, suddenly, they won't be the best any more. Here they're guaranteed to be noticed and watched. In the next class, they won't be anything special.'

'Maybe they really don't think they're good enough?' I whispered back.

Mario raised one eyebrow, then cupped the side of my face. 'Poor, innocent baby.'

I gave a stifled snort of laughter and batted his hand away.

Across the room, Beth flashed us a look and I stepped back behind Mario, trying to hide my sudden onset of giggles.

Jess caught my eye and grinned as she mouthed 'What?' to me.

I shook my head and did my best to focus my attention on what the instructor was now saying.

'You are a very bad influence!' I prodded Mario in the chest as the class ended with us all stood in a circle, giving ourselves a big round of applause. I clapped a couple of times before dropping my hands. Americans were very good at this sort of thing, but I always felt awkward and terribly British whenever I tried it.

'I am always a very good influence!' Mario protested, shocked, his dark eyes still twinkling with amusement.

'I find that hard to believe.'

'Me too!' Jess added, laughing as she put her arms into the coat Harry was holding out for her. 'This is the girl that never got in trouble at school. And you got her glares from the teacher in her first lesson.'

'It sounds like she has some catching up to do, then!' Mario laughed.

'No!' I bumped him. 'You have to behave. I want to learn.'

Mario gave a dramatic roll of his head. 'Fiiiiiiine,' he replied, before holding the door open so that we could all head down the stairs and out into the street.

'Thank you. Although I am glad you got partnered with me.'

'Me too.' He winked and gave me a squeeze before glancing up at a man walking towards us. He had his head down against the biting wind that had been whipping around all day, a knitted hat pulled low to his brow and a heavy wool pea coat wrapped around him. As he got closer, he lifted his head and caught Mario's eye. A bright smile suddenly creased the previously serious features.

'How was it?' he asked as he approached, his arm sliding around Mario's shoulder.

'Perfetto!'

'You managed to find someone to partner you then?'

'What, you mean as you refuse to?' Mario flashed, teasingly.

'Yep,' the man replied with no hint of regret.

Mario gave an eye roll and began the introductions. Andy, it seemed, wasn't a dancing man, preferring the quiet and books to the noisy atmosphere of salsa clubs, but was more than happy for his partner to follow his interest.

'Doesn't that make it difficult?' I asked, chatting with Andy as we sat in the small bar we'd all drifted to after the lesson. Still buzzing, none of us, apart from perhaps Andy, were ready to go home yet, but even he seemed happy to sit and talk. 'I mean, if you have such different interests?'

'No, we make it work. We give and take. And sometimes it's good to do things separately. You have things to share and talk about. I like to paint, but the thought of sitting still that long would, as I'm sure you've already gathered, send Mario into a frenzy. So, I go to painting class and now he comes here and learns to dance.'

'That's nice.'

'It is,' Andy agreed, smiling as he sipped his drink. 'And what about you?'

'What about me?'

'No one to learn this with, or do you have someone like me, who is desperately avoiding it?'

'The former. Well, there's Humphrey, but I don't think he'd be up for it either.'

'And Humphrey is?'

'My dog.'

Andy grinned. 'What type?'

'All sorts.' I quickly brought up a photo of my fuzzy pup and showed him.

He took the phone. 'Oh, he's so gorgeous! And what a great name!'

'See? That's what I think,' I said, accepting the phone back, 'but my friend, Seb, gives me grief about it all the time.'

'And who's Seb?'

'Seb is the man who's perfect for her!' Jess interjected as she swung herself onto the seat next to us.

'Ignore her. Seb is just a good friend.'

'More than that.'

'He is not.'

'So why isn't he here?'

'One, we're just friends.'

'He could still learn.'

'Fair enough. And he probably would give it a go.'

'Really?' Jess asked, a hint of surprise in her voice and I knew why.

'Yes. He doesn't let his injury stop him trying anything.'

'So why isn't he here?' Andy asked again.

'He lives miles away.'

'No distance is too much for love,' Jess swooned.

'Oh, for goodness' sake. All that Latin music and those last two cocktails have addled your brain.' I slurped up the last of my own mocktail, twirling its tiny paper umbrella as I did so.

'Not at all. I'm the one who sees things clearly now.'

'No, you are the one in gushy, romantic love and it colours everything you see,' I said, gently.

'I think you'd be surprised.'

'I would.'

Andy gave me a grin as, on the bar, my phone began to ring. Seb's picture showed on the screen.

'My, my! Who's that?' asked Mario as he and Harry joined our conversation, peering over Andy's shoulder at the phone.

'That's Seb!' Jess pointed, excitedly, almost bouncing in her seat. 'See, I told you?'

I juggled the phone and quickly answered, trying to angle myself in a way that would prevent everyone seeing Seb's ridiculously good looking face smile slightly crookedly from my phone screen. 'Hi, I'm just in the middle of something. Can I call you back in a bit?'

'Sure.' He paused for a beat and I saw his eyes take in the background. 'Oh sorry, I didn't realise you were going out after the class.'

'No. I didn't know I was. Kind of a last minute thing with some others from the class.'

At this, the other four crowded round me and waved at the screen. Seb gave an unsure wave back as I rolled my eyes and wriggled away to a quieter spot.

'Oh, right. OK. Great. That's good. Looks like you enjoyed it.'

'I did, thanks.'

'OK, Well, I'll let you get back to it. Have a nice evening and we'll catch up tomorrow or something.'

I glanced at my watch. 'Oh my god, is that the time?'

'Yeah. I was... just a bit worried about you.'

'Sorry. I know I said I'd call.'

'It's fine. I'm happy you're OK and having fun. I'll let you get back to your friends. Take care.'

'Bye, Seb.'

And he was gone. Turning back to the bar, four faces were watching me.

'Oh, for goodness' sake! We're just friends!' I laughed, exasperation in my words.

Mario gave me a look. 'Sweetheart,' he said, his Italian accent infusing the word with meaning. 'Friends is great. We are friends now. It is wonderful! But—' he took my phone from me and tapped at a couple of things on the screen before turning it back towards me. Seb's picture was back up on the screen, along with his contact details. 'If he looks like this, is straight, solvent and single, then you reaaaaally need to do something about the whole "just friends" thing!'

'Here, here!' Jess added, raising her glass.

'Oh... shush!' I said, grabbing my phone back and shoving it in my bag. 'I'm more than happy just as I am, and so is he. I'm not about to go ruining it.'

Mario crossed his arms and shook his head at me.

I looked to Andy for support.

'Sorry, kid. I'm kind of with them.'

I tipped my head back on my shoulders for a moment and let out a sigh. 'Ugh, Andy! I was relying on you for sensible back-up!'

He let that unexpected smile loose again and shrugged.

Shortly after, we gathered our coats and headed back out into the sharp wintry night air. There were, as always from the newspapers, rumours of blizzards, but the sky was clear and, away from the street lights, pinpricks of bright starlight shimmered in the blackness. We shared hugs and number exchanges with Mario and Andy, before Jess, Harry and I walked to the car park where we'd left our cars. After more hugs, we got in our respective vehicles, and Harry, who'd also been relegated to mocktails this evening, pulled away quickly, the tail lights of his Jag soon disappearing into the stream of cars along the road before turning off.

My breath steamed in the cold air and I rubbed my hands together quickly after putting them briefly on the freezing steering wheel, ruing the fact I'd left my leather gloves in my other coat. I gritted my teeth and laid my hands back on the wheel, turning the key as I did so. Nothing. No! Not now!

7

'Come on, little car, please! I'm freezing! Please start. Please, please, please. I've taken you to the garage and they've said you're fine, so please just let me get home and warm up!'

I tried again. Nothing.

One more time. This time, the engine started quietly and ran smoothly. No drama, no fuss. This was the pattern and had been for months. Of course, every time I took it to the garage, the problem never showed itself and I ended paying to take my car back, knowing something was lurking. I'd now given up on trying to get it fixed and had begun looking around at replacing the car instead. It had served me well, but I'd had a lot of years out of it and moments like tonight were not great for my peace of mind. I needed a car I could just get in and not worry about. Add it to the to-do list.

The rest of the journey home was, thankfully, drama free and I scooped up Humph as I came through the door and snuggled him against me, absorbing his joy at my return, as well some of his warmth. Changing into my jammies and big cuddly dressing gown, I then headed back into the kitchen to make a hot drink to try and warm up from the inside.

I snuggled into my favourite spot on the sofa, and Humphrey clambered up and over me, before flopping down on my lap. The TV was on low and I flicked aimlessly for a moment before glancing over at my phone. I felt bad that I'd forgotten to call Seb earlier and unintentionally worried him. When we'd talked in the past, he admitted that he knew he could be overprotective about people. He'd always been that way to an extent, but his deployment had sent ripples throughout his life, and although he'd dealt with a lot, and dealt with it brilliantly, it was naive to think that such an experience wouldn't change a person. I snagged the phone and rested my hand on Humphrey's sleeping back. Opening up the chat thread, I typed a message.

Hi. Sorry I worried you earlier. Hope you had a good evening

The message showed delivered but remained unread by the time I went to bed shortly after. It was pretty late, so I wasn't surprised, but something inside me felt a little strange that we hadn't said goodnight. It was a habit we'd fallen into quite a while ago now and it had stuck. I'd expected that to be the first thing to go when Seb had dates, but it didn't. He always said hi, checked I was doing OK and always said goodnight. Until tonight.

I shook it out of my mind. He probably assumed that our brief call earlier served the same purpose, which it may well have done.

* * *

The following morning was Saturday and I had plans to meet my parents for a food fayre in one of their local villages. Humphrey was even allowed to come, although I wasn't sure how fair it was to subject his nose to all those delicious smells and then him not be allowed anything. I dipped my hand back into the treat jar on the kitchen counter and added a couple more to my pocket, before grabbing his travel rug, a portion of dog food, and a couple of toys, as well as his lead and my handbag.

'You ready to see Nanny and Popsy?' I asked.

By his circular dance of delight, I guessed the answer was yes.

'Come on, then. Assuming the car starts, of course,' I muttered to myself.

Humphrey's ears twitched, catching my tone and his fuzzy head tilted at me in question.

'It'll be fine. Come on.' And we headed out, round the building towards the car park.

* * *

'Hello, darling!' Mum threw her arms wide and hugged me like she hadn't seen me in months. I'd popped round in the week, but I still loved that she did this every time. My older sister travelled a lot in her capacity as first-class cabin crew for British Airways and I knew she got the same greeting whether she'd been away for weeks to some far-flung destination or had been round the previous day.

Humphrey rubbed his body against Mum's legs and Dad, approaching from the kitchen, laughed, scooping him up in one large hand and plopping him against his broad chest.

'Feeling a bit left out, are you?' he asked as Humphrey wriggled in pleasure and snuggled himself against Dad's cashmere jumper.

'Don't ever let Sally see you cuddling him in that jumper she bought you? She'll go up the wall.' I pulled a face as I gave him a hug, temporarily pinning my dog between us.

Dad put a finger to his lips. 'Our secret.'

I loved my sister, but my idea of casual and hers were two completely different things. She didn't exactly object to Humphrey, but he had to stay in the kitchen if we visited her place, which, as we generally sat elsewhere, I and he hated. It felt like he was being punished for something he hadn't done, so, now, if I visited, I'd either leave him at home, or drop him off at my parents' place for a bit. In lieu of any grandchildren, they were always thrilled to have their granddog to visit. They'd ummed and ahhed over the years about getting a dog themselves, but they did quite often like to drop everything and go and do something, which, thanks to Sally, sometimes involved little trips abroad. A dog wouldn't really work with that lifestyle, so they stuck to what they knew and just enjoyed Humphrey's visits.

'What have you been up to then, love?' Dad asked, as he tucked my arm into his, my other one was holding Humph's lead, his toenails tapping on the pavement as we began our walk into the next village and the food fayre.

'Well, last night I went dancing.'

'Did you, darling?' Mum leaned across from the other side of Dad. 'What, at a club?'

'No. Those lessons I was saying about.'

'The lessons you've been talking about for years?'

I wobbled my head. 'Yes, all right. I took a long run-up.'

Dad grinned and gave my arm a little squeeze. 'So, how was it?'

'Good. Jess and Harry have started too.'

'Oh, that's nice.' I could hear the bright tone in Mum's voice and knew there was something else. 'Did you go with someone else too?'

'Nope. Just me.'

'So, who did you dance with?' Dad asked.

'I danced with the delightful Mario.'

Mum's head popped back around dad again. 'Mario?'

'Yes.'

'And?'

'And what?'

Mum gave me a look. 'I might be old, but I'm not daft. Spill.'

The hot breath from my laughter billowed into cooling clouds in front of me as I replied. 'There's nothing to spill.'

'He's called Mario. Of course there is!'

Dad tilted his head towards me. 'She's always had a thing for Italian men.'

'I have not!' Mum gave him a little push.

Dad slid his eyes to me and waggled his brows.

'OK, what do you want to know? Remember I only met him last night though.'

'So, what do you know about him?'

I gave a shrug. 'He loves to dance, he came over from Italy six years ago, works in graphic design, is very astute when it comes to people and has a wicked sense of humour.'

'Is he good looking?'

'Yep. Very. Tall, dark, Italian. The whole caboodle.'

'And?'

'And what?' I tried to ignore the hopeful look on Mum's face.

'Are you seeing him again?'

'Yep. Next week at class.'

'Not before.'

'No.'

'Why not? It sounds like you got on well.'

'We did. But he's my dance partner. That's all.'

'Darling, I know you're happy with Humphrey, but I don't want you to think that just because some things haven't worked out, that there isn't hope.'

I caught Dad's eyes and rolled my own. 'I don't think that, Mum.'

'Good. Good. So, you like this Mario?'

'Yes. He's very nice. We went out after class to a bar for a drink.'

'You did?'

'Yes. Me and Mario and Jess and Harry. And Andy.' Time to put Mum out of her misery. Or plunge her into it. Either way, it had to be done.

'Andy? Was he from dancing too?'

'No. Andy is Mario's partner.'

Dad snorted a laugh which he expertly morphed into a cough. Mum absentmindedly patted him on the back.

'Thanks,' he mumbled, keeping his eyes diverted from mine. We were the big gigglers in our family. Sally and Mum had a level of control Dad and I had entirely missed out on. We both knew that if he looked at me now, it was over.

'Partner?'

'Yes.'

'As in... boyfriend.'

'Yep.'

'Oh. Well. That's nice. And what was he like?' Mum said, trying to recover from the disappointment.

'Really lovely, actually. Much quieter than Mario, but they fit well together.'

'Good. Good. Well, it's nice that you have someone you like at the class. I imagine Jess and Harry are quite tied up with each other. I just didn't want you being left out.'

'I wasn't left out, Mum. It was fine. Also, talking of Jess and Harry, they're having an engagement party at some point. I don't know when, but Jess said to let you know there'll be an invitation wending its way to you.'

'Oh, how sweet. Will that be in London?'

I shrugged. 'I literally know as much as you do at the moment. But yes, I expect so.'

'And how's work?' Dad asked, and I gave his arm a little squeeze, thanking him for the swerve in conversational direction.

'Good, thanks. Been really busy with a new client and Seb's charity is having a big gala thing later in the year, so I'm getting involved in the organisation of that, which is quite full on.'

'You're not doing too much, are you, love?'

'No, Mum. It's all fine. I'm enjoying it.'

'And Seb is the veterans' charity chap, right?'

'That's him.'

'He all right? I know you said you're quite friendly now.' As this came from Dad, I knew there was no hidden depth to the question.

'Yes. Busy.' I assumed he was anyway, as there was still nothing to show he'd read my message from last night when I looked earlier, which was pretty unusual. And he always sent me a hi in the morning. Except that today he hadn't.

I pulled out my phone and glanced at it. Nothing.

'Talking of busy...' The fayre was packed, the bright crisp day combined with the artisan offerings having enticed people out of doors. Dad bent and picked up the dog, manoeuvring him into a comfy position for both of them. 'We don't want you getting trodden on down there, do we, little man?'

I smiled at them both. I loved that my big bear of a dad had such a soft side and, by the looks of things, so did Humph, who was now surveying the scene from this new, elevated position.

'Ooh, these look good!' Mum said, grabbing my hand and plunging us into the foody fray.

* * *

The trouble with these foody events is that you end up eating far, far too much. The sun had long set and I was sat sprawled on one of the sofas in the beamed living room of their cottage, while Mum and Dad sat opposite. Dad's feet were up on the pouffe cum coffee table thing and his head was back, as he snored softly. Dinner had been large and delicious and I was having trouble keeping awake myself.

'You can always stay here, darling. You know there's room. I know it's not far, but it seems silly to go home if you're coming back for Sunday roast tomorrow.' Mum looked at me for a moment. 'You are coming, aren't you? Sally's mentioned that she might be bringing someone with her.'

'Wouldn't it be helpful for you to know whether she is or isn't?'

Mum waved away the query. 'You know I always cook too much. I didn't like to ask too many questions as she hasn't been able to make it for a while, what with her shifts and hectic social life.'

As opposed to my very much not hectic social life which found me quite often around at my parents' place for Sunday lunch.

'What's this one then?' My sister's standards in her housekeeping and dress extended to her men. They were always, and without exception, groomed to within an inch of their lives, dressed expensively, and never earned less than six figures.

'Oh, I don't know. Something in the City, I think. Or is this one the pilot?'

Dad stretched as he roused himself from his nap and Mum looked at him for help, but he just shrugged.

'Best behaviour then? Better not show her up,' I said, straightening myself up and standing ramrod straight. I saw Dad grin and give me a wink.

'Come on, Lottie. You know she doesn't think that about you... us.'

I was less convinced, and if I was honest, I wasn't sure Mum was entirely sure of this fact either. Sally had always been ambitious and loved her glamorous lifestyle of jetting across the world, staying in top hotels, and meeting the rich and famous through the first-class cabin status she'd worked her way up to. I wasn't sure it was all that glamorous – at least not all the time. In the odd unguarded moment, Sally had mentioned that not everyone who travelled first class had first-class manners. As much as she loved her job, and had dealt with enough tricky customers over the years for it to be accepted that this sort of thing was all part of it, I think it did tend to take the lustre off things sometimes. But those moments of weakness were few and far between with my sister. She looked perfect, acted that way and wanted everyone to think that's what she was.

If I really thought she was unhappy, I'd have been more worried, but I knew she really did love her job and socialising. The men she met weren't ones that appealed to me, but then she and I had always been quite different, in everything from our looks to our ambition. Sally was the blonde haired (admittedly via a very expensive regular appointment at a top London stylist), blue eyed, slim, toned epitome of style and elegance. I'd kept my brunette tones, but we had the same eyes. I was less slim and less toned, although more so since I'd got Humphrey and our long daily walks had become part of my routine. As for the style and elegance, that was most definitely weighted in Sally's favour. Her nightwear was silk. Mine was fleecy with sloths printed on it.

'Thanks, Mum, but I've got some things I want to get done in the morning tomorrow, so I'd better go.'

'Only if you're sure.'

'Yes. But thanks. And thanks for today. It was lovely.'

She gave me a smile and nodded.

'I'm sorry if I go on,' Mum said as she hugged me goodbye. Dad was loading Humphrey and all his gubbins into the car for me, along with the food I'd got at the fayre earlier.

'What are you talking about?'

'You. Mario. You know. Dad says I go on a bit sometimes.'

'Oh, Mum. Don't worry about it. I know you mean well, and I'm fine.'

'I just worry about you, especially now Jess has moved away and in with Harry.'

'We still see each other.'

'I know, I know. You're good friends, and I hope you always will be. I suppose... I just want that happiness for you too.'

'So do I, Mum. But it happened for Jess when she was least expecting it, and that's probably the best way.'

'I suppose. I just hate to think you might be lonely.'

I shook my head. 'I'm really not. I promise.' And it was true. I wasn't. That didn't mean I would say no to meeting the right guy, but I'd also met quite a few wrong guys in the past year and I'd had more than enough of that. I had my business, my dog and my friends. Not to mention my family, and it was all good. I knew I'd have a hard time entirely convincing my mum of that, but hopefully Dad would be able to do a better job than me.

'Tell Mum I'm fine, will you?'

Dad nodded against me and gave me a squeeze. 'Let us know when you're in.'

'Will do,' I called, crossing my fingers and turning the key. The engine came to life and I gave a wave and turned the little car towards home.

Back in my flat, I unloaded everything I'd brought home and gave Humphrey a treat for being such a good boy in the car.

I pulled my phone from my pocket and quickly opened the chat app. There was a message from Seb that had come in a couple of hours earlier, but I hadn't looked at my phone for ages, as I'd sat chatting and watching telly with my parents.

Home! Love you xx

I sent the message to my parents and almost immediately received one back.

Good-oh. Love you too. Xx

Then I opened Seb's.

8

Hope you've had a good day

I frowned at it. There was something off, just slightly, but I couldn't work out what it was.

I did, thanks. Did you?

I set the phone down and picked up a magazine, but the reply ping sounded before I'd had a chance to even open it.

Took Scooby on a really long walk. Lots of fresh air

The message was followed by a picture of his dog on the sofa, resting his head against Seb's left knee, all four feet in the air.

Looks like someone enjoyed it. What about his owner?

His owner is knackered

I frowned, sending an emoji that conveyed the same message.

You didn't overdo it, did you?

Nope. All good

I wasn't entirely convinced. I knew that Seb still got pain from his leg and that some days were good and others less so and that it would always be that way. But I also knew that he had taken part in all sorts of activities and challenges with his prosthetic leg, things I wouldn't have even contemplated doing with two good ones. But it still didn't stop me being concerned. Or enable me to shake off the feeling that something wasn't right.

Is everything OK?

Yep

He added a thumbs up for good measure. The unconvinced, weird niggly feeling remained, but I didn't know what else I could do. I knew I'd forgotten to ring last night, but Seb wasn't the kind of guy to take offence at that. He understood, more than anyone, how easy it was to get caught up in stuff. And it wasn't like we were dating or anything. But there was something. And it was bugging the hell out of me.

So how was your class?

I pressed the video call symbol instead of typing. It rang a couple of times and Seb appeared on the screen, one hand rubbing over his cropped hair.

'Hi.'

'Hi. Is this OK, or are you busy?' I asked.

'Nope, this is good. You all right?'

'Yes, thanks. Are you? I'm a bit worried you did too much today.'

He pulled a face. 'I'm fine. Honestly.'

'I didn't know you had a big hike planned.'

Seb gave a shrug. 'Last minute decision. Nice day. Why not?'

'True.'

'Did you have a good day?'

'Yes, thanks. I went to a food fayre, so I've now eaten far too much and there are way too many tempting goodies in my fridge. Plus, I have roast dinner at my parents' booked for tomorrow, so, all in, I think I'm going to be rolling out of the weekend.'

'It's definitely a shame I don't live closer. I could have helped you out with some of that.' He gave me a grin.

My waistline agreed. Other parts of me also agreed based solely on that smile, but I was trying to ignore them.

'Nice to visit these sorts of things though.'

'It is. My parents love them so always know where the good ones are. I just tag along.'

'Oh... you went with your parents?' He pushed himself up a little straighter on the sofa as he spoke.

'Yes.'

'They OK?'

I gave a sigh. 'Apart from my mum despairing of me ever finding a man, yeah, they're fine.'

'I'm sure she's just worried that you might be lonely, or something.'

'That's exactly it, actually.'

Seb gave a sympathetic smile. 'Are you?'

'What?'

'Lonely.'

I rolled my bottom lip out and back. Probably not the most attractive trait I had but one I sometimes forgot to curtail when I was pondering over things. Seb didn't seem to notice.

'No.'

'That's good then.'

'That doesn't mean I wouldn't be happy to meet Mr Right, if such a mythical creature even exists, but, like I told my mum, I'm OK as I am.'

Seb nodded and smiled.

'Are you?' I asked.

'Lonely?'

'Yes.'

'Sometimes.'

Somewhere deep in my heart, I felt something shift and crack.

'Oh,' I said, which wasn't exactly the eloquent and meaningful reply I'd liked to have responded with.

Seb shook his head, smiling. 'Hey. Don't look at me like that.'

'Like what?'

'All sad and big-eyed and compassionate.'

'I'm not!'

'You are.'

'Well, it's not intentional. That's just my face. But I do hate to think of you lonely.'

'Everyone gets like it sometimes. It's no big deal for me. There are just moments. You asked and I answered, but I'm sort of wishing I'd fibbed now because I'm not sure I can take that pitying look from you much longer.' He laughed.

'I am not pitying!' I said, waving my free hand.

'You don't even know you're doing it!'

'Oh well, excuse me for having a compassionate soul.'

He rolled his eyes at me. 'Tell me properly about your dance class.'

I stuck my tongue out at him and rearranged Humphrey on my lap so that his paw was no longer pressing into my stomach.

'It was OK. Kind of awkward to start with, like I said.'

'But I gather it improved?'

'It did.'

'Thanks to the men you were out at the bar with?' He wiggled his eyebrows and I gave him a look.

'Just one of them. Mario.'

He nodded. 'Fair enough.'

'I just felt funny as everyone was already paired up, and I was sort of wondering if I'd done the right thing, but then Mario arrived.'

'And saved the day.'

'Well, that might be overcooking it a little, but it was nice not to have to sit out and wait to be swapped in with someone.'

'He any good?'

'He's done a bit before, so it was nice to have a bit of guidance, but basically we just had a really good laugh.'

'That's good. I'm glad you enjoyed yourself in the end. So, where does the other guy come into it?'

'Andy? We met up with him after and went for a drink with Jess and Harry too.'

'Oh right. Didn't you tell your mum all this?'

'Yes, why?'

'I just thought it might have taken the heat off a bit.'

'Ohhhhh, I see. Yes, well, initially she was terribly excited about Mario, you're right.'

'Initially?'

'Yes. But when I explained that Andy was Mario's boyfriend, her mind was immediately filled with images of me on a dusty shelf again.'

Seb let out a laugh. 'You will never be left on a shelf, dusty or otherwise.'

'Thank you for your vote of confidence.'

'Just saying it like it is.'

I smiled and tilted my head down, ostensibly to check on Humphrey but also to try and hide the blush that I felt creeping up my face.

'It's ever so cute when you blush.'

I looked back up. 'Oh, be quiet,' I said, laughing.

He gave me that slightly crooked grin again as he moved and adjusted his leg on the sofa, out of my sight. As he did so, I caught a flash of pain dart across his features.

'Is it bad today?' I asked.

He shook his head.

'You're a terrible liar.'

'I don't think you'd make a great one either, Ms Blushy Face, so we're a good pair.'

'True. Was it bad before you went on your marathon hike?' I pressed.

'Average.'

'Should you not have rested then instead of doubling down?'

Seb frowned at the phone screen. 'You've met me, right?'

'Technically, no. I haven't. But I know what you mean. You're stubborn. Sometimes too much so.'

'I prefer the word driven.'

'You would. But just changing the word doesn't change the fact you don't look after yourself as well as you should do sometimes.'

'Sorry, Mum.'

'Ughhh. Why do I bother?' I said, letting my head loll back on the sofa.

'I do appreciate it.' His voice was softer now and I pulled my head back up to look at the screen. 'Honestly. I really do.'

I pulled a face and nodded.

'So, I've been thinking,' Seb started.

'Oh dear. Is that wise?'

'Smartarse. Shoosh.'

'I beg your pardon?'

'Please,' he asked, breaking out a smile that would probably get a lot of women to do a lot of things.

'Hmm.' I said, non-commitally, pretending it had had no effect on me whatsoever. Even though it really, really did.

'What you said a moment ago. About technically not having met?'

'Yes?'

'How would you feel about changing that?'

How did I feel about that?

'OK...'

'We've been friends for ages, we speak most days and... I just think it'd be really nice to meet up and spend some time together in person. But I don't know how you feel about it. Whether you'd prefer to just—'

'I'd love to,' I blurted. OK, so I guess that's how I felt about it. Good to know.

'Really?'

'Yes. Definitely.'

'I mean, it's not like a date or anything. I don't want you thinking I'm trying to—'

'No, I know,' I replied, trying not to feel too disappointed that he'd been in such a hurry to point that out. The rational part of me knew that was just how Seb was. Upfront, honest. But the non-rational part of me, the part that had the crush on him, was now doing her best not to hurl herself into a corner and wail.

'Oh Good. Right. I just... I didn't want to scare you off before I'd even finished telling you the idea.'

Scare me off? You've seen yourself, right?

'Ha! No. Nope. Not at all,' I said, trying not to sound weird and, even to my own ears, failing miserably. 'So, what is the idea?'

'I remember you said ages ago that you loved Agatha Christie, right?'

'Oh crikey. That really was ages ago. I'm surprised you remembered.'

'You still do though?'

'Yes! Of course. Love her!'

'OK. So, there's a play of hers on at a theatre that's about an hour's drive from both of us and I just wondered if you might want to go?'

My smile answered for me. 'I'd love to.'

Seb relaxed and smiled back and it was only then that I realised he'd tensed up. Which wasn't like Seb at all.

'Did you honestly think I'd say no?'

He shrugged. 'Honestly, I wasn't sure. Your whole plan this year is to say no to stuff and I was just concerned about asking because I didn't want to ruin what we have and make things weird.'

'Fair enough. But it's not like I'm saying no to everything. Only the boring stuff. And why would it be weird?'

'Why is anything?'

'I'm not sure I understand the question!' I laughed.

He shook his head. 'Never mind. The important thing is you said yes. So, I took the liberty of looking up some times already and there's a showing next Friday evening that has some seats left, if you fancy that one? Depending on what time you can get away, we could always grab a bite to eat first maybe.'

'That sounds great.'

'OK. I'll send you through all the details and directions and I can order the tickets now while you're on. Where do you like to sit?'

'What have they got?'

'Let's see.' I heard him tap some keys and waited as he brought up the theatre's seating plan. 'Looks like there's some in the stalls. Fourth row back?'

'Sounds perfect. I'll be able to see what's going on without having to use those ridiculous little opera glasses things.'

'Do they still have those?'

'I've literally no idea. It's ages since I've been to the theatre.'

'I don't think I've been since I was a kid.'

'No! Really?'

'Yeah. Bad eh?'

'No, not bad. People have different interests.'

'That's the thing. I love the theatre. But I guess I just never get around to it.'

'Well, now you are.'

'I am indeed. There, done,' he said, picking the phone back up from where he'd balanced it while he booked the tickets on his laptop. 'We can pick them up at the box office on the night.'

'Ooh! I'm really excited now. Thanks, Seb. Can I give you the money when I see you?'

'Nope. My treat.'

'Oh no, you can't do that. I wouldn't have let you book them if I knew you'd do that.'

'You wouldn't have let me?' He raised a curious, dark brow.

'No. And don't look at me like that either. You might be bigger than me, but I have skills.'

'I don't doubt it for a moment. But the tickets are on me. As a thanks for everything you do.' I opened my mouth to protest. 'On top of what I pay you for.'

'Then thank you. And I look forward to it.'

'Me too.'

'Well, I'd better get off to bed. I need to clean my flat tomorrow and then make myself look presentable enough for seeing my sister.'

'You always look presentable.'

'She doesn't have the same relaxed attitude to my fondness for loungewear as you do.'

'She's not wearing it. You are.'

'Still. I have to make a bit of an effort. Apparently, she's bringing a bloke too, so we're all going to be on our best behaviour.'

'That sounds exhausting. Why don't you just say no? I mean, if not this year, then when can you?'

'I don't want to. Obviously, I understand the confusion as you've never had one of my mum's roasts, but, seriously, they're worth anything! And I'm probably making it sound worse than it is. Sally's just... particular. But she's harmless. She's just quite used to getting her own way. She doesn't really stand for much less, especially when it comes to men, so I think sometimes she forgets we're family and know her of old.'

'But you still try to please her.'

'She's my sister. I want her to be happy.'

Seb nodded but said no more. 'Well, I'd better let you go. Enjoy your roast tomorrow!'

'I shall. I hope you're going to rest a bit.'

'I am. Mostly. I'm going over to my brother's for the day, so apart from being a human climbing frame for my niece and nephew, it should be nice.' The joy that his family brought him was reflected in his features, his eyes smiling as much as that generous mouth.

'That sounds lovely, Seb. Family days all round!'

9

It turned out Sally's new chap, Oliver, was something in the City, but exactly what that something was remained a mystery to us all despite the fact he'd explained it more than once. I'd have had more luck trying to understand Klingon.

'That sounds very interesting,' my dad said diplomatically as he passed me the roast potatoes, the waft of them making my mouth water as I dished several onto my plate before passing them on to Sally, who took one. I looked at her, looked back at the dish full of golden deliciousness and then back at Sally. She caught my eye and gave the most delicate of shrugs.

'I shouldn't even be having one really, but you know I can't resist Mum's cooking,' she cooed, tilting her head at Mum, who reached over and patted her hand.

I looked at my sister's plate, one potato, a pile of French beans, two slices of lean roast chicken and some spinach. My eyes then drifted to my own, piled high with roast and mash potato, several pieces of chicken, plus some gorgeous, crispy skin, piles of veggies, all drowned in thick gravy. Apparently, her idea of not resisting and mine were two very different things.

* * *

I smothered the home made rhubarb crumble in thick, velvety custard the colour of sunshine and took a spoonful, feeling the wonderful textures meld in my mouth – crunchy topping, soft fruit and tangy custard.

'Don't forget, it's my book club this Thursday evening, Lottie.'

I shifted my eyes to my sister, the place setting in front of her entirely devoid of pudding bowl. She took a sip of tonic water as I swallowed my mouthful.

'Umm... OK,' I said, not sure what I was supposed to make of this announcement.

Sally turned a little and fixed her gaze on me. 'Have you forgotten?'

Apparently so.

She let out a sigh. 'I'm going to be in Kuala Lumpur so I won't be able to make it, so I need you to sit in for me.'

'Oh.'

'Good. Thanks.' And she turned away, giving a small, elegant hair flick to catch the attention of Oliver, who raised his eyes briefly from his bowl to acknowledge her, smile and then return his concentration to the food. Mum's puddings could do that to you. Sally accepted this and turned back.

'I can't do that, I'm afraid, Sally.'

Sally sat up a little straighter. 'Sorry?'

'Thursday. The book club thing. I can't do it.'

She frowned at me. Well, I assume that was what she was doing. Sally had been getting Botox for so long, figuring out some of her expressions now was guesswork on our part.

'You have to!' she said.

I gave a full-on frown that no one could mistake and loaded up my spoon. 'No, I don't,' I said, taking another mouthful.

'Yes! You do! I've arranged it all now. You can't cancel on me! How would that make me look?'

I did my best to keep my emotions low-key and stick to my guns. 'I'm sorry if you've made arrangements, but you didn't ask me if I could do it, or even if I wanted to, so you can't be cross now when I can't make it.'

'You know I rely on you to take over when I can't be here.'

'I know that you have done for the last three years, but things have changed and I don't enjoy doing it. I'm sorry if you feel I'm letting you down, but it's not up to you to host every time anyway. The others can take turns to work around your shifts. I'm sure they wouldn't mind!'

'It's *my* book club! I can hardly ask someone else to host it, can I?'

'You seem OK with asking me.'

'You're my sister. You don't count.'

'Wow. Thanks,' I said, shovelling in another spoonful, partly as a diversionary tactic for my mouth.

Sally gave an airy flap of her hand. 'You know what I mean.'

I gave a quick brow raise without looking up.

'Lots, please?' Sally moved from expectant to pleading.

My mind cast back over the past three years when I'd had to host her bloody book club. They always picked high-brow books that I didn't enjoy reading but Sally insisted I slog through so that I could take part in the discussion. Except I never did take part in the discussion. The five women who came to Sally's book club never made an effort to include me and pretty much only ever spoke to me to request more tea. I wasn't entirely unconvinced that they thought I was staff. Either way, the thought of getting back into that loop gave me stomach ache. And now was the perfect time to put a stop to it.

'I can't, Sally. I'm sorry. They're not really... my kind of people.' In for a penny, in for a pound.

'They're not your... What does that even matter? They're my kind of people! And you're making me let them down.'

'I'm sure they'll get over it,' I said, running out of patience.

Mum gave me a look, but I dropped my eyes to the bowl and concentrated on getting the last few bits of comforting deliciousness out of it.

'I see!' Sally said. It was just two little words, but they were absolutely loaded.

'I'm guessing by the tone of your voice, you don't. Not really.'

'I do. Entirely,' she said, her blue eyes flashing at me before turning to Oliver, who was now watching the interaction with a mixture of interest and wariness. 'Last year, my sister did this stupid year of saying yes, and now this year it's all about saying no. And apparently that applies to family too. Honestly, Lottie. Whatever will it be next?'

My face was burning with embarrassment and indignation. 'It wasn't stupid, Sally. It was to support Jess and to cheer myself up after my relationship ended. I don't think it was stupid at all.'

'You hated half of the things!'

'So? At least I tried them!'

'Oh, for goodness' sake, you hated it so much you've dedicated this year to saying no so you can sit indoors in your bloody pyjamas!'

'It's not about that at all! It's about saying no to things I don't want to do. And your book club happens to be one of the things I definitely don't want to do.'

She gave a dramatic roll of her perfectly mascaraed, aesthetician enhanced lashes. 'All you've got to do is sit there and serve tea!'

'I'm not a maid, Sally! And I have no interest in being one for you and your so-called friends.'

'They are my friends.'

'Well, then I pity you,' I snapped.

'Lottie.' Dad's soft tone brought me down from where I was beginning to climb the wall.

I let out a breath and shifted on my chair to face my sister. She was glaring at me with that haughty look she did so well.

'Look, Sally. I'm sorry you're upset and I don't want to argue with you. But I can't do the book club thing for you any more. I don't enjoy it. I don't feel comfortable with those women and I also have Humphrey now.'

Sally let out a sigh. 'What on earth has your dog got to do with anything?'

'Because he'd have to be shut in the kitchen the entire evening and he doesn't like it. I don't like it.'

She gave a small, sharp shake of her head as if me considering the emotional welfare of my pet, and apparently myself, was a ridiculous and inexplicable annoyance. 'Well, it's very inconvenient.'

'I'm sorry for that. It wasn't my intention, but I think it's for the best.'

'For you, obviously,' she said, before turning back to Oliver and giving him a huge, dramatic eye roll.

I bit my tongue and then decided that Humphrey could probably do with a trip to the garden. 'Mum, do you mind if I just take Humph outside for a moment? I'll come and help you make tea and coffee in a minute.'

'Of course, dear.'

I pushed my chair away from the table and headed over towards the kitchen and the large glass doors my parents had had fitted when they'd extended this room. My dog, who had been peacefully sleeping throughout the entire drama, rose, stretched and yawned and then trotted after me. He'd have been fine for a while yet, but I needed to get out and he was the perfect fuzzy excuse.

The cool air seemed to wake Humph up and, once outside, he set off charging around for a few minutes on an impromptu, and high speed, patrol just to make sure everything was as it should be. Having assessed that it was, he then set to exploring at a slower pace, giving everything a good old sniff and watering a few plants on his exploratory rounds.

I left him to it and wandered further down the garden to a seat my dad had built many years ago with timbers rescued from his own grandfather's shed. Things were built to be far more substantial back then and the bench had withstood many years of sunshine and rain and been with us in every garden. I'd sat on this bench and cried when I broke up with my first boyfriend, and when I'd broken up with my last one. And now I was doing my best not to have it witness to any more tears. Unfortunately, the burning in my throat, and pounding in my head, not to mention the fact things had gone a bit blurry, meant that my body had its own ideas about that.

I plopped down on to the bench, dislodging one of the tears. Through my watery vision, I looked up and saw my dad strolling down the garden, Humphrey trotting beside him, looking up at him as if they were deep in conversation. Dad reached the bench, and sat down, handing me my jacket.

'Chilly out here, love.'

'Thanks,' I said, pushing my arms into the sleeves. When I was done, he handed me one of his neatly folded and pressed white cotton handkerchiefs. I took it and wiped haphazardly at my eyes. Humphrey sat at our feet for a moment, watching, then trotted off to investigate the rest of the garden. 'Sorry, Dad. I didn't mean to ruin dinner.'

'Oh, Lots, you didn't ruin anything.'

'Is Sally still here?'

'Yes. Old Ollie boy got a look at that cake your mum baked this morning. I'm not sure even Sally's wiles will get him to shift until he's had some of that with a cuppa.'

'That's saying something.'

'You know your mum's cooking.'

'I do.' I prodded my tummy for emphasis.

'Ah, there's nothing there.'

'There's plenty there.'

'You'll walk it off. You've only just eaten.'

I made a noise that could have been dismissal, denial, or acceptance. Dad seemed to accept it as the last.

'You all right?'

I let out a long sigh and watched my hot breath cloud in front of me. 'Yeah. I just... Do you think this is stupid?'

'What?'

'The fact that I did that saying yes thing last year and now I'm saying no.'

'Nope. You needed a change. Something to shake things up a bit and take your mind off stuff. It's good to challenge ourselves sometimes, and that's what you're doing. That's never stupid. Sally's just annoyed because she's not used to you saying no to her.'

'Sally's not used to anyone saying no to her, apart from you and mum.'

'There you go. She's got a bit of a shock, that's all. She'll calm down.'

'Honestly? I hate arguing with her, but I don't really care if she calms down or not right at the moment. She called me stupid in front of a total stranger and laughed at me. Then she makes a big thing about family!' I could feel myself getting wound up again and the tears began burning against my cold face.

'If that Oliver's as clever as he thinks he is, he'll work it out for himself. If he gets to stick around that long. You know what Sally's like. Besides, it doesn't matter what he thinks. You have to do what you want to do. Did you really not enjoy doing that book thing for Sally?'

'No! I hated it. The women just completely ignored me the whole time, talked about their cosmetic surgeons, luncheon appointments and then gushed about books I couldn't see the point of! It was horrible. I know Sally's a pain in the arse sometimes, but she's not like that. Not really. I don't know why she even spends time with them!'

'We can't choose other people's friends. Why didn't you say something before?'

'Because I knew Sally would go off on one about it. Like she did today. But it's true that now I have Humphrey I hate shutting him in the kitchen if I go there. I get that she isn't really a dog person, and that's fine. But he doesn't understand and thinks he's done something wrong. It's not fair on him.'

'And it's not fair on you to ask you to do something you don't want to.'

'Actually asking me would have been a step up. Telling me, more like.'

Dad conceded that with a nod of his head. 'Either way, you have to stand up for yourself, even to Sally. You can't do stuff to make people happy if it's making you unhappy.'

I leant my head on his broad shoulder. 'Thanks, Dad.'

He put his arm around me and gave me a squeeze, just as Humphrey appeared at our feet, now eager to get in on the action.

'Come on. Let's get back inside and warm up with a nice cuppa.' He stood and I tucked my arm in the crook of his and we wandered back up the garden, Humphrey trotting in front of us, turning occasionally to make sure we were still there.

As we entered the kitchen, still warm and filled with the fuggy scent of roast and baking, Mum appeared from the living room.

'Just in time for tea.'

'I can do that,' I said, heading towards the kettle as I shed my coat, but Mum laid a hand on my arm.

'That's fine, love. I'll do this. You go through and warm up by the fire.'

My eyes darted in the direction of the room.

'Sally and Oliver are in there. Go and sit down and we'll be through in a minute.'

The last thing I wanted to do right now was go and sit with my sister and her trophy boyfriend, but I knew a veiled instruction when I heard one.

'OK.'

Sally's eyes flicked up when I entered before she adjusted herself on the sofa, long legs resting to the side elegantly like the Duchess of Cambridge. I plopped down on a squishy armchair and tucked my feet up so that I was a little ball. Humphrey hopped up and burrowed in beside me.

'Chilly out there?' Oliver piped up, breaking the silence.

'Yes. It is a bit. Nice though,' I replied, the words sounding banal.

'Good. Good.'

Silence fell again. I chewed the inside of my mouth. Oh, sod it. It wasn't really my style to air dirty laundry in front of strangers, but bearing in mind Oliver had already been witness to the original argument, his being here while I tried to make up with my sister wasn't exactly a huge deal.

'I'm sorry you're upset about the book club thing, Sally. I don't want to fall out with you over it.'

'It's fine. I've texted Delilah. She's going to host it when I'm not available. She's probably dying to show off her new kitchen anyway. Not that she ever cooks, of course. But it is beautiful.'

'What's the point if she never cooks?' I asked what I thought was a fairly reasonable question.

Sally looked at me and I guessed she was frowning. 'Some people just like beautiful things to look at, Lottie.'

'Oh... right,' I said, understanding and not understanding at the same time. Giving a glance towards Oliver, I couldn't help wondering if he was one of those people and, if he was, whether my sister cared. Perhaps just revelling in being that beautiful object was enough for her.

'Tea is served,' my dad announced in a deep, sombre voice as he entered holding a large silver tray filled with tea things. He put it down on the table and then bowed. He'd been doing this butler routine for decades, but it never failed to make us giggle. Even Sally.

'Tea, m'lady?' Oliver asked my mum, picking up on the thread and taking one of the delicate cups.

'That would be lovely,' she smiled, giving Sally an interested look, but Sally herself was distracted, a soft smile unseen by Oliver on her features.

Mum and Dad shifted their eyes to me and we all exchanged a quick look. Perhaps there was hope for this one after all.

10

'How was the roast?' Seb asked the next day as I scanned the email he'd sent at silly o'clock this morning, detailing the tasks he wanted me to do this week.

'The food was great,' I said, making a couple of notes, 'although dinner itself was a little tense for a while.'

'Anything you want to talk about?'

I shrugged. 'No biggie. Just my sister not really getting the whole thing I did last year or what I'm doing this year.'

'The years of yes and no, you mean?'

'Yeah.'

He frowned. 'Why does that make for a tense situation? Surely it's your choice, even if she doesn't get it.'

'I don't think she really cares what I do so long as it doesn't affect her.'

'Ah. And something is now affecting her? Let me guess. You told her no.'

I pulled a face. 'I did.'

'And it didn't go down well.'

'Let's just say it didn't go as well as I'd hoped it might.'

'But you stuck to your guns?'

'I did,' I said, a little smile creeping on to my face that might have been pride. On the screen opposite me, Seb was wearing a bigger one.

'Well done, you. I know you've said in the past that you've found it hard to stand up to her, so that's great.'

'It's not that. Well, it is a bit. I suppose I just grew up looking up to her, and I always wanted to please her. And I guess that got into being a habit.'

'Not just with her.' It was more of a statement than a question.

'Quite possibly. But I hate conflict—'

'Another reason you'd have made a rubbish soldier.'

'Yes. Thank you for that. Anyway. It was just as horrible as I thought it would be, saying no. But she did kind of catch me on the hop.'

'But you made it through.'

'I did.'

'Things OK between you now?'

'It was a bit icy for a while, but she thawed eventually. Helped by the new boyfriend, surprisingly.'

Seb laughed. 'Why surprisingly? We're not all bad, you know.'

'No, I know. But Sally has a type. And they're not usually ones that help her see a different perspective to her own.'

'Sounds like he might be good for her.'

'He might well be. If he sticks around.'

'Not known for the length of her relationships then?'

'Not especially. I think it can be difficult with her job though. Shifts and being away and so on. Some people don't deal with that very well.'

'If it's what she loves doing, then the right person should be supportive of it.'

'Oh, stop being so bloody perfect and start going through these requests with me.'

He grinned a slightly crooked, but utterly perfect, smile and tipped his head down to look at his own hand scribbled notes alongside his email.

* * *

OMG! Tonight's the night! Major Gorgeous in the flesh!

I shook my head at Jess' message but couldn't help laughing.

As I have said a million times – it's not a date

He'd made that pretty clear, but then that was probably a good thing. No wires to get crossed. No raised expectations. I was pretty sure Seb didn't have any of those, but still. Good to have all the i's dotted and t's crossed.

My phone rang, signalling an incoming video call from Jess. I swiped to answer and braced myself.

'That's a very negative attitude to go in with.' She frowned at me. 'A girl's got to go after what she wants these days. Don't you ever listen to Beyoncé?'

'Every time I get in your car.'

'She is a goddess. And wise.'

'I'm not disagreeing but not entirely sure how all that's related to me meeting a *friend* for a trip to the theatre.'

'Owning it, baby!' Jess did a move that involved her wiggling her head and doing something with her hands that seemed to work for her, but if I had even attempted would make me look like I was having some sort of medical episode.

'Owning what, exactly?'

Jess waved her hand over me, via the screen. 'All that.'

'I do own it.'

'OK,' Jess replied in a tone that suggested the exact opposite.

'What?' I said.

'Maybe you need to own it a bit more.'

'Jess, my lovely. I'm more than happy with my level of ownership. It suits me. I know who I am, and what I am. And, most importantly, I stopped trying to be someone else a long time ago. I spent ages growing up trying to be more like you, or Sally. Honestly, it's bloody exhausting! I'm me. And that's the only thing I'm going to own.'

Jess gave me a look. 'Well, all that's admirable, and I can see I'm not going to be able to persuade you to pull out your sexiest dress and your sluttiest shoes for this evening.'

'One, no. It'd look weird. And two, I don't own any slutty shoes!'

'Oh my god. You don't?'

'Not that I'm aware of.'

'OK, I need to come round very soon and see for myself. If that's true, we totally need to rectify that situation.'

'I'm happy with my shoes.'

'Lottie, every girl needs a pair of hot, totally eye distracting shoes.'

'And what exactly is the definition of such footwear?'

'Honey. When you see them, you'll know. And when your man sees them, you'll definitely know. Just don't be surprised if he asks you to leave them on.' She gave a wicked wiggle of her brows.

'Well, while I appreciate the information, it's definitely not relevant for tonight, which is all very platonic.'

Jess blew a spiral of hair from her face. 'Sounds kind of dull.'

'No, not at all. Quite the opposite actually. I'm far more relaxed knowing there's no pressure attached to anything. It's just two mates meeting up for a pleasant evening.'

'With at least one of those mates fancying the arse off the other one.'

'Which is not of any relevance whatsoever.'

'No. Of course not.'

'It isn't.'

'I know. I just agreed with you.'

'Then why didn't it sound like that?' I raised a brow at her.

She gave a shrug. 'Perhaps your unconscious mind is resisting the truth.'

I shook my head. 'Whatever. What I do know, though, is that my conscious bladder is in need of a wee, so I need to hang up.'

'Fair enough. Have a good time tonight. Let me know how it goes.'

'You're heading off on your retreat. And supposed to be switching your phones off. I heard Harry specifically tell you that. That you'd made each other a deal.'

'Well... yes. But what if something happens tonight? I'd have to wait until Monday to find out?' Jess sounded appalled at this possible turn of events.

'OK, first off, nothing is going to happen tonight and, secondly, if, in an alternate universe, something did happen, I'm pretty sure I'd have far more pressing demands on my time than messaging you. No offence.'

'None taken whatsoever. I only wish that would happen.'

'Well, it's not going to. The only thing that is going to happen is me making a puddle right here if I don't shoot off now. Talk to you later.'

Jess was making a 'shoo' movement with her hand as I quickly ended the call and scooted through to the bathroom.

* * *

Like I'd said to Jess, I was looking forward to it but I was still really, really nervous. Silly really as I had now known Seb for three years and spoken to him almost every day for a good proportion of that. The same Seb who had seen me on video call in the throes of flu, when I'd forgotten to brush my hair and when I had tomato soup smiles. The latter he'd pointed out, which had led to a moment of mortification, knowing I had been up to the supermarket between eating lunch and speaking to Seb and realising that I'd had a tomato soup version of The Joker's smile on my face the entire time. Seb had thought it hilarious. I'd been less amused, but he'd soon got me to relax and realise that there were far worse things in life than forgetting to wipe the soup smiles off your face before you went out.

Glancing at the satnav, I took the next turn and followed the little arrow on the screen. Noticing my fingers were gripping the wheel a little too tightly, I took a deep breath and loosened them.

Calm down. It's going to be fine.

Of course it would. There was nothing to worry about. No reason to think that although we were great as friends from a distance that it might be awkward actually meeting in person. Absolutely no problem about... My thoughts halted as my phone rang and I pressed the button on my daft *Star Trek*-type earpiece to answer it. I'd made a wish list for my new car and built-in Bluetooth was definitely on it but, for now, this had to do.

'Hey.' Seb's deep tones, with their well-spoken, Home Counties accent, drifted directly into my ear. To me it was the epitome of that classic Army officer voice, a fact I'd begun teasing him about early into our friendship.

'Hi. Everything OK?'

'Fine. I was just checking on you.'

'I'm OK. Not far to go now. Just a few minutes away according to the satnav.'

'Great. And how's the overthinking going?'

'Huh?'

'How many arguments have you had with yourself coming up that this might not be the right thing to do? That things might be awkward, and any other random scenarios you've cooked up between home and here.'

'I don't know what you mean.'

The deep laugh rumbled directly into my ear and sent a ripple of pleasure to places that it wasn't helpful for them to be right now.

'I already told you you're a horrible fibber.'

'Thanks.'

'I can see some lights turning into the car park. Is that you?'

'I am turning into the car park right now, so it might be. Don't watch me park. You'll put me off and I'll probably prang something!'

He laughed again and hung up. I glanced around but couldn't see anyone, so I aimed for a space and parked uneventfully. Grabbing my bag, I got out of the car and pressed the button to lock it before turning back to the car park to see if I could spot Seb. It didn't take long.

I'd known he was tall at six three, but he looked even broader in real life than he did on the screen, especially wrapped up as he was against the bitter chill of the evening, and together it made quite an impact. I did my best to look casual despite the swarm of butterflies that had just let fly in my stomach.

His steps were relatively quick, and there was less of a limp than I'd been expecting. In truth, I don't know exactly what I had expected but, I guess, in my naivety, I'd expected there to be a more telltale outward sign of his injury. His hair was freshly cropped, and as the light from a street lamp fell upon him, I saw those laughing eyes and the wide, smiling mouth. Oh crap. He was even better looking in real life than he was on screen. How was that possible? Was it even legal?

'I hid so I didn't make you crash.' Mischief shimmered in his eyes.

'Thanks, I appreciate that,' I said, allowing myself to be enveloped in the warm, comforting hug that Seb wrapped around me and a hint of a woody aftershave tickled my senses. 'Bearing in mind your size, I imagine that can't have been the easiest of tasks.'

'I've had practice. When you're in a war zone, you'd be amazed how small a big bloke can make himself.'

I pulled a face. 'I bet.'

'Besides, I aim to please.'

Oh crikey. And I had very little doubt that he did just that. I'd thought he looked good on a screen, but it seemed a computer screen image had nothing on real life. My crush indicator had already dinged up a few notches. Not at all ideal, but also not much I could do about that now.

'How was the drive?' he asked, leading us out towards the road and the brighter lights of the town centre.

'OK, thanks. Yours?'

'Good.'

'Have you been here long?'

'No. I hadn't long pulled up when I called you.'

'OK. So, looking forward to the play?'

'Can't wait. It'll be a real trip down memory lane. Is this place all right?' he said, slowing down by a small restaurant with a bay window, the bottom half of which was steamed up and above which was written 'Luca's' in a script font. 'I know you like Italian.' Seb winked and I whacked him on the arm with my clutch bag.

'Funny. And yes, it looks good.'

'Great.' He pushed open the door for me, and we both gave an involuntary shiver as the warmth of the restaurant contrasted with the chill of the evening we'd stepped in from.

A waiter headed over to us, took our coats and showed us to a table by the window, complete with single red rose and candles. Seb didn't seem to have noticed, so I took my cue from him and continued the casual chat. The romantic set-up was harder to ignore when the waiter returned, took our drinks orders and lit the candles with a flourish before disappearing again.

'OK, do we need to talk about the candles?' Seb asked, laughing.

'Candles?' I asked in what I hoped was a vague manner.

He shook his head. 'Just ignore them if they bother you.'

I shifted in my seat. 'They don't bother me. I like candles, but it's a bit... awkward, isn't it?'

'Why? Because it's a romantic table for two? Don't worry about it. I'm not.'

That's reassuring then. I think.

'Honestly, Lots. They'd be doing the same if I came in here with my brother, or Dad, or my ugliest, biggest mate. Don't get hung up on things that don't matter.' He reached over and physically unballed the fist I hadn't realised I'd even clenched.

'I just don't want you feeling uncomfortable.' I shrugged.

He shook his head. 'I don't. I'm out to dinner with a good friend who happens to be very attractive. If anyone thinks I could pull you, I'm not about to disavow them of that belief. It's not in my best interest.'

I couldn't help laughing. 'Pull me?' I asked. 'Charming.'

'Sorry. You can take the boy out of the Army...'

I smiled, shaking my head.

'OK?' he asked, his voice soft, the concern in it obvious.

'Yes,' I answered, honestly. 'Yes. I am.'

His smile was his only reply, but it was more than enough.

11

'So, what was the last play you went to see?' I asked, settling in to my seat and flicking through the programme Seb had insisted on buying me as a souvenir of our first official meeting in person – which still definitely wasn't a date.

'*And Then There Were None.*'

'No! Seriously? Agatha Christie again?'

'Yep. I know. Like I said, trip down memory lane.'

I tilted my head. 'Is that a good lane?'

His expression was soft as he looked back at me. 'Very. My mum used to take us to the theatre. It was really her thing. When Dad was away on exercise, but especially on deployment, she'd book us tickets to see all sorts of things. Christie was her favourite. I guess I'd forgotten that until we had the conversation ages ago about how much you like her work. It was a good memory to rediscover, so thank you for that.'

I smiled in reply.

'I think she'd have liked a lot about you.'

It was obvious by how he spoke just how much his mum had

meant to him and I flushed a little at the generous compliment. 'Thank you.'

It was his turn to smile.

'You've never thought about going with your dad? Or your brother?' I asked.

'It never even occurred to me. But Dad was never a theatre buff. More of an outside man. Even now he spends a good part of his day in his garden or up on his allotment.'

'Oh, he and my parents would get on well then. They like nothing better than chatting about new varieties they're going to try and concocting recipes with some weird new veggie they've discovered.'

'Exactly! I got given some purple potatoes last year. Purple!' he shook his head. 'So weird.'

'What did they taste like?'

'Just like normal potatoes, actually, which was oddly disappointing.' His smile broke into a laugh and I loved the sound of it, its deep rumble washing over and relaxing me even more. There was something about Seb. He had a calmness. A stillness in his soul that you couldn't help but be affected by. The only thing that worried me was just how much I was affected by it.

'Want one?' He offered the box of chocolates he'd bought.

'Ooh! Any I'm not allowed to take?'

He wrinkled his forehead. 'No. Of course not. Choose whatever you like.'

I took the orange cream and bit in, closing my eyes in delight at its yumminess.

Next to me, Seb laughed. 'You look like you're enjoying that way too much.'

I bumped against him. 'Oh shoosh. I just haven't had one of those for ages.'

'Because some were off limits before?'

Glancing briefly from under my lashes, I saw him watching me.

'It wasn't that they were off limits. More that I knew my ex really liked them, so I just always left them for him.'

'Even though you liked them too? Surely he wouldn't have minded sharing.'

I shrugged. 'I guess.' Honestly, I wasn't so sure, but as all that was in the past now, it didn't seem to matter too much.

'There's another one there. Have that too.' Seb pointed to the corner of the box.

'Don't you want one?'

'Nope. I eat pretty much everything in this box and having seen how much you enjoyed the first one, I don't think I could now deprive you of another.'

I laughed, taking the sweet and popping it in my mouth. 'Thanks,' I said, around it.

'Pleasure.'

Seb picked another chocolate out of the box without looking as the lights began to dim in the theatre. Without thinking, I squeezed his arm in excitement and he momentarily, and very gently, laid one large hand over mine in response.

The room quietened, the curtain rose and up on the stage, the set for act one was illuminated. I sat in the low light, feeling the warmth and strength of Seb's shoulder against mine as his broad frame filled the seat and did my best to concentrate on the action about to unfold in front of me, and not the man beside me.

* * *

Exiting the warm fug of the theatre into the cold, brisk air of the night took my breath away. The clear sky of earlier had been replaced with a layer of cloud from which hung the vague threat of snow. I shivered and wrapped my coat tighter around me.

'You all right?'

'Yes. Just chilly after being in there.'

'Here.' Seb held out his arm and I tucked my own around it as we walked quickly back towards the car park, gratefully accepting any and all transference of heat from his warm bulk to mine.

'Thanks for a great night,' I said, pulling away as we got to the entrance of the car park. By the direction he'd walked from when I pulled up, I guessed his car was nearer the entrance. I knew he had a disabled parking badge, but it wouldn't have surprised me in the least to find out that he didn't use it. 'It was lovely to meet you in person.'

'And not horribly awkward after all?'

I grinned. 'No. Not horribly.'

His smile broke the shadow of his face. 'I'll walk you to your car.'

'Oh, it's fine. You don't have to do that. Just go and get warm.'

He began walking towards my car, reaching back and tagging my arm when I didn't immediately follow.

'Do you ever listen to people?' I asked.

'All the time. When they speak sense.'

'What's not sensible about what I just said? In fact, I'd argue it was eminently sensible. You going to your car, which was closest, and getting warm is good for your health. Ergo sensible. Faffing around, needlessly walking me to car when I'm quite capable of finding it by myself is less so.'

'Finished?'

'Yes.'

'Good. So, here's my counter. I have no doubt that you're capable of finding your car by yourself. That's not why I'm walking with you. I just prefer, for my own peace of mind, to see you safe and sound to your car.'

'It's not far.'

'Doesn't have to be. Bad things happen, Lottie, and I would never forgive myself if something happened to you that I might have been able to prevent.'

'You're not an Avenger, you know.'

'No. This is true. More's the pity.'

'It is a pity.'

'Thanks.' He gave me a look. 'I'm not trying to be macho or anything. I know you're capable of looking after yourself and all the rest of it. This is just me. Maybe it's old-fashioned, maybe it's because of what I did for a living, maybe it's just the way I'm built, but I always see a woman to her door.'

'What if you'd had a horrible date?'

'We didn't.'

'I wasn't talking about us. And that wasn't a date. You said so yourself.'

'Oh. Yes.' He cleared his throat. 'Right. I did say that.'

'So?'

'So, no matter. I'd still do my best to make sure she got home safely.'

Without thinking, I put my hand up to his cheek. He smiled softly against it.

'Oh! God. Sorry.' I snatched my hand back. 'That was probably really inappropriate. I mean, I didn't... It's just that you...'

Seb smiled again and caught my hand briefly before letting it go again. 'Lottie, it's fine. Don't worry about it.'

I gave a wince. 'Sorry. Forgot where I was for a minute.'

'And where exactly did you think you were?'

'I don't know. It was just a really sweet thing to say... and I sort of got carried away. I guess I'm so comfortable with you, I forgot this is our first proper meeting and I need to rein in the tactile side of my personality.'

Seb waved a hand, dismissing it. 'Just because we haven't met up until tonight doesn't mean we don't know each other. And you don't need to rein anything in.' He stopped at my car and looked down at me. 'Anyone ever told you you worry too much?'

'Yes. You for one.'

He nodded. 'Sounds like something I would say.'

I let out a breath of laughter. 'Thanks for arranging tonight, and the tickets and everything. I've had a lovely time.'

'Thanks for coming.'

I reached up and hugged him, my feet on tiptoe to reach around his neck, even in my block-heeled boots. His arms wrapped around my body and I felt the heat rush through me. I tried to convince myself it was just physics. The sudden closeness of another human, his body heat transferring to me. But I knew that was a big fat whopper. The heat rushing through me right now was because I was wrapped in the arms of a bloke I'd had a crush on for ages and he was a really, really good hugger.

In a way, I'd kind of hoped that once we met in person, that image I'd built up of him wouldn't quite live up to the reality and I could gradually, and painlessly, let said crush slowly dissipate back into nothing. Unfortunately, that wasn't how it had gone. Seb Marshall in real life was even better than I could ever have imagined. Which was really, really inconvenient.

He stepped back and held the door as I unlocked it and got in.

'Drive carefully,' he said, closing the door.

I nodded and turned the key. Nothing. Glancing up at the window, I gave a little shake of my head to signify it was no big deal and tried again. Even more nothing.

Seb opened the door.

'Problem?' he asked.

I slid my glance across.

'Just call me Captain Obvious.'

'I thought you were a Major.'

'You're correct. Fair enough. Major Obvious. What's up?'

'Who knows,' I said, letting out a sigh. 'It's been doing this for a while now. I've taken it to the garage, but they just keep charging me to tell me it's obviously intermittent and they can't find anything wrong.'

'Worth another go?'

I wiggled the gearstick as though that would help and tried turning the key again. Nada.

'It's not the battery, as that was replaced the first time it did it.'

'Do you have breakdown?'

'Yeah,' I said, letting out a sigh and leaning across to the glove compartment to riffle through and find the card with the breakdown company's details on. 'I've been wanting to replace the car for a while but just haven't got round to it. And now I'm worried that when I try to part-exchange it, it'll do this and I'll be screwed.'

I dialled the number of the recovery company, gave them the details of what had happened and the postcode of the car park. When they asked if I was on my own, I said yes. Partly because I knew it might speed things up but also because I was hoping to get Seb to go home and get warm. As much as I enjoyed his company, it was bloody freezing.

'Where's Humphrey tonight?'

I looked across at where Seb was bent over at the door, peering in at me. 'With my parents, probably getting thoroughly spoiled.'

'Would they be able to have him a bit longer?'

'Why? What are you thinking?'

'You up for staying over?'

In the low light of the car's interior lamp, I tried to keep my face expressionless.

'OK. Here's the plan,' Seb began. 'I know a bloke who's a genius with anything mechanical. I'll call him and I'm pretty sure he will be able to take a look at it tomorrow. Whatever's going on with this baby, he'll find it. In the meantime, you can see if there are any cars you're interested in locally, and I can drive you to take a look at them while Angus works his magic on this one.'

'Oh, Seb. That's really kind of you, but I couldn't impose like that at the last minute. I don't even have any stuff with me.'

'It's not imposing. I have a T-shirt you can sleep in. You can wash whatever you want. There's a twenty-four hour supermarket not far from home. We can get this taken to my place, and I can whizz you up there for any other supplies you need. So, what do you think?'

I sucked in a deep breath and turned it over. If I was honest, I hadn't really been ready for the evening to end, but sitting in my broken-down car in a freezing-cold car park wasn't exactly what I'd had in mind. The prospect of someone actually fixing it was also pretty appealing. And it all came with the added benefit of spending more time with Seb Marshall.

'You sure you don't mind? I mean, didn't you have plans this weekend?'

'Nope. Just hanging out with Scoobs. And we can still do that. So long as you're OK with everything. I don't want you to feel I'm pressuring you or anything. I've been told I can be a bit—'

'Bossy?'

'Type A.'

'That A can stand for all sorts, you know. You might be better off sticking with bossy.'

Seb raised one dark brow. 'I'll take that into consideration. So, what's the decision because I'm freezing my arse off here and I've lost more than enough bits of me already, thanks all the same.'

'Oh my god, sorry. Look. It's fine. Just go home and get warm. I'll get the car taken home and message you when I'm back.'

'That wasn't what I meant. It's more that you're shivering and turning a fetching shade of blue too. And while I may, or may not, have had a thing for Smurfette in my younger days, I'm not sure it's going to be your best look.'

'Ughhhh,' I let out a sigh. 'I don't know what to do. And now I sound pathetic in front of you.'

'Hey,' Seb reached in and gently lifted my head off the steering wheel where I'd let it fall.

'Sorry. Bloody car. And it was such a lovely evening too.'

He gave me that smile that sent tingles to my toes, as well as a bunch of other places. 'It's still a lovely evening. At the risk of sounding—'

'Type A,' I interjected.

'Type A. When the guy comes, let me direct him to my place. You take it back to yours, you're just going to have to spend more money on trying to get it fixed, with no guarantee it will work.'

'There's no guarantee your friend will be able to fix it either though.'

'I'd put my money on Angus over a garage. He's kind of a savant when it comes to stuff like this.' He tilted his head. 'Come on, Lots. I know Scoobs is dying to meet you.'

The hot breath from my laughter froze into clouds in front of me. 'He's told you that?'

'Of course.' Seb put out his hand to assist me from the car. 'Let's get the heater going in mine while we wait.'

12

'You sure this is all OK?' I asked again as I pointed the beeper at the car and locked it. Although as it clearly had no inclination to start, the process seemed a little redundant.

'Definitely.' Seb gently laid a palm behind my back and we hurried across to where his Subaru Impreza was parked. The lights flashed and doors unlocked as we got there and Seb held the door for me before hurrying around to the other side and sliding in. Turning the engine over, he fiddled with some controls on the dash and pressed another couple of buttons. 'Heated seats,' he pointed. 'Just in case you wonder why it's getting warm down there.'

'Ha! Good to know that's the reason. Thanks.'

He held up his hand to the vent. 'Should be warm soon.'

'Sorry if I've made you freeze your behind off. I told you you should have just gone home.'

He faced me. 'We both know that was never going to happen.'

'Have you always been like this?'

'Like what?'

'Making sure everyone is taken care of?'

He leant forward and adjusted something and warm air began

blowing into the car, adding to the warmth now seeping up from the seats. His answer to my question was a shrug. 'Never really thought about it like that.'

'It's a nice trait. I'm not criticising. Just being nosy, basically.'

The interior light had clicked off, but I could see the wide, slightly crooked smile against the darkness of the surroundings.

'I'd go for interested,' he smiled at me.

'I'll remember that.'

* * *

A little over half an hour later, I peered out of the window, rubbing a patch of windscreen clear of hot breath with the elbow of my coat. 'Do you think that's them? He said he wasn't too far away when I called.'

'Could be,' Seb said, pulling the lever on the door.

I followed suit and we began walking over towards my car as Seb caught the recovery lorry driver's attention with a wave and pointed him in the right direction.

Twenty minutes later and the breakdown man was as puzzled as the garages I'd taken it to as to the problem. He rubbed his chin and shrugged.

'It's a strange one. Normally things like this are pretty cut and dried, but I think we'll have to leave it to the garage this time.'

In my head, I let out a long, painful groan.

'Ah, don't worry. I'm sure it won't be anything too serious.'

Guess that wasn't in my head then.

I nodded instead and tried to smile.

'So, your policy allows me to take it to a local garage or your destination. Where are we off to?' the breakdown chap asked.

Seb looked at me. 'It's up to you. You know the offer's open.'

I chewed my lip for a moment. God knew I'd already thrown enough money at several garages, so I had nothing to lose by letting

Seb's friend take a look. But that did, of course, involve spending a night at Seb's. And, innocent as his offer was, I couldn't help the tumble of emotions that shivered through me at the thought of that. Although I'd been ruing taking part in Jess' 'Year of Saying Yes' within days of it beginning, it had at least taken some of the indecisiveness out of my life. In theory, that same logic could be applied to this year. Only this year's plan of saying no was only to things I didn't want to do. And, as I stole a glance at Seb, saying no to him wasn't the immediate word that sprang to mind. In fact, however much I tried to deny it and write off any attraction towards him to Jess, having seen Seb in the flesh and spent some proper time with him, I was pretty sure my original suspicions that I had a full-blown crush on him had been realised, and the more likely response, given the opportunity would be 'Yes, yes, oh god! Yes!'

'Lottie?' Seb's gentle question nudged me, thankfully, off the path my mind had begun to race down.

I slammed the brakes on that particular thought and swerved back to reality, and rational thought. I needed this damn car fixed and Seb seemed to have utter confidence in his mate, so, firmly closing the door on my renegade libido, I turned towards Seb.

'You sure you don't mind?'

He smiled, soft and warm, and I could feel my libido charging against that door trying to shove it back open. I mentally threw another bolt across. 'Not at all. It'd be a pleasure.'

'OK then. Let's go with that plan. I'm just going to ring my parents and let them know what's going on and double check they're OK with keeping Humphrey a bit longer.'

He gave a quick nod, turned and headed over to the breakdown guy and began giving him the postcode of his house, spelling it out phonetically while I pressed the contact button for my parents.

'Hi, Mum.'

'Hello, darling. How was the play?'

'Really good, thanks. You OK?'

'Yes, thanks. We're just having a nice evening in front of the telly and Humphrey seems to be very comfortable indeed. He's currently sprawled across your father's lap like a small rug.' She laughed and I could hear the same love in it that I had when I spoke about my dog.

'Sounds good. Humphrey's actually why I was ringing. Would you be OK to have him a bit longer? I didn't know if you had anything planned for tomorrow or anything?'

'No, not at all. Is everything OK?' she lowered her voice. 'Or is it more than OK?'

Even in the dim light, I felt myself colour. 'Mum!'

From the corner of my eye, I could see that the breakdown driver had now hooked up my car to the towing rig on the back of his truck and was finishing securing it. Seb was stood by him, hands stuffed in the pockets of his coat, beanie pulled down low, chatting amiably as the task was performed.

'What?' she asked, innocence and laughter mixing in her voice. 'I'm just asking.'

'Hmm. Don't you start. I get enough from Jess about Seb,' I said, keeping my voice low. 'Anyway, it's far more dull than that. My flippin' car broke down again.'

'Oh, darling!' she said, all teasing gone now. 'Are you all right? Where are you? Do you need us to come and pick you up?'

I smiled and felt the wave of love travel across the miles and wash over me. I might have wasted far too many of possibly my best years on a relationship that had ended like a damp firework, but I knew I'd got more than my share of luck when it came to parents. 'No, Mum. I'm fine. Thanks. It's all in hand. The breakdown bloke is here now and he had about as much luck as the garages have in finding the fault, but Seb knows a chap who's apparently a genius with these things, so we're getting it towed to Seb's and hoping his friend will be able to take a look tomorrow and see if he has better luck.'

'So you're staying at Seb's?' The question was so loaded, I could practically hear the cartridge being locked into the shotgun.

'Yes. And no, before you ask.'

'Ask what?'

I couldn't help smiling. 'Whatever it was that you were going to ask or say. It doesn't mean anything. I'll be in the guest room. No funny business, don't worry.'

'Oh, darling. I'm not worried. In fact, I'm more than open to you having some funny business with this chap from the sounds of him.'

'Mum!'

She laughed and I couldn't help but smile. Although I still did my best not to show it, especially as the car now seemed to be ready. The driver had climbed up in to the lorry's cab and Seb was heading back towards me, head down against the icy breeze.

'Oh, darling. I'm just teasing.'

'I know. Thanks for looking after Humphrey. I really appreciate it.'

'It's our pleasure, honestly. You know we love having him.'

'Hopefully we're going to try and have a look at some new cars tomorrow while this chap's looking at mine and obviously it'll depend on how he gets on as to what time I get back, but I'll keep you posted.'

'No rush, Lots. Don't worry. Take all the time you need.'

'Thanks, Mum. Love you. Speak to you tomorrow.'

'Love you too, darling. And don't forget to have fun!' She gave a giggle that belied her years. 'Bye!'

'Bye, Mum.'

I hung up just as Seb got to me. 'Everything OK?'

'Yes, they're fine with it. All sorted?' I said, inclining my head towards the truck, which was now rumbling to a start.

'Yep. And I've messaged Angus. He'll be round at half eight tomorrow to fix it.'

I smiled. 'Don't you mean take a look?'

Seb opened the door of the car for me. 'Nope. I mean fix it.'

'Nothing like a bit of confidence.'

'When it's due.' He grinned and my libido gave another hefty heave. I did my best to squish it down, but now, in the cosy, dim interior of Seb's car, it wasn't exactly the easiest task. I decided distraction tactics might be the best option and began asking him about his friend.

'So, this chap. Angus?'

'Yep?' he asked, concentration on his face as the threatened snow instead became rain, pelting into the windscreen as we left the town and joined the motorway.

'How did he acquire these magical mechanical talents?'

'As far as I know, he was one of those kids who was always taking things apart to see how they worked, so I guess it goes back pretty far.'

'Bet his parents loved that!'

Seb glanced across, the flashes of street light highlighting for an instant a sad look in those dark eyes. 'Unfortunately, I don't think they took a lot of interest in what he did. From what I know, he had a tough time of it. Both his parents were alcoholics. Their main interest was in where the next drink was coming from rather than fostering any talent their son might be showing.'

'Oh. Sorry.'

'What for?'

I shook my head. 'I don't know. For making an offhand comment.'

Seb touched my knee in reassurance. It was so brief I wasn't sure if I imagined it, but there was a fizzing in my body that gave me a clue I hadn't. 'You weren't to know.'

'I know. But still. I forget not everyone is as lucky as me when it comes to the parental lottery.'

He flicked his gaze across briefly, before focussing back on the road. 'Don't ever feel you need to apologise or feel guilty for having a good relationship with your family.'

I nodded, not quite able to shake the feeling I'd put my foot in it. 'So, how do you know him? Did you serve together?'

'No. He's a bit older than me and we were in different units, but we did run into each other on deployments a couple of times. His skill with mechanics was kind of legendary throughout the base. Everyone took him stuff to be repaired and we chatted in passing a few times when he fixed some things for me, but that was kind of it.'

'Is he still in the Army?'

Seb shook his head. 'No. After three tours, he was done.'

'I can understand that. I mean, as well as anyone who's never been in that situation can.'

He gave me a soft smile. 'I know what you mean. And the fact that you try and understand these things is yet another of your great qualities.'

I wasn't sure what to say so I just smiled in response, but his eyes were on the road and I couldn't have said whether he saw or not.

'Readjustment to civilian life is an odd thing. Some people find it a hell of a lot easier than others.'

'I get the feeling Angus wasn't one of those people who found it easy then?'

'No. He'd enlisted as soon as he was able, in order to leave behind the life he had, and he made a new life, a new family if you like, in the Army. It suited him and gave him the structure that his early home life hadn't. He'd found his place in the world and knew where he belonged and who he was. But tours, and war, take their toll. Leaving wasn't an easy decision for him, but it seemed the right one. He had a wife and daughter to come home to, the stability of a loving home.'

I let out a sigh. 'But I have a horrible feeling it didn't go to plan?'

'No. Angus found it hard to adjust. Life outside can be completely different. He struggled with the lack of discipline he saw around him, and the lack of respect that people seem to have for one another a lot of the time now. He got a job in a garage and, for a while, that went well. He'd found a place again, doing something he was good at. And then the owner retired and handed the reins over to his son. He had dramatically different ideas for what he wanted the business to be. It was a successful operation, but this new bloke wasn't happy servicing the customers that had been coming to them for years with their little old Ford Fiestas and people carriers. He had this idea that they were going to be luxury car specialists – Fords were out, Ferraris were in. Angus is pretty easy-going and appreciates any sort of good engineering, but this guy's attitude rattled him from the start. I think the bloke knew that Angus could run rings around him and that rankled. He managed to get everyone's back up and was always questioning their work and treating them... well, I guess we're back to that disrespect thing again. Here are these guys who've been doing a job for thirty-odd years and in comes this upstart, for want of a better word, telling them how to suck eggs.'

'I can't imagine it went down well.'

'No. Not exactly. Pretty soon people started leaving. People Angus had built up a bond with.'

'That can't have been easy for him.'

'No. He'd left one work family and been lucky to find another, helping him make what had begun as a difficult transition a lot easier. And then it all began to fall apart again. He looked around for other work, but the recession wasn't helping things and although he tried to keep his head down, the new boss didn't like him. I think he was intimidated by him, if I'm honest. I know the guy's dad stood up for Angus, but it was this bloke's business now and there wasn't much the previous owner could do. In the end, there was some shady excuse given to get rid of Angus about how he didn't have the right experience for the new direction the company was going in. He did his best and offered to take any courses the company wanted to send him on, but the guy just wanted him gone. Legally, I still think it was pretty ropey, but Angus didn't have the money, or energy, to take on that fight.

'Unfortunately, stepping into a new job wasn't so easy and that really affected his confidence and state of mind. All he ever wanted to do when he met his wife was take care of her, and his kid was the light of his life. He vowed to give that little girl everything he hadn't had, not just materially, but more importantly the love and support he didn't get. And he did. Every day. Even when he was thousands of miles away. But the more he struggled to find another job, the more his confidence and mental state began to suffer too.'

'It must have been very difficult for both him and his family.'

'Long story, short, it was. The rows increased, tensions got to breaking point and Angus started drinking. The downhill slide came pretty fast from there.'

'Oh, Seb.'

'I know.'

'So, if you didn't know him all that well, how did you know all this was happening?'

'I didn't. I'd last seen him on a base in Helmand. The next time I saw him was several years later in a shop doorway as part of a home-less charity food provision programme I was taking part in.'

'And you recognised him?'

'Just about. But that was the easy part. Getting him help was less so.'

'Pride.'

Seb gave an outward breath that passed for a resigned laugh. 'You could say that. He'd lost everything, but there was still a sliver of that stubborn pride left. But there was no way I was going to leave him to rot in that doorway. He was a brother. Always will be. So, in the end, we managed to utilise that pride to our advantage, and again with the long story short thing, he's now pretty involved with the charity itself.'

'And what about his family?'

'Unfortunately, his marriage had paid the price, and for a long while he didn't see his daughter either. I think the loss of that was what really broke him. But once he got sober, and found a purpose again, he was able to build on himself. He'll never be who he was before he went to war. None of us will be. But he's a good man. He'd lost touch with his ex, but the charity managed to make contact and explain the situation. I don't think Angus held out much hope, but after giving her time to think, his wife contacted us again and asked to see him. She explained that she'd remarried and wanted him to know that beforehand, rather than just dropping it on him.'

'It sounds like she cared for him very much.'

'I think she did. I think she'd wanted it to be for ever too. But things don't always go to plan, as much as you want them to.'

'How did he take that news?'

'Pretty well. I think he expected it to be honest.'

'And the little girl?'

'The little girl had grown up, but thankfully her mother had never demonised Angus. Obviously, it was always going to be difficult. But she made her own decision to see him and Angus gave her the space she needed, when she needed it. It was a massive thing for both of them really. But I'm happy to say it seems to have worked out. His daughter has her own baby now and, I tell you, I'm not sure you could find a prouder grandfather.'

'I can imagine. I'm so pleased things have turned around for him.'

'Me too.'

'Thanks to you.'

'Nope,' Seb's voice had a definitive, non-negotiable tone to it. 'This is all down to him.'

'But if you hadn't seen him that day. Persuaded him to take that first step?'

'Then I like to think someone else would have.'

'Even you know that's not certain.'

'I do. So, I'm glad I saw him that day, yes. But the only person that can make a recovery – from anything – is the individual. Nobody else. I could have had the best doctors and nurses and physios – I did, in fact. I had a great team working with me. But none of them could help me walk again or get to the level of fitness I've got to without my input. I even proved that for a while by not giving it my all. Angus's recovery is down to that pride and the drive that I hoped he still had somewhere deep inside him. Turns out he did.'

'Well, I'm sorry to hear he's had such a horrible time, especially having already had a difficult childhood, but I'm pleased he seems to be in a good place again now. Especially so if he's going to be able to fix my car.'

Up ahead, the breakdown lorry began signalling a turn.

'If he can't, I'll eat my hat.'

I leant over and fingered the soft wool of his beanie that he'd taken off earlier and tossed in the centre console space. 'Then I really hope he can as I'm thinking that's going to take some chewing.'

Seb gave me that crooked grin and I felt a rush of warmth flood through me that had absolutely nothing to do with luxurious heated seats.

13

'OK, turn around.'

'Pardon?'

'Turn around. Please.'

'Lottie, believe it or not, I have seen women's underwear before. In fact, I'm pretty sure I've seen plenty of stuff that would make you blush. Just pick some.'

We were standing in a twenty-four hour supermarket, in front of the ladies' underwear section, stocking up on emergency supplies for me and I was desperately trying to get Seb to drop his usual nonchalant, nothing-phases-me attitude. Primarily because I didn't possess the same one.

'I've absolutely no doubt about that, but the truth of the fact is that one thing you haven't seen is my knickers and I'm not about to have you add that to the list.'

'Shame,' he said, a smile that now looked positively devilish, making him appear even more good looking than usual, which really wasn't ideal.

I gave a head tilt. 'Which part?'

'Both.'

Following the head tilt with an eye roll, I grabbed his arms and bodily turned him round so that he was facing away from the rows of knickers I was currently considering.

'If you're having trouble deciding, maybe I should just pick for you?' Even without seeing his face, I could hear the smile.

'That's really kind, but you're already putting yourself out for me enough this weekend, I couldn't possibly ask you to do more.'

'Really. It's no bother.'

'I'm done now anyway.'

Seb turned and I tucked the couple of pairs I'd chosen behind my back. He shook his head and caught my arm. 'Come on. I need to grab some milk while I'm here. What do you eat in the mornings?'

'Whatever I find in the cupboard, really.'

'Cereal? Toast? Eggs?'

'Seb. You don't need to go to any extra effort for me. I'm already descending on you unplanned. Whatever you have is fine. In fact, even better, I could take you out for breakfast to thank you.'

He hooked a carton of milk from the metal trolley it was stacked in and we began heading towards the tills. 'OK. One, you're not descending, I invited you, and two, you don't need to thank me for anything, much less take me anywhere. Besides, nothing can beat my cooked breakfast, so unless you have any objections, I'll just do that.'

We got to the till and, distracted by the thought of sizzling bacon and the like, I swiped my items through the self-service till before grabbing the milk from Seb and putting that through too.'

'I'll get that,' he said.

'Done now,' I said, flashing my supermarket loyalty card at the machine before paying and stuffing my purchases in my handbag.

'Thanks,' he said, leaning over to grab the carton. 'Nice pants by the way,' he added, winking as he did so.

I felt myself blush but couldn't help laughing too. There was something about Seb Marshall that made me relax, even when I thought I should be tense. And he was right, he probably had seen –

and even done – plenty of things that would make me blush. I tried not to think about those right now and instead gave him a nudge with my elbow as we turned and left the shop.

* * *

Seb's house was one of six fairly new houses off a country lane, not far from town. Each had a neat front garden and a drive, mostly with two cars parked on them in front of the garage door. The houses curved around so that none overlooked the other and the back gardens, although fenced, each had a gate, allowing access to the woods that lay behind them.

'That was a key attraction as I knew I wanted to get a dog as soon as I was able to get my fitness up,' Seb explained as he pulled up on to his drive, passing my car that was now parked on the road in front of his house.

'Saves faffing about with the car, I'm sure, if you can just open the back gate and go,' I replied, grabbing my bag and opening the door.

'He's excited to meet you. Scooby, I mean'

I laughed. 'He doesn't even know I'm coming.'

'Yeah, but you know what dogs are like. They sense things.'

'So, he sensed my car was going to break down again tonight? Perhaps you could train him to let me know beforehand next time.'

'It's a thought. Of course, then that would have meant I'd miss out on being able to help out and the chance to spend more time with you, so maybe things are best left as they are.'

I glanced up at him, his words about spending more time with me taking me by surprise, but he was busy unlocking the front door, his eyes away from mine, instead concentrating on the large mass of excited canine now charging down the hallway towards him.

'Calm,' he said in a voice that was firm but not intimidating. At this word, the barrelling lab slowed down, or at least made the best attempt he could on laminate flooring, and slid to a halt in front of us, his tail thumping fast on the floor and his whole body humming with excitement at the return of his master.

'Wow. That's impressive,' I said, as Seb closed the door behind me and offered to take my coat.

'He's a good lad, really. Just gets a bit excited sometimes and I didn't want him sending you careering over.'

'Oh, I'm fine,' I said, watching as Seb bent and gave the dog the greeting and cuddles he was clearly waiting for.

Scooby pushed his whole body against Seb's leg and made satisfied groans as his owner found the sweet spot under his chin to rub.

Standing back, he spoke to the dog. 'Right, Scooby. We've got a lady in the house now, so we need to behave. No lounging about in our pants this weekend. We need to at least pretend we're civilised.'

Scooby looked at his owner, cocked his head, gave a little whine and then sat in front of me, his wagging tail moving so fast he was sliding slightly from side to side on the shiny floor and inadvertently polishing a small patch of the pale wood. I crouched and he shoved his big, square head at me, which I rubbed and snuggled against until Scooby's excitement and weight tipped me onto my bum.

'Scoobs, mate. What did I just say?'

'Oh, don't be daft,' I said, waving Seb's concerns away as I made to push myself back up off the floor.

Seb put an arm down and hauled me up with minimum effort. I guess those muscles weren't just for show then.

'Let me show you your room,' he said, his hand still holding mine for a brief moment before he dropped it, indicating for me to go up the stairs.

I bent quickly and pulled off my heels, standing them next to a pair of expensive-looking hiking boots and some slightly battered trainers.

The guest room was gorgeous. All soft greys and luxury textures offset with a gentle accent of soft cream in the fluffy cushion on the chair and a vase of silk flowers that looked so real I had to double check.

I turned to see a hint of Seb's crooked smile focused on me. 'What?'

'You.'

'What about me?'

'Let's just say you wouldn't make a very good spy.'

I drew myself up a little. 'I might. I'm average, and unobtrusive and—'

'Your emotions are written all over your face.'

'They are not!' I blustered, really hoping that wasn't true as there'd been some moments in the past I *really* wouldn't have wanted him to know what I was thinking.

Seb's smile widened. 'Yeah, Lottie, they are. Also, I don't know where you got the idea that you're average from, but that's rubbish too.'

I did a head wobble that indicated I wasn't totally on board with that statement but let it pass for now. 'OK, Mr Psychic Mind Reader, so what am I thinking?'

Seb sat on the end of the bed and stretched his leg, his expression shifting slightly as he did so and I wondered just how much pain he was in right now. If I asked, I knew he'd dismiss it, but it wasn't in my nature to ignore things. And the fact was, I cared about him. Maybe more than I should, but that was a worry for a different day.

'Is it sore?' I asked, taking a seat next to him on the end of the bed.

'A bit. Nothing too bad. Sometimes the cold makes it ache more.'

'Yes. I don't suppose that helps. And then I made you sit in the freezing cold waiting for a breakdown lorry tonight when you could have been at home in the warm resting.'

He reached across and gave me a squeeze. 'Lottie. You didn't make me do anything.'

'But you should have just come home. I could have waited for the guy on my own.'

'And where would the fun have been in that?' he asked.

'That,' I said, pointing at where his other hand was gently massaging his leg, 'doesn't look like fun.'

'Stop worrying. I was happy to wait with you. And, if I'm honest, as much as I know your car breaking down is a pain in the arse, the fact that we get to spend some more time together isn't something I'm complaining about.'

I met his eyes, wondering where this was going.

'We've been colleagues and then friends for what feels like an age now. I can't believe it's taken us so long to actually get together. Now that we have, I'm really enjoying getting to spend the time with you and building on that friendship. It's really nice to just be able to go for a meal, spend time with someone and relax without any expectations, don't you think?'

'Absolutely!' I said, brightly, pushing myself off the bed and going over to peer out of the window. If Seb was right about the fact he could read me, then it was probably best if I made sure my traitorous face was pointed away from him. Even taking into account the reflection from the window, it was still an improvement on facing Seb head on. 'So, this psychic talent you reckon you have?' I said, calling Scooby, who was hovering at the door, over to me. 'Oh, sorry,' I pulled a face. 'Is he allowed in here?'

Seb smiled. 'It's his house as much as mine. I don't have him on the beds, but apart from that, he's got free rein.'

'Don't ever get together with my sister. She'd be changing that in a moment.'

'Yeah, that probably wouldn't work then. I'm kind of from the love me, love my dog school of thought.'

'I agree. And she doesn't dislike them. She just is very particular about her appearance and clothes. Admittedly, quite a lot of them cost a bloody fortune, so I can understand her point.'

'Yep. Different beliefs suit different people. It's what makes the world interesting, I guess. To a point. Obviously, some of those people take things to extremes...' he left the sentence unfinished, but there was no denying the prosthetic elephant in the room.

I snuggled my face against Scooby and wrapped my arms around his big, solid body. He gave a sigh of contentment and slid his bum across into a puppy sit next to me.

'You know that thing I said about you being easy to read?'

'Hmm,' I said, keeping myself occupied with the dog, which was far easier than reminding myself how delicious his owner was.

'You're doing it again.'

'Doing what?'

'Pretending you're fine when there's clearly something on your mind.'

I steeled everything I could into nonchalance as I came out from hiding behind the dog. 'Maybe your skills have slipped a bit because you're kind of off base this evening.'

Seb watched me for a moment. 'Am I?' he asked. In theory this was a question, but the way he said it told me he felt he already knew the answer and that answer was a big fat nope.

'Yes,' I said, pushing myself up from where I was sitting. 'Admittedly, I was a bit surprised that this room is quite so lovely.'

'Because?'

'Because you're a bloke who lives alone and this looks like something from a boutique hotel. But, of course, there are decorators and designers and even ex-girlfriends who might have been responsible for it, so perhaps it's not so surprising after all.' I gave a grin that was definitely verging on the side of sheepish. 'As various people have said, maybe I just need to get out more.'

Seb remained sat on the bed, his damaged leg stretched out. Scooby had now padded over and slid down to sit at his feet, or rather, had draped himself over Seb's other one like a shiny, but very heavy, rug. 'Then I think various people should perhaps mind their own business. You get out plenty. As for the other, no, no and definitely no. This was all my own fair hand.'

'Really?'

'I did ask for some advice from my sister-in-law, but that was once I'd chosen everything, which was probably a bit of an arse-about-face way of doing things, but still. Luckily, she felt I was pointing in the right direction and encouraged me to just go ahead.'

'Apparently you have an eye for design then.'

'Thanks.' He stood, gaining a height advantage over me. 'Are you going to tell me what unsettled you earlier when I said about building our friendship and no expectations? Did I say something wrong?'

I forced that nonchalant face back on and prayed to god Seb bought it. 'I honestly don't know what you mean. I'm fine and agree, it's been lovely to meet up. I just still feel like I'm imposing a little.' Maybe if I gave some sort of possible reason, Seb would stop sniffing around for any others like Humphrey did when he knew I had treats in my coat pocket.

He gave me a long look and I could tell he had his doubts, but, in the end, he decided not to push it and let it pass.

'OK. Well, you're not. Let's get that established once and for all. Deal?'

'Deal,' I said, sticking out my hand and feeling like I'd dodged a bullet. However, as Seb took my hand within his own large one, he met my eyes and I knew I hadn't dodged it at all.

14

Seb gave me a quick tour of the house, Scooby trailing us the whole time, and talked to me about the improvements he'd made and those he hoped to make in the future.

I took a seat at the breakfast bar as he made us hot chocolate. No powder and microwave here, as was my general procedure, but the full works, with hot milk and proper chocolate melted slowly in, his hand moving rhythmically with the whisk as we continued chatting, relaxed in each other's company.

I knew Seb still felt I was hiding something, but I was really enjoying the time I was spending with him. Not just because he was gorgeous, but because I had always felt, from the first moment I'd met him, that I could be myself with him and that wasn't something I wanted to lose, even putting aside the fact that he was my best client. He was fun and kind and entertaining. And, bonus, he had a great dog. I'd managed this silly crush well enough in the past and I could get past it now. Admittedly, it wasn't quite as easy as I'd hoped, knowing now that he was even better in real life than he was on a screen, which made the process a good deal harder, but there we are. It was still totally doable.

'Here you go!' Seb said, cutting into my reverie by placing a steaming mug of the most delicious smelling hot chocolate in front of me, along with a spoon for the whipped cream and tiny marshmallows decorating the top.

'Oh blimey!' I said, looking down at the creation. He'd had his back to the breakfast bar for most of the time he'd been creating these masterpieces, so I'd had no idea quite how much he'd gone to town. 'This looks amazing! It's a good job I don't live closer or else I think I'd be having to look for a bigger model car tomorrow.'

'Oh, nonsense,' Seb said, coming around the kitchen island and grabbing both the drinks. 'Let's go and sit in the lounge. It's more comfy.'

The living room, as with the guest bedroom, had no whiff of macho bachelor about it. Again, it was homely, comfortable and bright. It embraced the look of a show home but with softened edges so that it still looked like you could live in it rather than be afraid to sit down, unlike my sister's house. Beautiful but don't mess it up – but that suited Sally. It was very much her ethos in life.

It amazed me how we were even related sometimes, but, as Seb had said earlier, it wouldn't do for everyone to be the same, and when it had come to me moving out of the house I'd shared with my ex, Sally had been an absolute star. Her organisation and penchant for tidy and neat had been the help I needed to get myself organised when, in reality, I was still a little bit in shock at the fact the relationship I'd just assumed would be the one that would lead to marriage and possibly kids had fizzled out into nothing. I wasn't sure if I had much to offer her in return, but we got along and loved each other – so long as I didn't cover her in animal fur – so it worked pretty well and was certainly a lot less dysfunctional than a lot of sibling relationships.

'Do you mind if I just check in with my parents and Humphrey?' I said, glancing at the clock on my phone.

'Be my guest. I'll take these out.'

'No, stay. It'll be much easier that way as, I warn you now, Mum will be super interested in you.'

'That's fair enough. Her daughter is staying under my roof.'

'Yeah, I'm not sure she's too worried about that aspect. Like I said, she's kind of always on the lookout for potential suitors and,' I held my hands up, 'believe me, I've told her that you don't fall into that category, but you're a male, in the right age bracket, decent, single, straight and… well, that's kind of enough so far as Mum is concerned.'

Seb grinned. 'I like the sound of her.'

'That's because she's not trying to marry you off every five minutes.'

'I'm not sure she's trying to marry you off. She's just looking out for you. She wants you to be happy.'

'I know,' I said, pressing the call button on the video chat. 'It's all a bit Bridget Jones and the turkey curry buffet at times though.'

'I can handle it.'

'Don't say I didn't warn you,' I managed to get out just as Mum answered the call.

'Hello, love, everything all right?'

'Yes, thanks. Just thought I'd quickly check in before you went to bed. I didn't wake you or anything, did I?'

'No, not at all. We were binge watching something on Netflix actually.'

My parents had a habit of doing this. For someone who barely watched telly, it amused me that my parents were always watching the latest cult series and were up on all the gossip.

'Humphrey behaving?'

'As always.' Mum turned the phone around so that I could see Humphrey spread out like a lap rug across my Dad. I relaxed a little more, knowing that my dog clearly wasn't pining for me.

'You sure it's OK for you to have him a bit longer?'

'Of course. Are you all settled back at the house now?'

'Yes. The car's outside on the road and Seb's friend is due round first thing to come and take a look at it. Hopefully he'll have better luck than the garages.'

'He will,' a deep voice to my right said, an unmistakeable air of confidence in the words.

'Is that Seb?' Mum asked. The curiosity in her tone was also unmistakeable.

I glanced across at him. He was grinning and he gave a quick eyebrow raise in amusement. There wasn't much that got past Seb Marshall. Damn. He scooted himself up the sofa a little and I angled the phone.

'Hi, Mrs Wentworth,' he gave a little wave and that slightly crooked smile that always gave me tummy flutters.

'Oh, call me Tara,' my mum waved his formalities away with a smile that I knew meant Seb had already won her over with that killer smile of his. 'Thank you for helping Lottie out this evening.'

'My pleasure, Tara.'

I tilted the phone back towards me before Mum could begin questioning Seb about anything else. 'OK, Mum. I just wanted to check in. I'll keep you posted tomorrow and let you know what time I'll be home.'

'OK, love. No rush.'

I hung up and looked at Seb. 'Do you charm every woman you meet?'

'I try.'

I rolled my eyes and he gave my shoulders a quick squeeze before settling back. 'Do you want anything else?'

'No, thanks. That chocolate was delicious though. Where did you learn to do that?'

'It was another treat Mum used to do when Dad was away.' He shifted a bit on the sofa, getting comfier. 'I think sometimes she felt she had to make up for him not being there.'

I nodded. 'Or maybe it was a way of distracting herself too.'

He thought about that. 'Actually, I think you're probably closer to the mark. I suppose when you're a kid you don't think about it like that. It's all about you, isn't it?'

'I don't think we see our parents as real people with feelings and needs until we're much older.'

He nodded. 'She'd been an Army wife for a long time and she knew the deal, but I'm not sure she ever really got used to it.'

'Does anyone?'

'Good question. I know she wasn't thrilled when I wanted to follow the same path.'

'But she didn't stop you?'

'No, they always knew it was my choice. Thankfully my brother stayed in civvy street so that was one thing less for them to worry about.'

'If they're anything like my parents, they'd have worried whatever you did. I think it must be in the job description.'

'Yeah, you're probably right. I'll never forget the look on her face when she came to the hospital though. She had this brave, positive look on her face, but when I reached out to her, I saw the shattered look in her eyes. I'm not sure I'll ever be able to entirely forgive myself for putting that there.' He rubbed his leg absent-mindedly. 'I can't help but think the stress of me getting injured contributed to her heart attack.'

'Oh, Seb,' I said, reaching out and taking his free hand. 'You can't think like that. She knew you were doing what you loved and supported you in that. And she got to see you make a great recovery and start up the charity, didn't she?'

'She did. But she also got to see the mess I was in before I got my head in the right space.'

'You can't blame yourself for any of that. You didn't ask to be caught up in that IED blast, and she knew that not taking the path you'd chosen would have made you unhappy, which she certainly wouldn't have wanted.'

He looked down at my hand and laid his other over it before lifting his dark, thick lashed eyes to me. 'And how did you get to be so wise?' he asked softly.

There wasn't an answer I could give that didn't sound flippant, so I just tightened the hold I had on his hand for a moment in reply instead, before letting go.

* * *

We sat on the sofa talking until late, Scooby's soft snores the only other sound, until Seb glanced at the clock, apologising for keeping me up. I dismissed his apologies, knowing I'd have happily sat there until dawn, listening to him, exchanging ideas and thoughts and laughter, feeling more at ease than I ever thought I would have, bearing in mind it was the first time I'd been in his home and how awkward I'd felt initially about the unexpected sleepover situation.

'And so polite too,' he laughed. 'The perfect guest. You can definitely come again.'

'Is that a promise?' I smiled back, perhaps a little bit too emboldened by the nightcap he'd poured us a short time ago.

He stood up and put down a hand to me still sat on the sofa, which I took, allowing myself to be hauled up. Scooby was stretching and yawning, making that high-pitched squeak dogs do when they've got a really good yawn going. 'It most certainly is. Open invitation. I'll even put it in writing if you like.'

'Well, you know I like everything organised and easily referenced.'

'I do indeed. You're the queen of organisation. That's why I know I lucked out getting you to take me on as a client.'

My mind, relaxed by the surroundings, the evening and Seb in general, had been happily skipping ahead of me on a path that, as a rule, I'd kept myself off. At Seb's words, his reminder that, although we were friends, there was also a business element to our relationship, caused my imagination to pull up short, stumbling in its haste to stop. This effort apparently showed on my face.

'You OK?' Seb asked, his forehead creasing in concern. 'You've got a funny look on your face.'

'Thanks,' I said, a weird laugh escaping as I made an effort to cover any other feeling I was experiencing right then, of which I had a few to pick from, not least of all, lust, which wasn't awkward at all. 'Bit of a head rush getting up, that's all,' I said, bending down to pick up the glasses from the coffee table.

'Leave that, I'll do it.'

'It's fine. I think you have other priorities anyway.' I nodded towards where Scooby was now patiently standing by the patio door and looking hopefully between his master and the back garden, where a patch of grass clearly had his name on it.

I took the glasses through to the kitchen and gave them a quick wash as Seb sent the dog out into the darkness and stepped through after him. I was just popping them away in the cupboard I'd seen Seb take them from earlier when they walked back through, Seb locking the door behind them before he headed into the kitchen. The slight limp he walked with was more pronounced now, and I guessed the more tired he was, the more toll this took on his body.

'You OK?' I asked.

He nodded in reply.

I faffed about straightening the tea towel I'd just hung on the front of the oven. 'I'm sorry. I maybe shouldn't have asked that. I know you don't like people fussing, and it's not like I'm—'

'Lottie.'

I stopped, mid flow, but kept my eyes lowered. 'Hmm?'

Seb tilted his head and bent a little until I got the hint and met those dark, annoyingly sexy, eyes. 'You are allowed to say, ask and do whatever you like. OK? If you ever ask anything I'm not ready, or willing, to talk about, I'll tell you. Although, as I talk to you about pretty much everything already, I can't see that happening. But I never want you to feel that you have to tiptoe around me. Excuse the pun.'

I gave him a slightly embarrassed look up through my lashes.

'Understood?' he prompted.

I nodded.

'Good. So, in answer to your question, yes, I'm fine. My leg is aching and a bit painful, but that will be helped by some rest, which I think we both need.'

I ran a hand back over my hair. 'Oh god, do I look that bad?'

He gave me a look. 'Irritatingly, no. You don't. Which makes me feel quite old and haggard in comparison.'

'You're not that much older.'

'I know, which is what makes it even worse.'

'Oh, be quiet. You look just fine and you know it.'

He gave me a look which made me think he was genuinely doubting what I said.

'Seriously?' I frowned.

Seb shrugged.

'OK,' I said, accepting his motioned invitation to head towards the stairs. 'Example A. The charity's summer gala.'

'What about it?' he asked, 'And please hold onto the banister if you're going to insist on walking up the stairs and not look where you're going.'

'I'm fine,' I said, but holding on anyway, partly out of politeness, still half turned towards him.

'I'm sure but it makes me feel better, because if you fall, you're going to take me out too and that's going to be a real pain in the arse.'

I blushed and held on tighter.

He shook his head. 'You can let some blood flow through to your fingers though.'

By now we were at the top of the stairs and I headed towards the guest room, Seb leaning on the door jamb as we got there.

'What about the gala?' he asked.

'Is this for me?' I said, pointing at the neatly folded T-shirt that had appeared on the bottom of the bed.

Seb nodded. 'That OK?'

I shook it out and held it up against me. I could have got in it three times over. 'It's perfect, thanks.'

He gave me a smile that sent flashes through my brain which involved there being very little need for any clothing whatsoever. I really wished he wouldn't do that, although, as he apparently had no clue he was doing it, I couldn't hold it against him.

'I'm still in suspense,' he prompted, shifting position as he rested against the wall.

I'd sat on the bed now and, cross-legged, grabbed the make-up wipes I'd bought earlier from my bag. Pulling one from the packet, I swiped it across my face. 'You're tired. You should go to bed and get some rest.'

'I'll never sleep without knowing what you were going to say!'

I shook my head, laughing. 'Then at least come and sit down for a minute and take the weight off.' I shuffled my bum back up the bed more so that I was near the pillow and Seb took a seat next to me. 'Better?' I asked.

He nodded. 'So?'

'Patience isn't one of your virtues, is it?'

'Not really. Which isn't ideal sometimes, but I get by when I need to.'

'That sounds like a story.'

'And maybe one day I'll tell you, but right now I want to hear yours.'

'It's not a story. It's just facts.'

'Whatever it is, for the love of god, tell me,' he said, flopping himself back on the bed.

'You're such a drama queen.'

'Not the worst thing I've been called.'

'Really?'

He rolled his head, gave me a look and I got the message.

'Fine. OK. So, you're going on about feeling old and haggard, but as soon as we started brainstorming this gala, and ways to raise even more funds with the auction, one item kept coming up.'

'One auction item?'

'Yep.'

'Can we get it?'

'That's purely down to you.'

15

Seb rolled his head towards me again and opened the eyes he'd been resting closed. 'Why does the way you said that make me nervous?'

I waggled my eyebrows but remained silent.

'So, what is it then? This mystery auction item.'

'You.'

He shoved himself up onto his elbows. 'I beg your pardon?'

'You. More specifically a date with you.'

Seb said nothing. After a moment, he let himself slouch back down onto the bed. 'Very funny.'

I gave a shrug. 'I'm not joking.'

He pushed himself up again. 'Isn't that the sort of thing billionaires do in romance novels?'

'Read a lot of romance, have you?'

He gave me a smile that illustrated perfectly why a date with him would be a very popular lot on the auction list and I squashed down annoyance that I didn't have the funds to bid on it. 'You'd be surprised.'

'Brushing up on your skills.'

'Something like that.'

I raised a brow.

'Actually, I just read whatever I could get my hands on sometimes out on deployment. I'm not a book snob, and it was good escapism at times. And, as you say, enabled me to brush up on my skills as a bonus.'

'Ah, see? The truth comes out.'

'I still don't see how you've come to the conclusion that putting up an evening out with me would be a good way of raising money.'

'That's the thing,' I said, tucking my feet up under me. 'I didn't. That little gem came from several other directions.'

'Several?'

'Oh yes.'

He shook his head.

'You can shake your head all you like. It's going on the list, so you never know, those skills you picked up from the books might come in handy.'

'What am I supposed to do?' He asked, looking slightly awkward.

I did my best to squelch the feelings this momentary show of vulnerability had unleashed and instead concentrated on the conversation.

'On the date?'

'Yes.'

'What do you normally do on dates?'

'The usual, I guess.' He shrugged.

'Talk about yourself incessantly, ask your date how much they earn and then tell them they are clearly doing something wrong? Let the woman know that you're only there because your first, and second, choice fell through?'

Seb's mouth had dropped open a little. 'Is that really what you think of me?'

'Absolutely not. I'm just illustrating that "the usual" can vary, depending upon whom you speak to.'

He rolled onto his side, resting his head on his hand, the dark eyes studying me. 'Is that really your experience?'

I glanced at him, then focused back on the question. Much safer. 'Just the most recent highlights.'

'Lottie... we really need to get you a good date.'

I tilted my head as a sign of agreement. 'Sadly, I don't think I'll be able to keep up with the bidding.'

Oops! Damn that nightcap.

OK, so now I had two options. Pretend I hadn't said it and hope he hadn't heard or just laugh it off.

'You'd planned to bid?'

OK, so I guess hoping he hadn't heard wasn't an option.

'Only if the winning bid was looking a little terrifying, even for a tough customer like you.' I risked a glance. 'Friends take care of each other, right?' I shrugged, like it was no big deal and all a bit of a joke, even though I knew if I'd been attending the gala, watching some ridiculously wealthy woman gloat over her winning bid wasn't something I'd be in any great hurry to see. Of course, as well as the cougars, there was also the possibility that some of the younger socialites and celebrities would be holding up their cards. I wasn't sure which was worse.

'They do,' he said, quietly. 'Which is why I'm going to ask what that thought is that's racing round your brain right now.'

Ummm...

I waved him away. 'Nothing important. Just a... work thing.' Sort of true. 'So, anyway. That's just a heads-up. You're on the menu, so to speak.'

'Do I get a say in this?'

'Lady Genevieve Carstairs has already stated there's a ten grand starting bid with her name on it.'

Seb sat bolt upright. 'What?'

I smiled at his surprise.

'You heard. It's no secret she's got a thing for you. Besides, why are you so surprised people are interested? You've got a mirror, Seb. You know you're hardly the back of a bus.'

He gave me a look that was so adorably embarrassed, the butter-flies in my stomach I'd been fairly successfully keeping in check suddenly made a bid for flight. 'You know what I mean.'

'Your injury?'

He met my eyes.

'So? You're missing a bit. So what.' I shrugged. 'It's not exactly put a dent in your dating prowess from what I've seen.'

'Sometimes the women I've dated haven't known initially, depending on how we meet.'

'By which time, they're probably already half in love with you.'

He gave a laugh that caused Scooby, who had by now joined us and was snoozing at the foot of the bed, to open one eye. Seeing there was nothing much of interest to him, he closed it and went back to sleep.

'I hardly think so.'

'Says the man who already has ten grand bid on him.'

'I feel so cheap.'

I grinned and gave him a prod with my toes. 'From what I under-stand, that's just her opening bid. I'm pretty sure she'd go a lot high-er.' I shuffled my position. 'You don't have to do it, you know,' my tone a little more serious now. 'If you really don't want to. It was initially just said as a joke, but then it kind of took on a life of its own.'

His hand curled gently around my foot absent-mindedly. 'But if she's serious, that's ten grand for the charity.'

'True. But you shouldn't do things you're uncomfortable with, no matter what.'

'Let's just see nearer the time.' He glanced at the clock. 'I should let you get some rest. Sorry. Sat up keeping you talking.'

'That's OK. It's been nice.'

He pushed himself back onto his feet and looked down to where

I was now perched like a little gnome on the edge of the bed. 'It really has.' His voice was soft and a flicker crossed his face. At least I thought it did. But then it was gone. The only light was from the side table lamp and I was pretty tired, so it was entirely possible I imagined it anyway. 'There's fresh towels in the bathroom. Just use whatever you need in there and shout if there's anything else you want.'

'Thanks, Seb. This is all really kind of you.'

'My pleasure. Really.'

'What time is Angus coming over again?'

'He said eight thirty, but our Angus is an early riser, so he'll probably be round about eight.'

'Oh god,' I groaned, looking at the small, shabby-chic style clock on the bedside table. 'Maybe you should have told me that earlier.'

Seb shook his head. 'It's fine. Sleep as late as you want. I'll be up and can give him the keys. I already gave him a rundown of what's been going on, so he'll be fine to just get on and work his magic.'

'I can't do that. It seems rude.'

'Rude is your host keeping you up way past your bedtime.'

'You have no idea when my bedtime is!'

'We've been friends for long enough for me to have a pretty good idea. Although, to anyone else, your fondness for pyjamas might suggest your bedtime is more akin to a toddler's.'

'I like to be comfy. You're lucky I didn't wear them this evening.'

'I did wonder if you might. But, so long as you came, I wouldn't have cared what you wore, to be honest. It was just fun getting together. At last.'

And there it was. The biggest of red flags that Seb Marshall didn't think of me in *that* way. I'd made an effort, although in a way that hopefully looked like I hadn't made *too* much of an effort, but in the end, I could have rocked up in my pyjamas and he wouldn't really have noticed the difference.

'It was,' I said.

'OK. Night, Lottie.'

'Night, Seb. Sleep well.'

He gave a little wave and left, heading towards his own room.

I scooted along to the bathroom, did all the things I needed to and swapped my clothes for the T-shirt he'd left me. Made to fit him, and not me, it was generously sized and perfect as a nightie. Thanks to Seb's height, it was also long enough to cover all the bits required in order to maintain a certain amount of decency should I accidentally run into him on the landing.

* * *

I'd set my alarm and so was washed, dressed and downstairs by half eight the next morning. Without my make-up bag, I'd done the best I could to hide exactly how tired I felt with the basics of my compact and a slap of lippy. It'd have to do for now. Besides, as it was clear from last night that Seb didn't view me in a romantic way, it didn't really matter anyway. No pressure. Besides, he'd already seen me plenty of times on video calls looking knackered with scary hair, so this morning was probably not the worst. At least I'd brushed my hair.

I called out but got no reply and, poking my head into the lounge, couldn't see Scooby or Seb in the garden either. Wandering into the kitchen, I made my way over to the window. The weather was bright and sunny, but, judging by the way Seb and the man I guessed was Angus, were wrapped up as they bent over the open bonnet of my car, pretty damn chilly. Scooby was busy sniffing around the immediate area and, apparently having completed that task, now took a lazy puppy sit next to his owner, resting against him, and waited patiently.

As I saw Seb straighten from the car, I stepped back, ensuring that I didn't get caught watching in case it looked weird. Or in case he somehow got the telepathic message I'd accidentally been staring at his bum for a good proportion of the time.

Taking a seat on one of the bar style chairs at the breakfast bar, I waited for Seb and his pooch to return. Scooby made an appearance first, charging into the kitchen and sliding inelegantly to a halt in front of me as I hopped off the stool and crouched down to greet him. He pressed his head against me in delight as I fussed over him, deep groans of happiness emanating from him as I did so.

From the corner of my eye, I saw two trainers come to stand next to me and looked up at the unfairly gorgeous body and face they were attached to.

'I'm totally coming back as a pampered dog in the next life,' Seb grinned down at me. 'Good morning, by the way.'

'Morning,' I said, giving Scooby one last chin rub and standing.

'Sleep all right?' my host asked, heading over towards the kettle. 'Tea or coffee?'

'Tea, please. And yes, thank you. Very well.'

'You didn't need to get up so early. I told you that. It's all under control.'

'I know,' I shrugged. 'So, what does he think?' I nodded towards the window.

Seb dropped a teabag into a cup and then shoved a coffee pod into the machine next to the kettle. 'He's not fazed. Quietly confident.'

'Right.' I moved to the fridge and found the milk. Taking it out, I put it down next to where Seb was making the drinks.

'Thanks.'

'He knows I've had it looked at a couple of times though?'

'Ummhmm,' Seb nodded, concentrating on the task in front of him before handing me the milk back. 'Ta.'

I returned it to the fridge.

'So, you ready for breakfast?'

Apparently we were done with the car conversation, so I let it go. It couldn't hurt to have someone else look at it and, right now, I just hoped Angus really was the miracle worker he'd been touted as, because otherwise I was going to have to fork out to have the bloody thing towed back home. 'You don't need to go to any trouble, Seb. Really.'

'No trouble. I'm eating. Makes no difference to do extra. And if that was your stomach I just heard, I think I already got my answer.' He grinned as he leant over and snagged a box of eggs from the side, launching into the creation of his breakfast masterpiece.

16

A little over an hour later, Seb and I were cosily ensconced in his car, having left Angus to it, and on our way to a couple of garages in which we'd narrowed down some possible options over the insanely delicious breakfast he'd cooked. We pulled into the forecourt of the first and nosed around until a salesman came over and asked if he could help.

By early afternoon, I'd test driven three different cars and pretty much decided on the one I wanted. All I needed to do now was to see if Angus could work his magic, so I could get a decent part-exchange on my old one. Just as I was pondering this over a hot chocolate in a cosy café Seb had led us to, his phone rang. The café was quiet and snug, and Seb quickly rose, laid a hand on my shoulder for a brief moment and then stepped outside as he took the call. We'd chosen a battered but characterful leather sofa in the window to sit on, but the warmth of the café, contrasted with the chill winter air outside, meant that the glass was steamed and all I could see was a shadowy outline of Seb, huddled into his down filled coat.

A few minutes later he was back, rubbing his hands together and grabbing his mug to wrap them around and warm up.

'That was Angus,' he said, taking a sip and giving a little shiver as the hot liquid warmed him.

'And?' I asked, my fingers tensing around my own mug in anticipation.

Seb's eyes dropped momentarily to my hands before meeting my eyes again. 'Relax. It's all good. Running like a champion again.'

'Really?'

'Yep.'

'So, he found the fault?'

'Yep. Something in the wiring that's obviously got missed. Loose connection. It was kind of buried in there, which is probably why the others have never found it. Or they just weren't looking in the right place, but Angus is almost forensic when it comes to stuff like this. Hence, all done.'

'How much do I owe him?'

Seb shook his head. 'Nothing. And you can't offer him anything either. He'll be offended.' He shifted position on the sofa and turned to face me a little more. 'Angus sees things like this as his way of giving back.'

'But he doesn't owe me anything.'

'No, but he feels he owes the charity something, and ergo, me. Even though I've told him a million times that's not how it works.'

'But doing things for the charity, you, or anyone connected to you makes him happy.'

'Exactly.'

I took a bite of the gooey chocolate cake I'd ordered alongside my drink. There was another slice in a box on the table for Angus, who Seb had told me was a fiend when it came to chocolate cake. The soft buttery icing melted in my mouth and I had a feeling Angus wasn't going to be disappointed. 'I can understand that.'

Seb gave me a soft smile. 'Thanks.'

'It still feels weird though.'

'I know.'

He finished off the slice of cake on his plate and I saw him eyeing the box.

'No.'

'What?' he asked, looking innocent.

'Don't give me that look,' I replied, laughing. 'I've known you too long. You were definitely eyeing that box of cake and, in the light of knowing the man has miraculously fixed my car, I'll defend it with everything I have!'

'Is that so?'

'Absolutely!' To illustrate this, I moved the box as far away from him on the table as possible.

'You know I can still reach that, right?'

'You'll have to go through me first.'

'Lottie, I could sling you over my shoulder like a sack of spuds if I needed to.'

I drew myself up. 'Try that, buster, and your prosthetic will be the least of your troubles.'

'Oooh!' Seb winced and pressed his legs together a little. 'You've got a mean streak, you know that?'

'I have not. It's called determination.'

'Oh, I see. That's all right then.'

'I'm glad we agree.'

'I didn't say that.' But I saw the smile before the huge mug eclipsed most of his face. 'So,' he said, reappearing. 'You definitely decided on that car?'

'I think so. I think I'd like to go back and have another quick look and maybe another drive, but it's kind of what I had in mind anyway and it felt nice.'

'Great!'

'But if Angus has fixed my car now, you can just drop me back at the house and I can go back under my own steam.' I glanced up at the old station-style clock on the wall, the second hand bouncing as it edged its way around the face. 'You've got most of the afternoon left that way at least and I haven't entirely swallowed up your day.'

Seb kept his eyes on his mug as he finished his drink, tidying up the table once he'd done so.

I popped the box of cake on top of my bag to take back to Angus. When he still didn't say anything, I shifted in my seat. 'Not that I don't appreciate everything you've done so far.'

'I know,' he said, flicking me a smile as he pushed his arms back into his jacket. Zipping it up, he pulled the beanie hat out of a pocket and put it on.

'Seb?'

'Hmm?'

'You've gone weird.'

'What?'

'You. You've gone weird.'

At this, his smile broke through and the feeling dissipated, but there was no denying it had, momentarily, been there.

'I do not go weird,' he stated.

'You just did.'

He shook his head and motioned for me to go ahead of him. The car was parked close and, once inside, engine running and a warm breath of air filtering through, Seb turned to me. 'OK, so here's the deal. You were right. I did go a bit weird in there.'

'Was it something I said?'

'Kind of.'

I opened my mouth to apologise, or explain, or... something, but Seb held up his hand.

'But this is definitely a case of it's me not you.'

'Oh god. That's never a good thing to hear.'

He leant over and laid a hand over where I was now gripping my own together. Even if I got over the fact that Seb didn't fancy me, which I'd kind of worked out already as I'd been single for some time now and he'd never attempted to ask me out, I had to admit I'd been holding onto the tiny glimmer of hope that perhaps there might be a spark once he met me in real life.

'I didn't want to make you uncomfortable.'

'You could never do that.'

'It's just that I know you're on your Year of Saying No thing and I didn't want to put you in a position that would make you feel awkward, or us awkward.'

I swallowed and tried not to make that loud gulp noise that always happens when you're trying to be subtle. 'I don't think anything you say could make me feel that way, Seb.' My voice was soft and my heart had sped up. Maybe I'd got it wrong after all? Maybe—

'I didn't really have anything planned this afternoon. Angus has taken Scoobs off on a massive hike and I'd only be sat at home on my own anyway, so I'm happy to come back with you. Gives us a bit longer to hang out too.'

I nodded, the balloon of excitement and ridiculous romanticism deflating with a sad, slightly rude, noise inside my head.

Seb winced, and sat back, turning to the steering wheel. 'See? This is why I should have just kept quiet. You've already spent way more time than you expected with me and, unlike on the phone, you can't just hang up when you're bored.'

'I've never done that!'

He glanced over. 'That is true. And I thank you for that.'

'And I'd love for us to get to spend a bit longer together.'

'Lottie, it's fine,' he said, putting the car into drive. 'It's me. We made a pact ages ago about being polite for politeness sake. Let's not change that now.'

'I'm not,' I said, calmly. Honestly. 'I would love for you to come back to the garage with me.'

He gave me a sideways, slightly suspicious glance. 'So why the expression?'

'I didn't have an expression.'

'Yeah. You did.'

'No, I didn't. I have indigestion from that cake, that's all. It was kind of rich.'

Seb was driving, turning us back towards the direction of the last garage. Letting his eyes leave the road for the briefest of moments. 'I've already told you you're a terrible liar.'

'And I've told you I don't know what you're talking about.'

His eyes were back on the road, but I saw the sigh he let out.

'Honestly, Seb, I'm fine.'

'OK,' he nodded, without turning. 'Let's go and get this car then.'

I made a noise of agreement but felt the churn in my stomach. I hated lying to him, especially when it was so obvious he knew that I was, but I couldn't tell him the truth either. Wriggling in my seat, I shifted positions a couple of times, the discomfort in my head once more translating to my body.

Seb slowed as the traffic lights turned red and came to a gentle halt.

'Hey,' the word was soft and enquiring.

I looked across and gave a smile that felt a little awkward on my face, like it wasn't quite in the right position.

Seb studied me for a moment, reached out and laid one large hand over the little knot I'd made of my own. 'Relax.'

'I'm relaxed!' I replied, sounding about as relaxed as a turkey upon hearing a Christmas carol.

His laugh swirled around me and the sound of it helped release some of the tension that had built between us.

'OK,' he said again, but with none of the disbelief his previous reply had been laced with. His gaze flicked to the lights before resting back on me. 'You know you can tell me anything, right?'

My heart gave an unhelpful squeeze. 'I do.'

'Good.' He gave my hands a quick press before returning both his own to the wheel and pulling away.

Anything that is except this.

17

'I can't say I'm looking forward to Alice's baby shower on Saturday. Does that sound mean?'

'Nope,' I said, hooking my legs over the arm of the squashy chair I was sitting in, as Jess stretched her legs out along the length of my sofa and leant against Harry, who was tuned out to us and watching a sports channel. 'They're not my thing either. I don't really have any desire to play games called "Who's got the dirty nappy?"'

'Do you want me to pick you up on the way so we can go together? Strength in numbers?'

'Thanks, but I'm not going.'

Jess sat up. 'What?'

I shrugged, stroking Humphrey, marvelling at how quickly he had become an indispensable part of my life and how much I loved this little fuzzy ball of fur. 'I'm not going.'

'What... how...?'

'I said no.'

'You said no?' Jess screwed up her face at this apparently impossible concept.

'Yep.'

'And she just... accepted that?'

'I guess so. I was polite about it. I told her I'd see them all once she's had the baby, which is what I'd planned to do anyway.'

'Wow.'

'What?'

'You're really doing it.'

'What?'

'This year of saying no.'

I frowned. 'I am. Most definitely. Why? Did you think I wouldn't?'

Jess gave a little shrug. 'I just know how much you hate upsetting anyone. You're a people-pleaser.'

'Which is probably how I got roped into that bloody year of saying yes last year.'

'I think the bottles of wine we got through probably helped.'

'True.'

'But look what came out of it!' Jess grinned, flashing the huge diamond on her left hand.

'Yes. I think we've already established it was good for you.'

'Wasn't it for you? I thought you were mucking about when you moaned all the time.'

'I didn't moan all the time!' I said, offended. 'But it was way out of my comfort zone and I can't say I was sorry when it was finally over.'

'But didn't you get anything out of it?'

'I got to spend some fun times with you. I got to see you made incredibly happy and I also got the inspiration to stop all that people-pleasing and say no sometimes. We spend all this time rushing around, saying yes to things we don't really want to, then feeling upset and annoyed that there's no time left for us to do the things we actually want to.'

'Very true,' Harry added.

'I thought you were watching telly.' Jess lolled her head back to look at her fiancé.

'I am. But, contrary to popular opinion, I am capable of doing two things at once.'

Jess gave me a look that suggested she disagreed.

'And I saw that too.'

I gave Harry a smirk, and he caught my eye, giving me a wink in return.

'Anyway. The upshot of all this is that now I don't even have you there to keep me company on Saturday,' Jess stated, a little sulkily.

I gave her a what-can-you-do look and she let out a dramatic sigh and flung herself back against Harry, who rubbed her arm soothingly, his eyes back on the screen. He was a quick learner.

'Can't you say you've changed your mind?' Jess whined.

'Nope. Because I haven't.'

She let out a huff. 'I'm not sure I'm such a fan of this saying no thing.'

'You were when you didn't realise it was going to apply to you too,' Harry said quietly.

'I'm leaving you at home next time,' Jess pouted at him.

'Lottie invited us both.'

'Yes, but I have final say.'

'Actually, it's my flat and my food, so I do. And Harry's agreeing with me, so he's definitely invited again.'

'Ugh! I know I said I wanted you two to be friends, but this is ridiculous!'

I swung my legs to the front, reluctantly dislodging Humphrey, who made a small leap to the floor and then began stretching elaborately as if to point out to me how comfy he'd been, having apparently picked up some drama cues from my best friend. Getting up, I took Jess' wine glass from her and gave her a hug.

'So, what are you doing instead?' she asked, padding after me into the kitchen, where I refilled her glass and flicked the kettle on to make Harry another tea.

'I'm going to pick up my new car.'

Jess straightened, her attention focused like a dog that's just spotted the possibility of a cheese snack. 'With Seb?'

'No, I'm going to the garage on my own.'

The proverbial cheese was back in the fridge.

'Oh.'

'But I'm supposed to be seeing him after.'

Cheese!

'Supposed to be?' Jess raised a perfect brow.

'Well. Yes. I am. I think. He's suggested I bring Humphrey so we can take the dogs on a ramble together. It's obviously quite a distance, so he's invited us to stay over.'

She tilted her head. 'What's going on?' her voice was softer now, the drama gone, replaced by concern.

I flicked off the kettle and poured water over a teabag, prodding it occasionally with a spoon as thoughts tumbled in my brain. 'I don't know.'

'I think I might.'

I gave Jess a sideways glance.

'Seb Marshall.'

Flicking the teabag out, I leant back against the fridge. 'It's stupid, I know. I just...'

'Hoped he wouldn't be as great in the flesh as he was.'

'Pretty much,' I sighed, yanking the fridge door open and grabbing the milk before sploshing some into Harry's cup. 'And then he was all tall and dark and gorgeous. And funny. And caring. And—'

'Perfect?'

'Nobody's perfect.'

'Present company excepted, obviously.' This was followed by a loud cough from the other room. 'I don't have to marry you, you know!' Jess tossed back, receiving a laugh in reply.

I couldn't help smiling. I loved this new side of Jess. She was tall, bright and beautiful. When she walked into a room, it really did light up and men were drawn to her, laughing at her jokes, flattering her, and all hoping to be the one she might choose to go home with. When she'd met Harry, he'd been like this too for the first few moments. Jess had the kind of presence that could temporarily make you lose your train of thought. But then, unexpectedly, he'd teased her. Like I would tease her. But the difference was, we'd known each other since we were four years old. I'd held my breath, waiting for Jess' reaction. Knowing how prone she was to a bit of drama, I was weighing up whether it would be a total blanking or a turn on her five inch spiked heel followed by a dramatic strut. Instead, she'd laughed. Really laughed. And in that moment, I knew. And I think Jess did too. Harry was different. Harry was the one.

'Anyway,' I waved the thoughts away. 'It doesn't matter. I'm just being daft. I guess he's just the first guy I've liked since I broke up with Tom and I got a bit carried away.'

'You never get carried away, Lottie. Which must mean you really like him.'

'I do.'

'Why don't you just ask him out?'

'Because I don't want to.'

Jess rolled her eyes. 'Harry darling? Could you call the fire brigade? Lottie's pants are on fire. Get them to send several engines. It's a full-blown inferno.'

* * *

'You look happy!' Seb smiled, as he set me back after one of his way too good hugs.

'I am. I have a new car!'

And a new, far more sensible attitude about you. I can do this.

'Also, right now, if I hadn't had my yearly plan in place, I'd be sat at a baby shower I didn't want to attend, pretending I was enjoying myself while everyone talked about things that currently have abso-lutely no relevance to my life.'

'Instead you're here.'

'Exactly!'

Seb grinned. 'Then, I for one am very glad of your plan for the moment. And I'm pretty sure Scooby and Humphrey are too,' he added as the two dogs had now said hello and started charging round the house playing.

'For the moment?'

He smiled again, taking my coat. 'Yes. Because it works in my favour.'

'You sound like Jess.'

'Your best friend?'

'Yes. She was saying the same thing in a roundabout way just the other day.'

'Wise woman.'

'Sometimes,' I said, pushing her advice to just 'bloody well ask him out' as she'd left my flat the other night to the back of my mind. 'Sometimes not so much.'

'Because of last year?'

Yep. Let's go with that.

'The perfect example. But, like I said to her, I'm taking the positives from that. I learned stuff about myself and if I hadn't done that, I might not be saying no more now.'

Seb nodded. 'Want a drink before we head out?'

* * *

After a long walk with the dogs, Seb and I had gone back to his house, to be greeted by the delicious aroma of a hearty and warming stew he'd put in the oven to slow cook before we left. Over this, accompanied by fresh, crusty bread and good wine, we'd talked and laughed and completely relaxed. The slight awkwardness that had arisen the weekend before was washed away, replaced by comfort and ease. I'd come to my senses at last. There was no denying I thought Seb was gorgeous and all the things I'd told Jess. But I'd also confirmed to myself he was totally off the menu, accepting instead that we had a fabulous friendship and that was better than anything that might be risked by letting my crush continue. So I'd had a long talk with myself and I was done with it. Totally. Absolutely done.

'Night, Lottie,' Seb said, hugging me as we finally said goodnight, having sat up talking into the early hours once again.

God, he smelled good... I stomped on the thought. *It's the year of saying no, remember?* I reminded myself. And getting high on Seb Marshall's aftershave was a definite no.

'Night, Seb. Thanks for today.'

'You're welcome,' he said, leaning on the door jamb, watching as I tucked Humphrey into his bed beside me. 'You know you're both welcome any time. It's nice having company.'

I plonked down onto my bum and looked up at him, the outlines just slightly fuzzy from a combination of wine and tiredness. 'You know you could get company really easily, don't you?'

He frowned.

'You're kind of hot,' I blabbed.

Seb smiled. 'Kind of.'

'Quite.'

'Oh. I'm not really sure what to say to that.'

I shrugged. 'Just saying.'

'Thanks,' he said, focusing on the little dog beside me. 'It's not that easy to meet people sometimes though, is it?'

'No. That's true. But you could try online dating.'

Seb slid his eyes to me. 'No thanks.'

'Why not?'

'Because I've been there, done that, and it was awful.'

'You have? I didn't know that.'

'It was before I met you. But, pretty much, I had the same experience as you did when you did it last year. Not something I'd be in a hurry to repeat.'

I pulled a face. 'I know there are plenty of people who do find someone special, but, for the most part, everything I hear tends to veer to our end of the experience scale.' I shifted positions. 'Something I read recently said that over eighty per cent of people on dating websites don't have representative profile pictures! Over eighty per cent!' I threw my arms up.

'Yep. I definitely had a few of those too. But it was just a weird experience for me. People, in general, don't seem to be satisfied. They might like you, but there's this hang-up. It's like they feel that if they keep seeing you, they could be missing out. They might think you're great and tick all the boxes, but there's this niggling doubt that maybe, just maybe, there's something around the corner even better.'

I flopped back, slouched against the side of the bed, still looking up at him. 'They're likely in for a big disappointment. Especially if they passed you up for that slight chance.'

'Sometimes they were keeping all their options open. But I'm not really into sharing.'

'Really?' I asked, trying not to be intrigued. And, judging by the smirk on Seb's face, failing.

'No. Probably not a very modern outlook, but if I'm with someone, I'm with someone. Heart and soul.'

Oh bloody hell, Seb. I'm really trying here and you're so not helping the situation.

'No, I'd agree with that,' I said, trying to ensure it sounded casual. 'I don't get that whole "we're not exclusive" thing. That doesn't really work for me either.' I smothered a yawn and Seb smiled.

'Get some rest. Thanks for today.'

'I didn't do anything! You cooked and hosted and everything else.'

'You came. That's enough.'

OK, he needed to go now. I knew I could do this, but it was a lot harder with him standing there looking drop-dead gorgeous and ticking all my boxes.

'You should get some rest too. Night, Seb.'

I was still sat on the floor next to Humphrey who had long since passed into the land of nod. Seb took the few short steps from the door, bent, placed the lightest of kisses on the top of my head and turned back to the door.

'Sleep well.'

With that, he headed out, Scooby sleepily padding just in front of him, and pulled the door to behind him.

18

'Got everything?' Seb asked late the next morning as I finished securing Humphrey into his doggy harness.

'I think so. Thanks again for helping me with the car shopping. I really appreciate it.'

Seb shook his head. 'My pleasure. I'm glad you found something you liked.' He bent to look in at the dog who was already curled up and looking sleepy. 'Someone seems comfy enough.'

I smiled at Humphrey. 'He's had a great time with Scooby. I think we've worn him out.'

Seb straightened back up and shifted his weight. 'I hope you had a good time too.'

'I really did,' I said, looking up at him. He was close now and I could smell the citrus tang of the shower gel I'd borrowed this morning. 'Thanks for having us.'

'Do you think we could do this again?'

'Of course. If you don't mind, that is. You could come down to me, although I don't have a spare room so it'd be—'

'Lottie.'

'Hmm?'

He rubbed a hand across his jaw, shadowed from a day's growth. 'I'm normally much better at this.'

'At what?'

'Asking a woman out.'

'Asking... I...' I felt my eyes widen as I lifted my gaze to his. 'Is that... umm... what you're doing now?'

'Very badly, apparently. But... yes. I'd really like to take you out and maybe have that romantic table for two used for its intended purpose.' He shrugged a little self-consciously, his face half smile, half uncertainty.

A chill breeze had been blowing all day and, having thrown my hat in the car already, my hair was now at the mercy of the wind. I lifted a hand to push it back from my face, but Seb's was already there, gently, tenderly moving it and tucking it behind my ear. The word 'thanks' was in my head, but I couldn't get it to make to the journey to my mouth as my brain was too busy processing his words.

'I...' I began, suddenly realising that I had no idea where I was going with that sentence.

Seb straightened away from me, his Adam's apple bobbing as he swallowed.

Come on, Lottie. This is a simple question! Seb Marshall, the man of some very X-rated dreams, has just asked you out. He does like you after all. This is what you wanted! It's a simple answer. All you have to do is say yes! Yes, Seb, I'd absolutely love to!

'No.'

Huh?

'I'm really sorry, Seb. I can't.'

He shook his head, a smile on his face as he briefly raised his palms. 'No, not a problem. I... just thought...' The words tailed off as he looked off into the distance, one hand running briefly back over the short dark hair.

Shit. What was I thinking? This was Seb. The man I'd had a crush on for ages. The man I most felt myself around. The man whose smile made my stomach flutter like no one else ever had – and I'd just turned him down.

'It's just that you're a client and I don't want to mess that up.' I sighed. 'I can't afford to mess that up.'

He waved it away, the smile still there, but we both knew it wasn't his usual, easy-going expression, however much he tried to cover it.

'And now I'm worried it's messed up anyway.'

'Of course not,' he said, airily. 'You're absolutely right. I just...' he blew out a breath. 'I've just had a really great time these last couple of weekends and I guess I got a bit carried away. I'm sorry. I should never have said anything.' He lifted his hands and scrubbed them across his cropped hair, his eyes on the distance again momentarily before focusing back on me. 'Are we still good or have I blown it?'

I shook my head. 'We're fine. It's for the best. I think we both know that really.'

'Yep.' He cleared his throat. 'Yeah. Absolutely. Probably best if we both forget I ever said anything,' Seb replied, nodding, as I felt my stomach twist.

'I'd better be going.'

'Yeah. Drive carefully.'

'I will.' I gave a wary glance. 'Do I still get a hug?'

'Of course.' He hugged me for a moment before standing back. 'Message when you're home.'

'Will do,' I said, sliding into the driver's seat and pulling the seat belt across me. Seb smiled and pushed the door closed for me. Turning the key, I gave him a thumbs up at the novelty of a first-time start, turning it into a wave, which he returned with a brief movement of his hand.

In the rear view mirror, I saw Seb and Scooby walk back to the house and I let out the breath I'd been holding. I knew I'd done the right thing. So why did it feel so entirely wrong?

* * *

'How's it going?' Jess asked.

'What's that?'

'The denial that you're in love with Seb?'

'Oh pffft. I am not.'

'So, it's going well, then.'

I rolled my eyes. 'Actually, it's fine. I told you it was just a crush. And I'm over it.'

Mostly.

'Is that so?'

'Yes.'

'Good. You won't mind that I've invited him to our engagement party then?'

I snorted tea out of my nose.

'You did what?' I asked, mopping up with a tea towel as I glared at Jess on the screen. 'Why? You don't even know him!'

'We kind of do. Harry was looking for a charity to do his next triathlon challenge for and I suggested Seb's, so he contacted him and mentioned that they had a mutual acquaintance and got chatting. They really hit it off.'

I didn't doubt this, but I also knew my friend of old and it appeared Jess had been doing some serious scheming.

'You could have just asked me to bring him. He'd probably have said yes anyway.'

'It wasn't like that. It was more...' Jess tailed off as she saw the look on my face. 'OK, fine. But you're doing this whole saying no thing and I really want to meet him!'

'Ugh, Jess!' I dropped my face into my hands.

'What?'

'You're not helping things!'

'I thought you just said you were doing OK with the whole crush thing.'

'I am! But it's far easier at a distance!'

Jess cocked her head. 'There's something else, isn't there?'

I blew out a sigh. 'He asked me out.'

'What?' Her eyes were wide. 'When?'

'The weekend I went to pick up my new car. As I was leaving.'

'So what did you say?'

I cleared my throat. 'I said no.'

'Come again?'

'I said no.'

'Yeah, that's what I thought you said, but that can't possibly be right because this is the man that's perfect for you. Looks hot, has manners and a great personality and apparently fancies the arse off of you, as I *know* you do with him!'

I dropped my head back momentarily. 'I know. But it's complicated.'

Jess pulled her head back. 'No, it isn't. You're single, he's single, you both like each other. It's far from complicated. In fact, it's entirely the opposite of complicated!'

'Jess, please.'

'You know this year of saying no thing doesn't mean you have to say no to everything, especially not to hot men you've been lusting over for ages!'

'It hasn't been ages!'

'It bloody has! Why on earth did you say no? You like him, Lottie. I know you do.' Her voice was softer now, trying to understand. 'I think he'd make you happy. He obviously cares about you.'

'I know. And I care about him. But I have to be sensible, Jess. He's my biggest client. If I started something with him and it went bad, there's no way he's going to keep his business with me and that could be really bad for my income. I just can't afford to mix the two. Yes, I think he's lovely and, yes, I do have a bit of a crush on him.' I ignored Jess' unladylike snort. 'But I can get over that. In time. It's for the best,' I repeated, a phrase that seemed to have become a personal mantra since that day.

'So how did he take it?'

'OK, I think.' I paused. 'Yeah. Fine actually. He agreed it was for the best too. We're great as friends and neither of us want to ruin that, so it's all good.'

It's definitely all good. Great, in fact. Absolutely perfect!

'So how are things now?'

'Good. Back to how they were before.'

'Really?'

'Yep. He's been pretty busy with work and I think he was out on a date the other night, so it's definitely not like I've broken his heart or anything.' I gave a one shouldered shrug.

'Right.'

'What's that supposed to mean?'

'Nothing. I just said "right".'

'It's the way you said it.'

Jess shrugged but offered no further explanation. 'I can try and take back the invitation if that helps.'

I laughed, tension seeping out of me. 'You can't do that!'

'It's my party. My prerogative.'

I shook my head. 'It's fine.'

'He might not come anyway,' she added.

My phone dinged with a WhatsApp message. I reached for it. Seb and I were doing OK and had seemingly managed to move on from the hiccup. The fact he'd been on some dates certainly seemed to indicate that was the case. I knew I had no right to wonder about those dates, but I couldn't help it. I couldn't help wish that I'd met him some other way than through work. Maybe Jess was right. Maybe he wouldn't or couldn't come. I opened my phone.

Hey. I just got an invite to an engagement party from Jess and Harry. He's doing a charity challenge for us. You OK with me coming? I won't if you'll think it's weird or makes you uncomfortable. (As I know you're happy to say no, I feel able to ask this in complete confidence that you'll answer me honestly 😊)

I turned the phone screen towards my computer.

Jess squinted. 'I can't read that. I haven't got my contacts in. As it is, you're kind of fuzzy round the edges.'

'I'm fuzzy round the edges at the best of times.'

Jess rolled her uncorrected eyes. 'What does it say?'

I put the phone back on the coffee table. 'That Seb's just received your invite and would I mind if he went.'

'I hope you've replied and told him you wouldn't.' Jess said, clearly forgetting she'd just offered to uninvite him.

'Not yet.'

'Why not?'

'It's just come in! And I haven't decided if that's the right answer yet.'

'Oh pfft. Of course, it's the right answer.'

I gave Jess a look, which she immediately shrugged off. Possibly because she couldn't see my expression clearly or possibly because it was Jess and her curiosity was a force to be reckoned with. Also, even with my plan in place, I knew that she knew that I was never going to stop Seb from going to the party.

'Your mum and dad have already said they'll be there. And Mario and Andy, of course.'

'Are Harry's parents coming?'

Jess let out a bit of a sigh. 'Yeah.'

'How's that going?'

'Slowly. I guess it will just take them some time to get used to the fact Harry's not chosen from the stable of "suitable types" they'd expected him to.'

'They can't not love you, Jess. And just look how happy you make Harry. That's got to count for something.'

'Yes. But I also didn't go to private school, and I'm mixed race. I'm pretty sure, as far as they're concerned, that's two strikes against me.'

I pulled a sympathetic face, but Jess batted it away.

'It's fine. They're an old money family and Harry's their golden boy. It was unlikely ever to be free from drama. And you know me, I love a bit of drama.' She gave me a wink. 'I think it was a bit of a shock initially. He was expected to hook up with some titled pony club type after a deal their parents did while they were both in their prams.'

'Does that still happen?' I asked, a little surprised.

'More than you'd think, apparently. Anyway, this lady wotserface rather put paid to that when she eloped last year with a penniless Romanian musician.'

'Ah.'

'Yeah, so I think at the moment they're considering that, although I don't have the titles, or monied background, I may actually have a lot more sense. And, of course, I'll look fabulous in all the photos.'

I grinned. I loved this aspect of Jess' personality and it reassured me that she had that inner strength not to let prejudice ruin the life she was choosing.

'What does Harry think about it all?'

'He stood up at the first family dinner he took me to in order to meet his parents, toasted me and, in a roundabout way, told them that we now came as a package. Without me, they didn't get him either. But in that kind, adorable, cute way of his.'

'That still left them in no doubt that he wasn't about to take, or let you take, any shit over his choice.'

'Bingo.'

'I bloody love Harry.'

Jess laughed and fiddled with her ring, a soft, wistful expression floating over her perfect features for a moment. 'Me too.' And then they cleared. 'Now we just have to get you sorted.'

'Excuse me, I do not need "sorting"!'

'Oh, honey, I think we both know you're in need of a damn good sorting!' she said, letting out her filthiest laugh.

'OK. I'm hanging up now.'

19

My flat suddenly seemed a lot smaller with Seb Marshall stood in it. I'd always known it was kind of tiny, but it was all I could afford at the time after the split with my ex, and it had been fine, even when I had Jess round. But Seb was a lot bigger than Jess and he definitely filled the space a lot more. Or maybe it was just that there suddenly seemed a little less room to breathe...

'You look nice,' groaning to myself at the lameness of my comment, I took his coat and hung it on the peg in my tiny hallway.

'Thanks.' He gave a little self-deprecating glance and then paused. I could practically see the cogs in his head going round as he searched for the right thing to say.

'It's a new look I'm trying out,' I said.

'Oh! Right,' he smiled, nodding at the same time as his eyes quickly scanned the rats' nest of pigtails currently kirby gripped to my skull. 'Cool!' he added, crooked smile fixed in place. This was the real giveaway. I'm not sure I had ever heard Seb say 'Cool' before and the look of awkwardness that flashed briefly on his face showed it sounded as odd to his own ears as it had to mine.

'Cool?' I couldn't resist.

The grin widened. He knew he was caught.

'Don't worry,' I said, waving him through to the living room. 'I'm taking them out in a minute. You were just a little earlier than I expected so you got the full effect of my pre-presentable self. Sorry about that.'

'You always look presentable. More than presentable.'

'I spend half my life in pyjamas!' I laughed, as I watched Humphrey stretch and jump down from the sofa, before toddling over to investigate the new human in our midst.

'Yes, true. But they're nice pyjamas. From what I've seen.' Seb laughed, bending over to fuss with Humphrey, who, in his excitement, stood on his back legs and placed his front paws against Seb's leg.

'Oh, Humphrey, no. Get down!' I made to crouch and scoot my pup away, but Seb caught my arm.

'He's fine. Two tiny little paws leaning against me aren't going to do any damage.'

I flicked my gaze up hesitantly before glancing away again. 'I know. I mean, I don't, but I just didn't want him damaging anything accidentally and...' I stopped as Seb's hand gently tucked under my chin, encouraging me to turn back and face him.

He waited, letting me adjust my position myself, not forcing, just following, his finger resting beneath my chin, the touch itself soft, but the skin having the slightest hint of roughness. And then I was looking directly into those chocolatey brown eyes, long-lashed with a frown line set between them.

'Stop overthinking.'

Right now, that definitely wasn't a problem. Thinking in any capacity was actually proving to be a bit of a job, if I was honest.

'OK?' he prompted.

'Ummhmm.'

He let his hand drop but didn't step back. 'You won't break me, Lottie. I'm big enough to look after myself.'

I felt my chest rise as I tried to suck in more air and push out the thought that had just zipped its way in while I was momentarily distracted by Seb's touch, and his closeness. A thought that sent heat in some directions, and panic in others.

'I know.'

'Then you know you don't need to fuss over me.'

But what if I want to?

'I know,' I repeated, digging deep to find my breeziest voice. 'Just habit. With everyone. Don't worry. You're not special.'

He stepped back and nodded. 'Yep, I know. I'm just saying. A tiny dog leaning on me isn't going to break me. I'm pretty sure you wouldn't have said anything if I didn't have a prosthetic. All I'm asking is that you treat me the same as you would any other bloke.'

'Sorry.' I shuffled my feet and bent down, scooping up Humphrey and cuddling him to me, partly for comfort and partly for something to do rather than just standing there feeling awkward.

'There's nothing to apologise for,' Seb said, reaching forward and fluffing Humph's fur as I held him, his eyes not meeting mine. Tilting his wrist, he then glanced at me. 'Do you need to finish getting ready, or did you decide you liked this look after all?' He gave a tiny quirk of his dark brows, the eyes beneath them smiling once again, easing the feeling that I might have made a blunder.

'I don't know. What do you think?'

Seb flicked the ends of one of my pinned up plaits. 'I think you'll look gorgeous whatever you choose,' he shrugged. 'You know that.'

'I'm not so sure about that, but so long as I'm sort of presentable, and don't show either you or my parents up, I'll take that as a win.'

Seb gave an eye roll, took Humphrey from my arms with one large hand and gave my hair another flick. 'You're not, and never will, show anyone up. Now just get your arse in that bedroom and do whatever it is you're going to do.'

I gave him a sarcastic salute. 'Yes, sir.'

He let out a warm, rumbling laugh. 'Oh, Lots, you wouldn't have lasted five minutes.'

There was probably some truth in that.

He checked his watch. 'I'm happy to continue this later, but if we're not going to be late, and you're planning to wear something other than that dressing gown, you might want to get a shifty on.'

I leaned over to look at his wrist. 'Oh crikey! Is that the time? Why didn't you say something?'

'I just did.'

'Earlier! Make yourself at home. I'll be back out shortly.'

* * *

When I came out of my bedroom, Seb had taken my suggestion seriously and was sat on the sofa, Humphrey on his lap, glancing through a gardening magazine I'd borrowed off my dad. I hesitated for a moment, unused to having a man sat in my living room and slightly overwhelmed by the fact that having Seb there felt so entirely natural, as if he'd been there a hundred times before, when, in truth, it was his first time visiting me and we'd only actually met up in person three times. And one of those times had resulted in him asking me out and being turned down flat. Thankfully, his ego seemed to be fairly robust, and proceeding with his suggestion of us both forgetting he'd ever said anything seemed to be working pretty well.

'I didn't know you had access to a garden with the flat,' he said, giving the magazine a little flap. 'That's—' he stopped as he turned his head. 'Umm... nice. Having an outdoor space, I mean.'

I pulled a face. 'I don't, actually. I have about two and a half paving slabs. I'd love a garden, but for the moment I have to just enjoy reading those mags and pretend.'

He stood, shifting his position slightly once he was upright.

'You're always welcome in mine. You know, if you ever have an overwhelming desire to... dig stuff.'

'Dig stuff?' I laughed, grabbing my door keys off the side and glancing at my phone.

Seb shrugged, broad shoulders rippling the fine cotton of the pale blue shirt. 'I'm not very green fingered, as you might be able to tell. Much to my dad's chagrin. He'd love you!'

'Nobody is born with green fingers, but we all have to start somewhere, don't we?'

'That's true. Trial and error.'

'Kind of like life really.'

Seb took the coat I had slung over my arm from me and held it out, allowing me to slip my arms into it. As I swiped blindly for the belt, my hand brushed his as he passed it to me.

'Thanks,' I smiled, turning back to face him.

'You look beautiful.'

The words were simple and honest and took me completely by surprise.

'You also looked shocked,' his expression was half smile, half frown.

'I just...' I wasn't sure where I was going with that sentence so I gave up.

'Thought I was too uncouth to compliment a woman?'

'No!' I replied, my apparently already shocked face getting another dose. I cleared my throat. 'In fact, I somehow get the impression that it's quite the opposite.'

He grinned and I tried not to notice. 'What's that supposed to mean?'

'It means,' I said, glancing at my phone as a message dinged, 'that I think you can probably be pretty damn smooth when you want to be.'

'Why do I get the idea you might think that's a bad thing?'

'Nope. Not at all. I was just stating a fact. Taxi's here, by the way,' I replied, dropping the phone into my clutch bag.

'I see. This might be another topic to circle back to when you've had a few.' He said, holding the door for me before stepping through behind me and waiting while I locked up.

'Why when I've had a few?' I laughed.

'Because I'm intrigued as to what you might reveal once your guard is down a little more.'

We got to the kerb and Seb leaned over before I could get the door, holding it for me before sliding in next to me. I gave the driver the address of Harry's apartment and settled back against the seat.

* * *

'Oh darling, he's even more gorgeous in the flesh!' Mario whispered to me in a voice loud enough for everyone in the vicinity, including Seb, who was stood right in front of me, to hear. Heat immediately smothered my face, which I had a feeling was already turning a fetching shade of pink thanks to the free flowing champagne Harry had provided for the occasion.

I risked a look at Seb, who met my eye with the tiniest hint of a raised eyebrow. Turning, I gave Mario a glare, which seemed to amuse him even more, laughing as he squeezed me in a hello hug.

'Mario,' he said, releasing me and extending his hand towards Seb. 'We've heard *all* about you. It's fabulous to finally meet you.'

Oh my god. Where was a hole in the ground when you needed one?

'Ah! The famous Mario. It's a pleasure to meet you too,' Seb replied, smiling. 'I know you're responsible for Lottie enjoying her dance lessons as much as she does.'

Mario batted his gorgeously long eyelashes and laid a hand on his chest. 'Well, I can't take all the credit – just most of it.' He did the wicked grin that had got us more than one warning look from the dance instructor, but even those were easing now as Mario began winning her over too. 'And from what we hear, you're responsible for Lottie enjoying her work as much as she does.'

'Right!' I needed to stop this before Mario got too carried away. I could have nobbled Jess right now for ever bringing up Seb's name in Mario and Andy's company. I could deal with the teasing on our own but with him standing right there, it was just on the wrong side of mortification. 'Who's for food? Seb, you're always hungry. Come on, let's go and see what we can find.' I wrapped my hands around Seb's arm, bodily moving him away in the direction of the buffet as he was mid-wave to Mario.

'Stronger than you look,' he said, glancing down at me, amusement dancing in his eyes.

'Needs must. And stop looking at me like that.'

'Like what?'

'Like that,' I said, drawing an imaginary circle around his face.

His smile widened. 'Literally still no clearer.'

I gave a huff and turned back to the food handing Seb a bamboo plate, which he inspected for a moment before beginning to fill it. Popping a warm, artisan sausage roll in my mouth, I tried to calm my nerves and laugh off Mario's teasing like I normally did. Seb clearly wasn't bothered. Trying to pretend that he had no idea what Mario had meant was stretching things a little far, even for me. So now I just had to decide whether to actually address it, and laugh it off, or just say nothing and hope Seb didn't either.

'So, how come he's heard so much about me?' Seb asked, stealing a cheese straw off my plate.

'Oi, get your own,' I said, slapping his hand away as he went in for the second one, although I was secretly grateful the food seemed to have distracted him from his question. At least temporarily.

'I didn't see those.'

I stuffed the snack in my mouth before he could make another attempt at it and pointed at the far end of the table.

Seb assessed the room left on his plate, then looked back. 'I'll get some second go round.'

'I don't know where you put it all,' I said, genuinely curious. I'd seen the size of the meals he could put away, but there wasn't an ounce of fat on him. Muscle, yes. Oh lord, there was plenty of that, but definitely no fat.

He shrugged. 'Burn it off.'

An idea of a very efficient and what I dangerously imagined to be a very enjoyable way of burning it off shot into my head unannounced and uninvited.

'Do you want to go outside?'

'What?' I squeaked, my interrupted thoughts still very much not PG and momentarily misinterpreting Seb's question. Fortunately, or unfortunately, depending on whether or not you were my libido, he clarified the matter.

'You just look like you could do with a little fresh air. It's quite warm in here.'

I knew he'd been involved in several negotiations when he'd been deployed and I could see that his skills in tact hadn't left him. Sadly, I didn't possess the same ability to sip champagne, look glamorous and remain a nice, normal colour as my sister and Jess did. Instead, it had the regular propensity of creating two high spots of colour on my cheeks which gradually grew the more I drank.

'Oh crap. I look like bloody Noddy already, don't I?' I groaned, dropping my head and studying some crumbs on my eco picnic plate.

'Nope,' Seb's steady, calm voice replied.

He adjusted position in front of me and tilted himself down a little until I looked up and met his eyes.

'Liar.'

Unruffled, he shook his head. 'You're a tiny bit pink on your cheeks, but then so are a lot of people. It's warm and there's alcohol.' He shrugged as if that was all that needed saying.

'You're not pink! You're a nice normal colour and you've had alcohol too.'

'But I don't have your beautiful peaches-and-cream skin tone.'

'I don't think it's all that beautiful right now,' I said, aware that there was an edge of petulance in my voice.

'Well, I do, and always will,' Seb replied, matter-of-factly, taking my now empty plate from me and putting it on the side. 'Come on, let's go out on the balcony for a few minutes and get some fresh air.'

'We're in London. I'm not sure there's a lot of that about.'

'You do have a point. OK. As near to it as we can get then.'

I raised my eyes, unexpectedly finding Seb watching me. 'What?'

'You. I... just don't get why you don't have more confidence in yourself when it comes to anything outside work.'

I shrugged. 'I don't know.'

'Then I reckon that's something we need to work on. You already took the step of saying no to stuff you don't want to do. Now it's time to start saying no to stuff you don't want to feel too.'

'Like Noddy?'

He grinned, standing aside for me to step through onto the wrap-around balcony of Harry's penthouse apartment.

'I was always a fan of Noddy, actually. I think it was the cool car.'

I rolled my eyes at him and walked out, feeling the chill air hit my burning cheeks as a shiver rippled through me. Immediately, Seb was close, and I felt another shiver, but this one was far more pleasant. And possibly far more dangerous.

20

'Are you OK? Do you want me to go and get your coat?'

I shook my head, staying him with a hand on his forearm. 'No. Thank you. I'm fine.'

Seb watched me for a moment, taking the time to make his own decision on this before lifting his head and looking out at the view. 'Wow.'

'Yes, it is a bit, isn't it?' Below and around us, London twinkled, shimmered and glowed. The modern skyline soared upwards, dwarfing its historic counterparts, although they refused to be overwhelmed, standing strong and reminding residents and visitors that this city was a complex place with much more to offer than just commerce.

'Can you imagine waking up to this every day?' Seb asked.

'I like it more like this with all the lights twinkling. Cities always look better this way, I think.'

Seb leant on the banister rail.

'Is that safe?' I asked, still a couple of steps back from the edge.

'I didn't know you were afraid of heights.'

'I'm not. I'm afraid of falling from them. It's an entirely different thing.'

'Come here.' He held out a hand.

I hesitated.

'Come on. I promise I won't let go.'

'I can see perfectly well from here.'

Seb gave me a patient look, his hand still held out towards me.

I sucked in a deep breath and reached out. Gently his large, warm hand closed around my cool, smaller one and I took a step nearer the glass of the balcony surround.

'One more.'

I did so, and then I was there, one hand gripping Seb's for dear life, the other almost welded to the cold steel of the rail, knuckles showing white in the stylish but low outdoor lighting Harry had had installed.

'All right?' Seb asked, his voice soft but without any hint of condescension.

I suddenly realised I'd been holding my breath. I let it out in a whoosh, the word 'Yes' being swept along in it.

He nodded, remaining silent, letting me take in the view better as I felt my muscles gradually relax.

'Why do you like cities more at night?' he asked.

'I suppose it's a different feel. It's like it has a mask on like this.'

'A mask?'

'Yes. Like we both know there's dirt, and greed, and crime and so on going on out there, and in every city all the time, day or night. But when you look at them like this, it's all hidden. It looks pretty and sparkling. Like a swathe of Christmas lights, and you can forget about all the bad stuff because it's out of sight.'

'You can't just pretend the bad stuff isn't there though,' Seb argued, his tone gentle. 'At least, that's not a great long-term plan. It fails eventually. Real life has a habit of intruding.'

'Yeah, I know. But you asked.'

'I did.'

He turned back so that we were both facing the river, our hands still joined and now both resting up on the rail.

'You'd tell me if there was something you were having trouble with, wouldn't you?'

I turned towards him. 'Me?'

'Yes.'

'There isn't anything.'

'That's not what I asked.'

I let out a sigh. 'You're so pedantic,' I grouched, bumping my shoulder against him lightly.

'Again, not the worst thing I've ever been called.'

'I really need to find out what is.'

He laughed then, warm, deep, relaxed. 'You really don't.'

'I do!'

He pushed himself up, grinning down at me. 'So not going to happen.'

'Why not?'

'For several reasons.'

I sighed. 'Such as?'

Seb shook his head. 'Man, you're persistent.'

'And you're stubborn. Tell me.'

'No. One, I don't want to cloud your judgement of me, especially as, from what I gathered from Mario, it's not too bad at the moment.'

The colour whooshed back to my face.

'And, secondly, it's not language I'd repeat in front of a lady.'

A giggle bubbled out of me, and I glanced around. 'I'm sorry. Did we just step out of a time machine into 1892 or something? I'm sure I know just as many bad words as you do.'

'Actually, I doubt that. Army life is very enlightening. But that's irrelevant. My reasons still stand.'

'I don't need protecting.'

'What if you don't get the choice?'

'I always have a choice,' I said, in a tone that didn't encourage debate on the subject.

He shook his head. 'Of course. That's not what I meant. It just came out wrong. I meant—'

'There you are!' Jess bounced up to us, clearly slightly the worse for wear but looking as happy as I had seen her in years. We exchanged a hug. 'Harry said you were here, but, oh my goodness, I didn't realise we'd invited so many people! I've been trying to get over and see you for about an hour!'

'Just wait until the wedding!' I winked.

'I know, right?' Jess nudged my arm with hers, the champagne in her glass sloshing dangerously up the sides of the crystal. I eyed the glass, and Jess followed me, immediately steadying it. 'Honestly, I told him we shouldn't have this stuff for today. But he insisted that he wanted us to toast with proper crystal.' She rolled her eyes, but I could tell she was loving it. 'And he said it was more eco-friendly than plastic disposable ones, which was a low blow but obviously right.'

Ever since watching the *Blue Planet* programmes, Jess had been steadily doing her bit to reduce the plastic usage in her life, and the lives of those around her. Harry was clearly on board, although not many of us could afford to swap out the picnic cups for crystal, even if they were hired, but I liked his style.

'Why not?' I said, clinking my glass against hers, laughing as we agreed that the pleasing *ting* it made was so much better than anything else could ever have been.

'I'm sorry, I'm being so rude.' Jess then turned to Seb, charm-o-meter switched to high. To be fair, that was pretty much Jess' stan-dard setting, but it was always fun to watch people fall under her spell. Normally, she'd elegantly extend her hand, with its perfect nails, and execute a firm but friendly handshake. But champagne and excitement had obviously made their mark as tonight Jess just launched in for a hug, catching Seb slightly off guard. She pulled back. 'I'm so happy to finally meet you. I've heard so much about you.'

Seb slid his glance to me momentarily. 'People keep telling me that tonight. I'm still trying to work out if that's a good thing,' he said, giving her the killer grin that I was pretty sure he didn't know he even possessed.

'Oh, it's definitely a good thing.'

'They don't get out much,' I said, shrugging.

'Fair enough,' he smiled, taking a sip from his glass as we all headed back into the main room.

'Have you seen Harry yet?' Jess asked, glancing round for her fiancé, and beckoning madly when she caught his eye.

'Briefly, when we came in,' Seb replied, as across the room Harry excused himself from the guests he'd been talking to and ambled over, sliding his arm around Jess' waist and placing a kiss on her temple as he arrived.

'We're so glad you could both come,' Harry said, waving over one of the hired catering staff to top up our glasses. 'And it's brilliant to meet you in person, Seb. I was so excited to get involved with your charity once Jess told me about it. The support you've already given me with the training and so on, it's been great.'

'Anytime. Obviously, the charity is hugely grateful for the publicity you've generated, as well as the donations, so anything we can do to help, just give us a call. Actually, can you hold that a minute, Lots,' Seb asked, passing his drink to me before pulling a slim wallet out from his back pocket. Withdrawing a business card, he handed it to Harry. 'That's got my personal number on too, if you ever need anything. I know you're pretty experienced at these things, but just in case. You know, pep talks, training ideas, emergency jelly babies, whatever.'

'Thanks, mate. I really appreciate that,' Harry said, looking at the card for a moment, before pocketing it in the back of his designer jeans.

'No problem.' Seb smiled as I handed him back his glass and he took a sip. 'What?' he asked as I continued to focus on him. A focus that was, admittedly, now slightly fuzzy around the edges.

'Emergency jelly babies?'

'Excellent for an energy boost as well as delightfully tasty!' Harry added.

'You've never offered me emergency jelly babies, and we've been friends for ages,' I complained.

'I would have, had you been training for a triathlon.'

Harry and I exchanged a smile as something caught Jess' eye across the room. 'Oh Lots! Your parents are here. Fabulous! I'll go and get them.' And with that, she dashed off, returning moments later with my mum and dad in tow as Harry signalled a waitress for two more glasses of champagne.

'Hello, darling!' Mum said, reaching out for a hug, followed by Dad. 'Sorry we're late. Traffic was a bit snarly coming into town.'

'I thought you were getting the train?'

'That strike they were threatening went ahead today, unfortunately,' Dad replied.

'Oh.' I made a point of avoiding as much news coverage of everything and anything as far as I could. It was another aspect of me saying no to things I didn't want to do. And being inundated with doom and gloom every day with twenty-four hour rolling news was definitely something I didn't want. It had already made quite a difference. The effect of seeing all those depressing headlines every day had, apparently, been something I'd underestimated and cutting it out had certainly been beneficial. 'Mum, Dad, this is Seb. And please don't tell him you've heard so much about him as he is developing a complex about it.'

Mum smiled and shook his hand, covering it with both of her own. 'It's lovely to meet you, Seb.' I could see she was itching to say more, but, much to my relief, kept to my wishes.

'Pleased to meet you,' Dad said, one shovel sized hand taking

Seb's equally sizeable one. 'We've heard absolutely nothing at all about you.'

Everyone laughed and I doinked my head against Seb's upper arm, hiding my face.

As my dad released his hand, Seb's arm curled around me and gave a reassuring squeeze. 'I'm tougher than you think. Don't worry about it.'

I lifted my head and raised my gaze. 'Oh pfft. You're as much as a softie as the rest of us.'

His eyes widened and he put a finger to his lips. 'Ssssh! You can't just go blurting slander like that about. I've got a reputation to maintain.'

'Oh yes, adding sensitive to good looking ex-military man is *really* going to hurt that reputation.' Jess frowned momentarily, before her wide, even smile burst through.

Seb returned the smile but quickly lowered his eyes to his glass and took a swig.

'So, Seb, Lottie tells us your dad is into gardening too? Is that right?'

The relief on Seb's face to have the attention drawn away from himself and onto far safer ground was palpable as he proceeded to tell Dad about his own father's green fingered habits.

'He seems very nice,' Mum said as I took her over to the buffet, where we began loading up two plates, me holding one for Dad as he continued his chat with Seb.

'He is,' I replied, in as casual and non-committal a tone as I could possibly muster before sneaking a glance at Mum, who was busily engaged in filling Dad's plate with all the things she knew he liked. And then she caught my eye and smiled. Not a huge smile. Just one of those tiny but knowing smiles that mothers have a habit of giving just when you think you've managed to sneak something by them.

* * *

The view from Harry's apartment really was quite stunning and I stood staring out of one of the large picture windows onto the scene below, mesmerised a little by the champagne but mostly by the shimmering, glinting lights of the city spread below me.

'Not a bad view.' The slight whine that underpinned the aristocratic accent burst the bubble of magic. It was the voice I'd last heard making me a very easily rejected offer on New Year's Eve. I'd described him to Jess later and apparently he was Tarquin double-barrelled something or other, an old friend of Harry's. She'd added the word 'unfortunately' to the end of this explanation and it was easy to see why. 'You should come and see mine. It's rather superior to this.'

I glanced at him, assuming he was making a joke, but he met my eyes and there was no humour there. Unbelievably, he really was that obnoxious.

'What?' he asked.

I never was much good at hiding my emotions.

I shrugged, hoping he'd take the hint that I really had no interest in continuing the conversation.

'So? Back to my place after this? You can see for yourself then.' He smirked. 'In fact, there's quite a lot there that's superior.'

Oh. My. God.

I shook my head in disbelief and swigged the rest of my fizz.

'Is that a yes?' This was, in theory, a question, but the manner in which he said it possessed an overtone of privileged expectation.

I turned to face him. Yep. There it was. That look on his face – one that said 'there is absolutely no chance of me not getting my way on this'. Well, I had news for him.

'No. That's a no. A most definite no. What the Americans call, I believe, a hard no.'

He looked confused. 'Are you sure?'

I felt my mouth drop open. 'Yes. I'm sure. In fact, I don't think I've ever been more sure of anything in my life.'

'You do know who I am?'

I know what you are, that's for sure.

'My father is an earl. That's going to be my title when he off and pops his clogs. I've got more money than god, and I'm very good looking.' He squinted at me. 'Or am I just barking up the wrong tree, so to speak?'

'You are barking up the wrong tree entirely. But not for the reasons you're suggesting. I like men. I just don't like you.'

With that, I grabbed a glass off a passing waitress and stalked back to where Seb was stood laughing with Harry and Jess. Unfortunately, I was followed.

21

'Harry, old man,' Tarquin began, cutting across the conversation and not even acknowledging Jess or Seb, as though they were beneath his notice. 'What's up with this one?' He waved his champagne flute in my direction.

I've never felt the desire to push anyone through a window before, but this bloke was sorely testing me. Did his insensitivity and rudeness know any boundaries at all?

Harry gave me an apologetic look. 'Nothing. She's lovely. Why?'

'I've just asked her out for a second time and she's turned me down. Again.'

I rolled my eyes. 'Propositioning someone and asking them out are two very different things.'

Tarquin snapped his head towards me. 'If you're playing hard to get, you've blown it. I won't ask a third time.'

I looked to the ceiling. 'And people say there's no god.'

Jess attempted to cover her snort by burying her face in Harry's shoulder as Seb's face disappeared quickly into his champagne glass. Tarquin just looked at me, a stunned expression on his face, his mouth opening and closing like a very posh fish. And then Harry burst into laughter.

Tarquin glared at Harry before snatching a glass of drink from a nearby waiter and downing a good proportion of it.

Harry, unbothered by his friend's expression, threw an arm around his shoulder and, ever the gentleman, made the proper introductions that Tarquin himself should have done before butting in and taking over the conversation of our small group.

'Tarquin, you obviously know Jess, and have also met the delightful Lottie properly now.'

'Actually, I didn't know her name.'

Harry pulled a face. 'You said you've asked her out twice and you've not even bothered to ask her name.' He shook his head, laughing. 'No wonder she turned you down.'

'Shouldn't you be using Charlotte by now? Lottie is rather a childish moniker, don't you think?' He said, a sneering tone lacing the words.

'I like it,' I said, defiantly. Out of sight, I felt Seb's hand lightly touch my back in support. He knew I didn't need him to defend me, but it was nice to know he was there all the same.

'And this is Seb Marshall. Seb, this is a good friend of mine, Tarquin Farquar-Stour-Pendleton,' Harry said, frowning slightly as Tarquin shoved his free hand in his trouser pocket instead of extending it as his friend had obviously expected him to do. Clearing his throat, Harry continued, 'Seb is the founder of the charity that I'm honoured to be doing a triathlon in aid of later in the year.'

Tarquin tipped his chin up a little, acknowledging this information. 'I see. I suppose you must be very grateful that there are good, fit men like Harry here willing to put themselves out and do that sort of thing for you. I mean, as you can't do it for yourself.'

I exchanged a glance with Jess, who was clearly seething. Neither of us had missed the veiled dig. I risked a glance at Seb, hoping that he might have missed it, but one glimpse was enough to see the slight flicker in his jaw. Tarquin was looking particularly smug and my eyes drifted once more to the window. It was enough to insult me but quite something else to be so casually callous. Not to mention uninformed. Had the Para Olympics passed him by entirely? Had he never heard of the Invictus Games? But the more I got to know Tarquin Farquar-Stour-Pendleton, the easier that possibility was to believe.

Seb swallowed and gave a brief, practised smile. 'The charity is always grateful to people who are good enough to give up their time to help us, in any way.'

It was a good answer. Tactful and inoffensive. Unlike Tarquin, who raised his eyebrows briefly as if to acknowledge the answer, but it was clear that he hadn't got the rise out of Seb he'd wanted to. His eyes slid to me, then flicked back to Seb, pausing a moment before switching back to me again, his brain trying to work out if there was a connection and what it was. Apparently, he came up with something, because a small sneer curled the edge of his mouth before he turned away, looking for yet another drink.

'Why do you never hire enough bloody staff, Harry,' he snapped before stalking off to replenish his glass.

Harry gave a small, noticeably awkward laugh. 'Sorry about that. Tarq never seems to think before he speaks, so things can sometimes come out sounding different from how he actually means them.'

It was a valiant effort but one lost on Seb.

'He knew exactly what he was saying, Harry. But don't worry about it. You're not responsible for him and shouldn't be apologising for him.'

Harry ran a hand over his hair. 'He does say the most ridiculous bloody things sometimes. Why he's having a dig at you, I don't know. A lot of his family were in the military, so he holds them in the highest regard.'

'Right. Yes, I can see that.' Seb smiled at Harry, softening the reply, letting him know that this wasn't Harry's fight.

Harry's shoulders sagged a little and Seb moved slightly and bumped one with his own.

'Don't worry about it, mate. Like I said, not your fault. Don't give it a thought. You've got a wonderful fiancée there – you're supposed to be enjoying your engagement party, not excusing other people's poor manners.'

'I know but...'

Jess tucked her arm through Harry's. 'He's right.'

He looked down at her, the smile breaking onto his face softly as he did so. 'I know.'

She paused for a moment. 'Is that true then, about his family all being in the military?'

'Absolutely,' Harry replied. 'I mean, obviously going back, a lot of the commissions were bought and so on, but there's been genera- tions of Farquar-Stour-Pendletons wearing a uniform.'

'So how come old Tarq didn't join up?' Jess asked.

'That's the thing. He did. I think he quite fancied himself in a uniform.'

'I think he quite fancies himself full stop,' I interjected and Jess grinned.

Harry wobbled his head a little in acknowledgement, and possibly agreement, of this statement. 'I'm not sure how much he'd considered the realities of Army life past the swanky uniform and formal dinners, but he did sign up as an officer.'

'So, what happened?'

'Oh, there was some sort of health complication in the end which meant he couldn't finish his training. Even I don't know exactly what it was. Tarquin was pretty upset about the whole situation, to be honest, so we didn't really press him on it. I know he regrets it though,' Harry added, as if hoping that would excuse his friend's earlier behaviour.

'I see.' Seb nodded.

'Yeah, it was a tough break for him.'

'Ummhmm.'

Jess glanced around before speaking, lowering her voice when she did. 'I still struggle to see how someone as lovely as you and someone as... unlovely as him can be such good friends.'

Harry dropped a kiss on the top of her head. 'I know he doesn't always present himself in the best light, but I've known him since Prep. Our families have been friends for generations.'

'That doesn't mean it's compulsory for you.'

'I know. He was out of line tonight, and I'm not happy with him for that. I already have plans to talk to him.'

'Don't worry on my account. Seriously,' Seb reiterated.

'No. He embarrassed me and he needs to learn to think a bit more before he opens his mouth.'

'Fair enough, but for now let's just focus on what we're all here for and celebrate.' Seb lifted his glass and we all chinked together. 'Cheers!'

* * *

'You OK?' I asked as we walked back from the bank of lifts, having seen my parents off, but not before them having secured an agreement from Seb that he'd come to Sunday lunch the following day.

'Me? Sure.'

'OK.' I nodded.

'Honestly, Lots. If this is about earlier, put it out of your mind. I have.'

I wrinkled my nose. 'I just don't understand why he was like that. I can understand him being rude to me, but he's never even met you!'

'People are what they are. But I can think of a couple of good reasons.'

'You can?'

'Yep.'

'Which are?' I asked, leaning against the wall next to the front door that we'd left ajar.

Seb tilted his head at me. 'One, you.'

'Me?'

'Yep.'

'Why me?'

'Because he clearly fancies the arse off you and you turned him down. Twice. And then he sees you standing with me and, by the look he gave, obviously thinks something's going on.'

'But it's not,' I said, wrinkling my brow.

Seb looked at me for a long moment, then shook his head. 'No. It's not. But it's not hard to see old Tarquin isn't one worried by the facts.'

'So, what's number two?' I asked, readjusting my position on the wall and trying not to slide down it. All of a sudden, I was really, really tired.

'You all right?'

'Mmmhmm. Number two is what?'

'He's got a chip on his shoulder about not making it in the military.'

'But, and it pains me to say this, if he had a medical condition, it can't be helped.'

'True. But that doesn't always stop people regretting stuff. It can be hard to let go if that was your dream.'

I shook my head and then put a hand out, finding Seb's chest to steady myself on. *Note to self, do not shake head after that many champagnes.*

Gently, Seb rested a hand at my waist. 'You OK?'

'Yep. Just... old brain got a bit loose in there for a moment.' I looked up and saw his smile. 'What's funny?'

'You are. But in a good way.'

'I will accept in a good way.'

'Excellent.'

'But you're still wrong. Tarquin's not that bothered about me. Certainly not enough to insult you over. He's just annoyed with me because he thinks someone of my comparatively lowly station should be so impressed by all his money and trinkets that I should be forever grateful he chose me to bestow his cheap propositions on. The idea that someone, anyone really, but especially someone like me should dare to say no has just put his aristocratic nose out of joint.'

'I think there's more to it than that. Being turned down by you would be upsetting for anyone.'

I looked up, but the light was low in the hallway and I couldn't see his expression. 'You're teasing me.'

I saw his head tilt briefly. 'Maybe. Maybe not.' His voice was soft, low and deep and I felt something shift within me. A flame that I'd been trying to keep doused made a flicker into life from the embers.

'Seb, I—'

'Where have you been?' Jess burst into the hallway. 'I've been looking for you everywhere.'

'We were just seeing my parents off. Why, what's wrong?'

'Oh, have they gone? I wanted to say goodbye and thank them.'

I gave her a hug. 'They didn't want to interrupt you, but they said to thank you very much for inviting them.'

'Aww, I'll message your mum in a minute.'

'So why were you looking for us?'

'Harry's got someone he wants Seb to meet and my bloody feet are killing me. Come and sit on the balcony with me while they talk boy stuff?'

'Of course. You OK with that?' I turned to Seb, able to see his face a little more as we headed back into the main living area, which was just atmospherically lowlit rather than slightly dark as the hallway had been.

'Talking boy stuff? Absolutely.'

I gave him a little look and he brushed my fingers with his own.

'Go and sit with Jess. Relax. Have fun.' He squeezed my fingers gently before letting go and taking the outstretched hand of the first man Harry introduced.

Immediately Jess grabbed hold of my hand and tugged me towards the balcony. Sliding the door open, we stepped through before she slid it back across, leaving just a small gap. The night was cool but a welcome contrast to the heat of the party room. Jess flopped onto a lounger and I sat sideways on one opposite, facing her as she kicked off her shoes.

'Seven hundred quid and they're murdering my feet!'

I stared down at them. They were pretty. Gorgeous, in fact. Jess had always had fabulous taste in fashion, but I just couldn't imagine spending that much on a pair of shoes.

'I know,' she said, reading my expression. 'It's stupid money, but I made the mistake of admiring them online and, the next thing I know, I have a delivery.'

'Wow.'

'I've told Harry he needs to stop doing it or I won't say anything any more.'

I gave her a grin. Jess not saying what was in her head would be a first, but I knew what she meant. 'Not a horrible problem to have.'

'No, I know I'm super lucky and probably sound like a spoilt cow moaning that my fiancé buys me expensive gifts, but I don't want to feel... I don't know. Kept. I earn my own money. Obviously it's nothing like in Harry's league, but I work hard for it and I like spending it on stuff.'

'Somehow I don't think you'd ever struggle to find stuff to spend money on, Jess.'

She returned my giggle. 'That is true. I am exceptionally talented in that regard. But you know what I mean.'

'I do. And what did he say?'

'He got it. Eventually, I think.'

'He just enjoys spoiling you. Like I say, not the worst problem in the world.'

'I am lucky. I do know that.'

'I know you do. He's lovely. And completely adores you, which makes me so happy. I really like him, Jess. I'm so happy for you both.'

She sat up and gave me a big hug. 'Thanks. I'm so glad you like him. He thinks you're wonderful as well. I'm so pleased it's working out. He thinks Seb's great too. They've really hit it off. It's lovely.'

'It is,' I agreed. 'He did mention he's spoken to him a few times.'

'Yeah, Harry really enjoys his company. It's just such a shame he's so far away from all of us.' She sent me a mock innocent look as she said this and I rolled my eyes. 'Oh, come on. You can't say you're not sorry too. And what was all that in the dark hallway?'

'Nothing! We were just coming back in.'

'Hmm, low voices, close together.'

'It was nothing. Honestly.'

Jess shook her head, her corkscrew curls dancing as she did so. 'Well, looking at you two, it should most definitely be something.'

'We've been over this.'

'And you haven't changed your mind?'

Had I?

Jess took my silence as affirmation. 'What if I had a word?'

'Don't you dare!' I said, grabbing her arm. 'Oh my god. That would be so... Just promise me you won't! I'm fine, Jess, really.' I lowered my voice. 'Yes, I admit I still have a bit of a crush on him, but that's all it is, and I don't want what we have messed up. Promise me you won't say anything!'

'I won't. I promise. I was just trying to help. You two look so perfect together.'

'You said that about me and The Ex.' Jess refused to let me mention him by name as she blamed him wholeheartedly for me having possibly wasted some of my best childbearing years on him.

The fact I'd been in no way ready or even inclined to have a child during that time was irrelevant. The idea was enough for Jess.

'I know. But this time I'm right.'

'OK.' I laughed, a slight shiver catching me as a breeze ruffled the water below and wound its way around the planters, rustling the leaves of the bamboo within them. 'I think I'm going to head back in. It's getting a bit chilly out here. How are the feet?'

Jess gave them a quick rub and rummaged around to find the shoes that had tumbled beneath the lounger. 'We'll see when I get them back on,' she said, her words slightly muffled due to her position and the breeze now building. 'Where's the other one bloody gone?'

I bent down and peered, reaching out to grab the missing shoe.

'What on earth are you doing?'

22

I felt my heart sink as those snobbish tones cut through the wind.

I stood up, handed Jess her shoe and turned to face Tarquin. I refrained from explaining myself as, frankly, it was none of his damn business, and I'd already had about as much conversation as I wanted with this man to last a lifetime.

He made a little movement of his head as if to prompt me to reply, as though he were some university don and I'd been caught walking across a quad despite the 'keep off the grass' sign. Smug git.

I tilted my head up in response and remained silent, seeing his jaw harden as I did so. Jess was strapped back into her shoes now and I turned, holding out a hand to haul her up off the lounger.

'So, you and this Seb bloke a thing then?'

Normally I'd have happily replied, but after his dig earlier and the underlying tone that rippled through his question, I was in no hurry to answer.

Tarquin took my silence as enough of an answer. The sneer curled back onto his lip. 'Interesting choice. I expect you were always the kid bringing home injured animals too, weren't you?'

I dug my fingers into my palms and made to step past him. The slightest of movements by him blocked my way.

'Excuse me.'

'You don't know what you're missing,' he said, moving a step closer to me. 'Tell you what, when you're ready for a *real* man, give me a call. Maybe I'll give you a go after all.'

'Who the hell do you think you are?' Fury shone in my eyes. 'Seb Marshall is far more man that you could ever dream of being, and frankly, if you were the last man on earth, I still wouldn't call you, and now, unless you fancy taking a short walk off this balcony, I suggest you get out of my way.'

Tarquin stared at me for a moment and then laughed.

'God, you're a nasty piece of work,' Jess snapped, coming to stand beside me. 'You don't deserve a friend like Harry. I have no idea what he sees in you.'

'Well,' he sniped, wheeling on Jess, 'I could easily say the same, although it's very evident to everyone what you see in him.'

'I beg your pardon.'

Tarquin gave a dramatic roll of his eyes. 'Oh, come on, Jessica. Everyone knows what you're after and well done you on hooking him, but let me enlighten you. If you think for one moment, even with that rock on your finger, that you're set for life, then you're in for a rather nasty surprise. Harry's got a set type he goes for. You're...' he looked her up and down, 'obviously quite different from that, but that's your attraction, I suppose. You're a novelty. And novelties wear off. Harry might be smitten now, but he's loyal to his family, who we all know aren't exactly thrilled about welcoming you into the fold. He's got generations of standards to live up to. He'll know what to do when the time is right.'

We both stood staring at Tarquin, hurt and astounded by his words. Not only the content but the harsh, vicious delivery of them, carried out with such apparent glee.

I turned to look at Jess, a woman who, as her mum had often

despaired during her daughter's teenage years, would 'have an answer for the devil if he popped up in front of her'. She was silent. Being mixed race, Jess had heard a lot in her time and rarely let it get to her, but Tarquin's words had cut her more deeply and more unexpectedly than any others. The boiling rage inside me bubbled up and exploded.

I opened my mouth, set to let loose a vehement tirade, but before I could say a word, Harry's educated tones cut through the air.

'Tarquin. I think it would be best if you left now.'

Jess and I looked round to see Harry and Seb standing further down the balcony, having apparently exited from the kitchen doors of the apartment. I had no idea how much of the conversation they'd heard, but, judging by the look on both their faces, my guess was pretty much all of it.

Tarquin looked momentarily surprised and then began to smile. 'Harry, old chap, you had me going there for a minute.'

Harry didn't smile.

Tarquin's face clouded with anger. 'You're not actually serious?'

Harry said nothing. It was all the answer needed.

'So, just let me get this straight? You're choosing people like this,' he gave a tilt of his chin towards the three of us, 'over years of friendship? Over people of your own kind? Your own level?'

'Like I said, I think it's time you left.' Harry's normally smiling face now held an icy expression.

Tarquin's eyes narrowed, disbelief mingling with disgust. He turned on an expensive heel and yanked open the door, stalking through. The front door slamming reverberated throughout the room, stilling the conversation for a moment before the level rose again. Out on the balcony, though, everything was still silent.

'I am so, so sorry,' Harry said, looking distraught. 'Jess, my darling,' he said, cupping her face, and tilting it to his own. 'You know none of that was true, don't you? I will never, ever be tired of you. If I am tired of you, I will be tired of life and I have no plans for being either.' He moved his hands and wrapped them around her, Jess' own doing the same and holding him close. 'And to you two, what he said...'

Seb spoke for the first time. 'Like I said before, not your fault, mate. I've heard it all before and Lottie had already decided he was an idiot months ago. No harm done. So long as you two are all right?'

'We are.' Harry looked down at Jess, hesitating. 'Aren't we?'

'Of course, we are!' Jess said, pushing her hair back and sneaking a quick wipe of a stray tear as she did so.

Jess loved drama and was a pretty good actress in the amateur productions she'd been in over the years, but I'd known her since playgroup and I wasn't fooled. Tarquin's words had done damage. I only hoped it was reparable.

'It's actually getting kind of late,' Seb said, glancing at the face of his complicated looking watch. 'We should probably make a move anyway, if Lottie's ready.'

I was more than ready. I'd been feeling the long day before the showdown on the balcony, but the emotional impact of that, plus the champagne, and now I felt like my body was swaying. I wasn't entirely sure if that was in my head or actually happening, although as Seb came to stand next to me and gently took my hand, the sensation stopped, so I guessed it had certainly had some physical element to it.

'Oh, don't go because of this, please!' Jess said.

'Don't be silly,' I said, reaching out and hugging her hard. 'It's nothing to do with that. You know I'd normally be in my pyjamas about five hours ago. It's just time to go and sleep.'

A sparkle of the real Jess then showed as she pulled back and gave the tiniest raise of one HD brow.

I widened my eyes in warning in return, receiving a smile in reply. That alone was worth the tease.

'Harry, darling. There you are!'

We all turned at the well-spoken words and saw a woman

moving swiftly towards us along the balcony. If I had to choose one word to describe her, it would be elegant. Another would be expensive.

'Ginny, how are you? We're so glad you could come,' Harry replied, as she kissed him on both cheeks.

'Jess, how lovely to see you.' The greeting procedure was repeated. 'I'm dreadfully sorry to be so late. I had another engagement which rather ran on, but I did so want to make sure I at least said hello.'

'That's OK. Thank you for coming.' Jess smiled back at her, before turning towards us. 'Lady Carstairs, may I introduce my best friend, Lottie and—'

'Seb, darling man. You didn't tell me you were going to be here.' She gave him a slightly pouty look, which she really made work for her. Something if I tried just made me look like a petulant five year old. 'Hello, Lottie,' she said, tearing her eyes away from Seb momentarily to meet mine. 'How lovely to meet you.'

'And you,' I replied, automatically.

'Seb and Lottie were just leaving, unfortunately.'

'Oh?' Her gaze flicked between us. 'Can't I persuade you to stay a little longer so we can get to know each other better?' She smiled at me, but her gaze lingered on Seb.

'It's been a long day,' Seb returned. 'Another time.'

'I'll call you.' I'd never heard three words loaded with so much promise and kicked myself for the knot in my stomach it created. I'd had my opportunity and I'd turned it down. What Seb did, and with whom, shouldn't bother me.

It shouldn't – but it did.

Seb gave a brief smile and a short nod but said nothing. Lady Carstairs gave me another smile, before leaning over to kiss Seb on the cheek, her lips lingering there momentarily. Pulling back, she met his eyes, then turned, waving as she disappeared back into the main throng of the party.

We said our goodbyes to Jess and Harry with a lot of hugs before Seb gently took my hand and led me to the balcony door, still open from Tarquin's dramatic exit, before standing aside for me to go first and then stepping through after me. Turning, we gave the others a quick wave and I blew a kiss before Seb shut the door to give them the privacy they needed.

'I hope that was OK to suggest leaving. It just seemed like Jess and Harry needed to talk.'

'I was about to suggest it anyway, so it was good timing. Unless you want to stay a bit longer now?' My glance slid to where Harry's latest guest was laughing with a couple more of Harry's friends.

He followed my eyeline briefly, then shook his head. 'Nope.'

'You all right?'

Seb frowned as he picked up my coat and proceeded to stand behind me, holding out the arms for me to slip it on. 'Why wouldn't I be?'

'I just...' I tucked my scarf around me as Seb shrugged into a smart wool pea coat, pulling the apartment door closed behind us as we stepped out into the hallway. 'I'm just sorry you had to hear all that. I mean what Tarquin said about—'

'Lottie. I already told Harry it's fine and I'm telling you the same thing.'

A lift arrived and we stepped in, before silently and smoothly descending to the marbled lobby of the exclusive apartment block.

'I know but—'

'Lottie,' Seb said, turning to me, his size stopping me in my tracks. I looked up, meeting the dark eyes, serious in the handsome face. 'I don't give a shit what people like Tarquin think about me, and while I appreciate the thought, I definitely don't need you to defend me. I'm more than capable of defending myself, if and when the need arises.'

I got the distinct feeling I was being told off. He turned to walk away.

'So, why didn't you then?' I asked, annoyed. It had always been second nature for me to defend my friends and here he was, getting all uppity about it.

Seb stopped, glancing at the concierge, who was, in accordance with his job, doing a wonderful impression of not being able to hear our conversation as it echoed around the expensive décor. Seb pushed the door to the street open and waited for me to go through. Once outside he turned back.

'I didn't because there was no need for it. One, it's Jess and Harry's night and I didn't want to make a bigger deal than was necessary, and two, I don't need to dignify comments from people like Tarquin Twit-Idiot-Pendleton with a response, and I'd appreciate it if you didn't either. I know you meant well, but I don't need your protection.'

'You know what? If you think I won't always defend my friends, any of my friends, then perhaps you don't know me as well as you think you do.'

His hands were shoved in his pockets now and his body, still held with the upright bearing of a soldier, was rigid. He felt distant. Unreachable.

'Fine,' I said, looking away. 'And thanks for the clarification on how to behave.'

'Lottie...'

'Here's the taxi now. Perfect.' I'd called it on an app from upstairs and had never been more pleased of a distraction. I grabbed the door handle before Seb could and slid in the back, across the seat, and as far away from him as I could manage.

Seb manoeuvred in, wincing for a moment as he tried to fit, his leg bumping against the seat in front. I could already see the problem, but, having apparently already said too much once this evening, I remained silent, letting him deal with it.

'Could you push the seat up a bit, please, mate?'

'Oh, yeah sure,' the driver replied in a slightly dazed manner that made me think that hailing a black cab might have been a better option.

Seb settled his long legs in and shut the door, leaning back against the seat. Confirming the directions, I settled back too and turned my head away to look out at the streets of London, still busy with locals and tourists. Neither of us spoke, the air filled instead with the offerings of a Punjabi radio station as the driver bopped his head softly to the beat.

Having paid the taxi, we walked to my flat and I unlocked the door, Seb following me in, both of us silent, the air between us thick enough to slice. Hearing us enter, the two dogs hurled themselves around the corner, greeting us both as though we'd been away for months, not a few hours. That doggy greeting never got old. Even on a night like tonight, those canine snuggles raised my spirits.

I stood back from cuddling the dogs and slipped my coat off, hanging it on the hook. From the corner of my eye, I saw that Seb was still wearing his.

'Aren't you taking that off?'

Seb let out a sigh and absent-mindedly ruffled the fur on the top of his dog's head.

'What is it?' I asked.

He tipped his head back momentarily before looking down at me. 'I'm just thinking it probably would have been better if I'd not had a drink and I could have just left now, and not be stood here, making us both feel awkward.'

'Right,' I said, for lack of anything else to say as thoughts pinged about my brain.

'I'm usually up early anyway, so I can be gone before you—' He stopped mid-sentence, his eyes widening at me in surprise.

He wasn't the only one surprised. I'd had absolutely no intention of bursting into tears in quite such a spectacular manner. If at all! And I still had no idea where they'd come from. One minute I was busily ensconced in my annoyance at him and the next minute I had a virtual torrent streaming down my face and had started making weird hitching noises as I juggled breathing and crying, my body apparently trying to get a rhythm going but struggling in that particular endeavour.

Then Seb's arms were around me, pulling me gently against him, one large warm hand behind my head, the other at my back. But just because I was crying didn't mean I wasn't still upset with him and I pushed him away. At least I tried. He didn't really budge, which was kind of annoying. Instead, he pulled away a little, looking down at me.

'Lots, I'm so sorry. I never meant to upset you. I know you were just being who you are.' He moved his hands to my face. 'Please forgive me. I haven't handled this very well and the last thing in the world I want is see you like this.'

'Then don't look,' I snuffled out between hiccups.

He pushed my hair back with one hand. 'Not an option.'

I gave a little huff and he pulled me back against him and I relented a little, resting my head against his chest as he stroked my hair with one hand, the other cuddling me to him. 'I just hated hearing him speak like that. I couldn't help it. It just came out. It's nothing to do with me thinking you can't defend yourself. It's to do with you being my friend.'

'I know. I realise that now. It was kind of an automatic reaction.'

I pulled my head back in order to meet his eyes. 'Why?'

'Why what?'

'Why is that your automatic reaction? What's so bad about your friends standing up for you. You'd do it in a heartbeat.'

'That's different.'

I pushed away from him, but more gently this time. 'No. It's not. It's exactly the same. Just because you're all big and... like that...' I said, with exactness, waving my hand at him, 'doesn't mean people don't still feel protective about you. And before you say anything, it's got nothing to do with anything else. Tarquin would have found something to dig at you about, even without your injury, and I would have told him exactly the same thing. You are worth a hundred of him.'

Seb's Adam's apple bobbed as he swallowed. 'Thank you,' he said, his voice soft.

'Even if you are a pain in the arse sometimes.'

'Only sometimes?'

'Don't push it. I'm being kind.'

Seb stepped closer, hugged me tight and dropped a kiss on the top of my head. 'Thank you. And sorry for being a pain in the arse. At any time.'

I relaxed into the hug and we stood there in silence for a few moments.

'You should get some rest. You looked done for in the car.' Pressed close, I could feel his deep voice reverberating through his chest as well as hear it.

'Mmmhmm,' I agreed. He was right, but a part of me, perhaps the part still happily doing the backstroke in champagne, felt more than happy to stay right where I was. Thankfully, the majority of me had already taken a lurch towards sobriety and won out. I stepped back, Seb's arms falling away. He was, however, still looking at me. 'What?'

'I'm just checking you're OK,' he paused. 'That we're OK.'

'Of course we are.'

He rubbed a hand over a chin that held a shadow of stubble. 'Like I said, I'm just used to dealing with this stuff on my own. Not having someone else dragged in.'

'And like *I* said, no one dragged me anywhere. If Harry hadn't come out when he had, I'd have been starting on Tarquin for what he said about Jess too, so don't go thinking you're special or anything.'

That made him smile. 'I wouldn't dream of it.'

23

I'd already piled the blankets and pillow into a little pile on the end of the sofa and, after getting the two dogs off the space, an action they did most reluctantly, I set about making the linen into a cosy bed for my guest.

'I can do that.'

'It's fine. I'm nearly done.'

'You don't need to fuss, Lots. I've slept in far worse places than this.'

I slid my eyes to him and I could see him replaying the sentence in his brain.

'Yeah, that came out different from how it sounded in my head.'

'I should hope so!' I teased, standing back to survey my work.

'Looks great,' Seb came to stand beside me. 'Very inviting.'

I let out a sigh. 'I really wish you would take my bed. It'd be much more comfortable for you. I'm more...' I'd always wanted to be taller and wasn't about to say the 's' word, 'compact. I fit better on here. You're definitely not compact. You're the very opposite of compact.'

Seb stepped past me and sat down, as if staking his claim. 'What exactly does that mean?'

I shrugged. 'You're big. Bulky. Large.'

'Yes, to all the above. But I'm still not taking your bed.'

'Why not?'

'Because it'd be rude.'

'No, it wouldn't,' I said, sitting down next to him and bouncing slightly on the sofa as though I was testing out a mattress in that completely pointless way that everyone, including myself, has done while shopping for one.

'Yes, it would. Plus I'm far more used to sleeping in different situations than you, and can pretty much sleep anywhere.'

I thought about that. 'I'm pretty sure I could do that too. And I've fallen asleep on here plenty of times.'

'Not the point,' Seb said, gently nudging me out of the way with his hip. 'You're not sleeping here. I've claimed it.'

Now stood, I looked back down at him. 'It's my house. My rules.'

His grin was wide. 'Nope.'

'You're impossible,' I huffed.

'Quite probably,' he replied, leaning back and swinging his legs up on to the sofa, Both hung over the end.

'Oh, Seb! Look. You can't sleep like that.'

He caught my hand. 'Will you stop fussing and go to bed?'

'But you—'

'I generally don't sleep like a laid out corpse, so you're worrying about nothing. Plus, this is coming off in a minute, so I'm already a little more... compact.' He winked at me, as he tapped his artificial leg.

'That's not funny.'

'It's kind of funny.'

'You have a weird sense of humour.'

He gave a head wobble. 'Admittedly, there's probably a little more darkness than there used to be, but that's often part and parcel of the life I had. Most branches of the armed forces can have a pretty dark sense of humour at times.'

'I guess I can see how that would develop.' A huge yawn enveloped the last word.

'Go to bed, you.'

'OK. I can see I'm on a losing streak here.'

'You are.' He reached out, catching my hand. 'But don't think I don't appreciate the thought behind it all.'

I bent and hugged him, wished him a goodnight and pottered off to my room.

Ten minutes later, I was just dragging myself into bed when I realised I'd forgotten my glass of water. Damn. I pulled my dressing gown on and padded to my door. Cracking it open a little, I listened for movement. Hearing none, I stuck my head through and listened again. Still nothing.

I pulled the door open and tiptoed through. The living room was shrouded in darkness, the street lights outside having now turned off for the night, and it took a moment for my eyes to adjust. Misjudging the corner of the hallway, I stubbed my little toe on the skirting. The tiniest of noises escaped from my lips – which was actually pretty good going considering how much it bloody hurt – and I crouched, squishing my toes in my hand to try and ease the pain.

'Let it out. It'll make you feel better.' His voice, low and gravelly with a hint of sleep, drifted around me.

'I'm sorry. I didn't mean to wake you up.'

'I wasn't asleep yet. You all right?'

'Hmm.'

'What did you do?'

'Stubbed my little toe.'

'You should have put the light on.'

'I thought you were asleep.'

'It's your house.'

'You're my guest.'

'Put the light on now.'

'It's all right, I can sort of... Oh! For fuu-argh...' Seriously? Again?

'Lottie. Put the damn light on.'

'Are you decent?'

His laugh was low and way too sexy for this time in the morning. 'As near as I get to that, yes.'

I flicked the light on, immediately hitting the dimmer switch so that it was just enough to move without any more injuries but not too much of a shock to either of our systems.

I grabbed a glass of water and poured another for my guest. Making my way over, I saw Seb, sprawled on the sofa, one leg hanging over the end. Sprawled in turn, on top of his master, was Scooby, who apparently hadn't woken at all. To the right of them, resting within easy reach, was Seb's artificial limb.

I set the glass down just in front of him on the coffee table. When I looked up, even in the low light, I could see him looking at me. He'd seen my gaze take in the leg and my memory flashed back to what he'd said a while ago about an ex getting a bit freaked by it all. His face was blank as he met my eyes.

'What?' I asked.

He rolled his head from side to side. 'Nothing.'

I looked back at the leg. 'Did you want me to say something?'

'Nope.'

'So why are you looking at me with that non-expression?'

He let out a chuckle. 'What's a non-expression?'

'I don't know, but you have one and you do it whenever you don't want people to know what you're thinking.'

'Is that so?'

'Yep. And honestly, it's kind of annoying. It might be easier just to tell people things sometimes.' Apparently, that sobering plunge pool in my brain hadn't quite done its full job yet. My mouth was still a little unfiltered thanks to the alcohol.

'Probably.'

'It doesn't bother me, if that's what you're worried about,' I said, nodding towards his leg.

'I've heard that one before.' His voice, like his face, held little expression at this statement.

I shrugged. 'Yes. But this is me. And, as we've already established and as you never hesitate to point out, I'm a terrible liar. Especially when I've been drinking.'

'That is true.'

'Honestly, Seb. I really don't care. I know tonight probably didn't help, what with Turnip Tarquin and his comments, but...' I shrugged. 'I just don't think it's a big deal. You're an amazing bloke and I l—' I stopped and cleared my throat. 'Like you just as you are. All the stuff you've been through is what makes you you. Who knows? Maybe you were a real arse before and this has changed you for the better? Either way, just relax the hell out about it, will you, and stop trying to protect me from everything.'

He didn't say anything for a few moments and I took a sip from my glass. I wasn't sure where all that just came from. Mostly a champagne bottle, if I was to take a guess, but I suddenly wasn't sure if it had been wise.

'Maybe I was a real arse?' Seb asked, unable to hide the amusement in his voice.

I felt a knot unwind. 'Maybe.'

'I wasn't.'

'So you say.'

The low chuckle came again. 'It's a good job I like you.'

'Just saying it as it is.'

He tilted his head so that he was looking more directly at me. 'So am I.'

I bobbed my head. *Yep. Definitely need that water.* There was still way too much alcohol sloshing about in my brain. And with Seb lying on my sofa, looking sexily rumpled, that was not a good thing.

'Not much of a guard dog, is he?' I nodded my head at the still softly snoring lab sprawled over him.

'Not really.'

'Isn't he heavy?'

'He's not exactly light.' He smirked. 'My own fault. I did this with him all the time as a puppy and now, if I'm ever prone on a sofa, he thinks that's a cue. He doesn't really get the fact he's a tonne heavier now.'

'You OK?'

'I'm tougher than I look.'

I rolled my eyes. 'Machismo is not attractive.'

'Isn't it?'

'No.'

'Never?'

'Not really.'

'Bugger.'

I gave a muscular arm a prod with my toes. 'Right. I'm going to bed. Do you want me to pass you this?' I pointed to the glass. 'No, I'm OK. He'll wriggle a bit in a while, stand up and stretch, probably tread on something delicate and then get down and spread out on the floor. I'll get it then.'

'Something to look forward to.'

'I always think so.'

'OK. Well, goodnight. Again.'

He lifted his hand off the dog's back and caught my fingertips. ''Night, Lottie. Thanks.'

* * *

When I got up the next morning, the blankets and pillows were stacked with what could only be described as military precision, and there was no sign of either Seb or Scooby. Humphrey, however, was still spread out like a fur rug in his bed at the side of my bed and hadn't bothered to follow me in to the lounge. He'd get there in his own time.

I looked around. Seb's bag was gone. The only sign that he'd ever been there was the neat stack of bedding.

I frowned, casting my mind back to the previous night, or more accurately early this morning. Oh god, had I told him he was probably an arse before his injury? I leant on the counter, my head in my hands, not only because my brain was dancing a samba in my skull but at the thought of how I'd just blabbed on.

'That doesn't look like a happy pose.' Seb's voice broke into my thoughts and I simultaneously stood up way too fast and jumped, neither of which was good for my balance and I stumbled back, bouncing off the sink.

Seb was across the room a lot quicker than I could have moved this morning. At least without the added incentive given by someone scaring the crap out of me, of course. Actually, he moved a lot faster than I ever did.

'You all right?' he asked, as I grabbed at the counter top, trying to steady myself. My sudden movements had done nothing for the skull samba, apart from perhaps encourage an encore. He tilted his head. 'Try not to look quite so surprised. I'm pretty good on this thing now.'

I gave him a pathetic punch on the arm. 'It's nothing to do with that. You were drinking just as much as me last night and I have no intention of moving anywhere near that fast for at least a week, judging by how I'm feeling right now.'

His hand was at my waist, warm and strong and I tried not to think about how nice that felt.

'You just made me jump. I thought you'd left.'

'Nope. Just nipped out to get these.' His hand dropped and he turned back to where he'd deposited two large coffees on the table. 'Thought we could both do with one.'

I took a sip of the one he handed me and felt it sear down, the caffeine racing round, kicking out at my system, trying to boot it back into some semblance of life. 'Thanks.' I looked him up and down. 'Why don't you look like you have a hangover? That's hardly fair.'

'Maybe I'm just a bit better at disguising it than you. But I'm also less... compact,' he winked at me, 'than you. That's going to make a difference.'

'Not necessarily. I could drink my ex under the table.'

'He a big guy?'

I looked at Seb and thought of Tom. Hmm. 'Not really. I mean, he was sort of tallish but not as tall as you. And kind of rangy.'

Seb shrugged his eyebrows in reply.

'Yeah, fair enough. Thanks for this though.'

'Did you really think I'd leave without saying goodbye?'

I took a sip, looking at him over the top of my cup, but didn't reply.

He gave a little eye roll and smiled. 'Just for the record, I wouldn't. Besides, unless I imagined it, I think your mum invited me to Sunday lunch today and I said yes.'

'OK. And no, you didn't imagine it. You're definitely invited.'

'Good.'

'I should feed you something. I think I have bacon...' I squinted at the light in the fridge.

'Here.' Seb gently took my cup from me and headed over to the sofa. 'Come and sit down for a bit and drink this. Let it work its magic.'

I gave him another look as I followed his instruction. 'And who waved their wand over you?' I asked, grumpily.

'I'm just better at hiding it.'

'I'd feel better if you looked as rough as me.'

'You don't look rough. Believe me. You look just as lovely as always.'

'OK. At least now I know you've definitely got a hangover. Your eyesight is still shot.'

He gave me a look and then glanced around. 'Where's Humphrey?'

'Still in bed. Like a normal person.'

Seb's lips twitched. 'Doesn't he have to do ablutions like normal people?'

'Of course. But he just does it in his own time. There's no rush.'

Seb grinned, and my tummy, which had been quietly churning, did a flip that had nothing to do with champagne or late nights and everything to do with Seb Marshall. I ignored it. My defences were down right now, but once I was fully sobered up and not fighting a raging hangover, I'd be right back in control. I just needed a minute or two.

As if hearing his name, Humphrey chose this point to wander out of the bedroom, survey the area, have a moment's play with Scooby before toddling to the door. Turning, he looked back at me, expectantly.

'See? In his own time,' I said, pushing myself up extremely reluctantly.

Seb placed a gentle hand on my shoulder. 'Stay there. I'll take him. I've already got shoes on.' He ran his eyes over me. 'And, you know... clothes.'

'I have clothes on!' I said, flushing bright red.

He did that grin again. He *really* needed to stop doing that for about the next hour or so. 'I meant outdoor clothes.'

'It's only the garden for the flats and I'd put a coat on.'

'I know. But I'm dressed.'

'I wish I had a house with a proper garden that Humphrey could go out into whenever he wanted.' I suddenly felt a bit emotional. 'Do you think I did the right thing getting him? Was it selfish to bring him into a flat?'

Seb had wandered over to Humph and popped a lead on him, but he turned now, watching me for a moment. Scooping up my little pooch, who looked swamped by the broad chest and also remarkably comfy resting on the one muscular arm that held him, Seb walked back and sat on the edge of the coffee table in front of me.

'Oi.' The word was soft.

I lifted my eyes.

'You are the least selfish person I have ever met in my entire life. And yes, I think you did the right thing in getting him. You gave him a home where he's loved and cared for and gets everything he needs and more.'

'But if he had a garden...' I let the thought trail off.

'If he had a garden, it would be nice, but he's no less happy for not having one.'

'You sure?'

'I'm positive.' He stood, towering over me. 'I'm also positive that if I don't get a move on, he will be tiddling all down my arm, which is not a situation I'm eager to find myself in. Drink your coffee and relax. And stop overthinking.'

I closed my eyes and heard the door shut softly behind them. All of a sudden, I jumped as a weight bounced on my knee. Scooby looked up at me with doleful eyes, one paw on my leg, and I immediately bent to cuddle him.

'Sorry boy, I didn't realise you were still here. I thought you'd gone with your master.' He emitted a little groan of pleasure at the cuddles and I smiled. 'But I'm glad you stayed.' I curled up on the chair and Scoobs put his other paw up and looked at me. We both knew he was going to win. 'OK, fine, but you can't sit on top of me like with your dad. You'll squash me flat. Here,' I scooted back in the armchair so there was a little spot in front of me, which Scoobs manoeuvred himself into, curling his body round like a Cumberland sausage until it fit. His bum was shoved into my stomach and my arm was round him, cuddling his solid frame and enjoying the comfort and warmth his presence gave out. And then I went back to sleep.

24

Two hours later, I was feeling a lot more human thanks to the extra bit of kip I'd nabbed, a thick smoky bacon sandwich courtesy of Seb, and a long hot shower which was entirely of my own doing. We gathered up the dogs and ourselves and headed out to Seb's car as he'd offered to drive and I had no objections.

'I just need to grab something. We OK for time?'

I glanced at the clock on his dash. 'Yep. Plenty.'

'OK. Do you need anything?' he asked as he pulled into a free car parking space at the supermarket.

'Nope. Shall I wait with these two?' I inclined my head at the two pooches sat happily peering out of the boot window. Humphrey hadn't been able to see out when we first put him in, but without a word, Seb had reopened the boot, swept a couple of jackets and a blanket into a pile and, looking at Humph, pointed to it. Humphrey had scooted on to it, wiggling his bum in to get comfy and given a small bark as he now surveyed the surroundings from his raised dais.

'You're welcome,' Seb grinned, before shutting the hatch.

I laughed at the two faces peering out, and at Seb's conversation. 'And you say I'm daft.'

'I've never said that.'

'You don't have to. It's usually written all over your face.'

'I thought you couldn't read my expression.'

'I'm special.'

He led me to the passenger side and opened the door. 'That you are,' he smiled, before closing it behind me.

* * *

'Oh Seb, dear! You really didn't have to do that,' Mum said, her face flushed with pleasure as she admired the enormous bouquet he'd come out of the supermarket with.

'You'll be popular!' I'd said as he'd passed the bouquet to me to hold and I peered round it, giving him the directions to my parents' house. 'You didn't have to do this, you know. My mum already thinks you're pretty great.'

'I wanted to. And why does she think that?'

'Because of your heroic stance of staying with me until the breakdown truck came, not being prepared to leave me undefended against dragons and brigands.' I'd placed a hand against my chest, doing my best impression of a damsel in possible distress.

He'd given his head the briefest of turns, then looked back at the road. 'The dragons were less of a worry. Plenty of brigands about though.'

'I'd have been fine. Just have locked myself in the car. No biggie.'

'It was a biggie to me. And obviously to your parents. If my daughter was sat in a car park in the middle of the night alone, I wouldn't be too thrilled about it either.'

I'd studied him for a moment.

'You've gone quiet.'

'I was just pondering on you as a dad.'

'Oh.' There'd been a pause. 'Dare I ask what conclusions you came up with?'

'If you like. I think you'd make a great dad. I do, however, pity potential love interests for any daughters you may have though. Man, they're going to be in for a grilling. I mean, look what you're like with me, and I mean nothing to you compared to what a daughter would.'

'You mean a whole lot more than nothing to me, Lottie.'

I'd smiled and held his gaze for a moment before I'd flapped my hand. 'You know what I mean. Oh, turn here. It's the one on the end. Just park anywhere.'

We'd entered via the kitchen, immediately ensconced within the warm fug of cooking and home. The dogs had charged in, Scooby following his new best friend around as Humphrey went off to inspect his grandparents' house, just in case anything had changed since his last visit. Seb had made a bid to catch hold of his dog's collar but to no avail, calling him back.

'I'm sorry. He's normally really good.'

'He is.' I backed Seb up.

'Oh, they're not doing any harm,' my dad chuckled. 'Just off checking to make sure there's no intruders. Don't worry. They'll be back. This is where the food and company are, after all.'

Seb smiled and nodded, and my dad gave him a hearty clasp on the shoulder.

'Now, what can I get you to drink?'

'I'm driving back later, but anything non-alcoholic would be great.'

'Good, good. We can do that. I've got a little selection here. Come and take your pick. You into rugby at all?' My dad led Seb through into the annexe off the kitchen where he stored all the drinks bottles and we soon heard them laughing.

Mum glanced over at me and gave a little smile. I pretended not to know what it meant and just returned it innocently, happy that my dad was putting Seb so much at his ease. Not that I'd had any doubt of that.

It had always been in our house that friends had gathered after school and at weekends, and not only because of Mum's fabulous cooking but also for the atmosphere – the ease, the humour that pervaded the house. I'd always loved coming home, even on my odd stroppy teenage day. I'd never really gone through a phase. I always thought that made me sound boring – the fact that I hadn't gone through a rebellious stage, dyed my hair black or pink or blue and declared anarchy on the System. To be honest, whenever I saw others at school doing this it just looked bloody exhausting!

Sally, of course, definitely didn't have any teenage angst. She'd been far too busy being pretty much perfect, getting good grades, looking beautiful and aiming for the career she wanted. I was good at the academic side, did my best to look presentable – sometimes with Sally's help when she was feeling in a generous mood – but had absolutely no idea what I wanted to do with my life. That hadn't fazed my parents either. They'd just told me I'd find out eventually. It took me a while but I had. And, as a bonus, this career came with a free Seb Marshall included.

* * *

Dinner was, as always, totally scrummy and ridiculously filling. I knew I shouldn't have another roastie, or another anything really, but they were so delicious it was often hard to resist. Not that I tried that hard. I had nothing like my sister's willpower when it came to Mum's cooking.

'No, no,' Mum said, whipping the washing-up liquid out of Seb's hand with the swiftness of a ninja. Seb opened his mouth but she held up a finger. 'I'm serious. I'm just going to stuff it all in the dish-washer anyway.'

'Well, let me do that then.' Seb made to step towards the machine.

Mum raised an eyebrow. 'I shan't invite you again if you're going to insist on being helpful. Lottie, do take him away. Go and show Seb the view from the top of the lane, give the dogs a chance to stretch their legs.'

We both looked to where the dogs were curled up by the Aga, sleeping.

'Yes, they look eager to do that,' I giggled, laughing at how Humphrey was using his bigger pal as a pillow.

'Watch this though.' Seb moved to where his coat was hanging and pulled the lead from a pocket. Scooby was up and across the kitchen, leaving Humphrey looking slightly dazed and appearing to wonder what just happened. 'Come on, Humph. Time for a walk.' He knew that word and was now just as keen as his friend, despite having been in the depths of what looked like a very contented sleep moments ago.

I wasn't entirely sure how I felt about Mum effectively shoving me out the door with Seb, but there wasn't a lot I could do about it.

We walked leisurely up the lane, towards the area Mum had suggested. 'Sorry about this. I hope you didn't mind a walk.'

'Of course, I don't mind. It's lovely round here. I just feel bad not helping.'

'Oh, don't worry. She's always been like that. The kitchen is kind of her domain. Stay long enough and she might let you help one day.'

He smiled. 'Something to look forward to.'

'There's a lot of dinners to get through before you get that golden ticket though.'

'It's a tough job, but I'm trained for this kind of thing.'

I bumped his arm and we walked on companionably, talking about everything and nothing, until we got to the fence that separated the lane from the view beyond.

'Wow.'

'Not bad, eh?'

Before us, a field curved gently away, and below that lay the next village, an enchanting little hamlet that was just a scattering of houses, a tiny shop and a beautiful Norman church, with Gothic Victorian additions. Stood here, with the promise of spring in the air, a gentle warmth on our faces as the clouds of earlier had cleared away, the view was like something from a picture book. Or perhaps a history book of times gone by. From here there was no sight, and no sound, of the mechanical intrusion of humans. All was quiet, the only sounds being the gentle rustle of early leaves on the trees around us, birds fluttering and chirping as they swooped across and gathered on branches, and the long grass in the field swooshing gently as a breeze caught it.

'You should see this in June. It's an absolute mass of wildflowers. The owners don't mow it as they want to encourage wildlife. It's absolutely breathtaking. It's just this humming mass of colour, buzzing with insects.'

'That sounds wonderful. I'd like to see that.'

'Well, behave and I might bring you again.'

He gave me a little salute and rested his hands on the fence. 'Where's that?' he asked, pointing to the next village.

'Tinkerton. It's beautiful. Tiny. I've always wanted to live there.'

'Sounds like a place from a kids' TV programme.'

I smiled, bending and placing my elbows on the top bar of the fence next to him before resting my chin in my hands.

'It does. I think that's part of its appeal. It's got a timelessness about it. I love it.'

'Pricey?'

I pulled a face. 'Way out of my price range, unfortunately. Houses don't come up very often there, but I always keep an eye and, when they do, I spend ages looking at them on the estate agency site.' I rolled my head to one side to look at him. 'Daft, eh?'

His gaze remained focused on the view as he shook his head. 'Not at all. People's circumstances change all the time. Who knows what tomorrow might bring?'

'Unless it brings a lottery win, I don't think I've got any hope there. Still, it's nice to dream.'

He turned then, his smile as gentle as the sunshine. 'It is.'

I pushed myself up. 'Shall we head back?'

The dogs trotted alongside us as we meandered back a different way so I could show Seb the village and the little nursery my parents frequented much of the time. The owner smiled and waved as we came in.

'They OK with dogs in here?' Seb asked, hesitating.

'Yep. Totally dog friendly. Even the café. It's great. Their plants are brilliant too. Really strong and healthy. God, I wish I had a garden,' I said, rubbing the soft furry leaf of a stachys between my thumb and forefinger. 'Feel that. Isn't it gorgeous?'

Seb did as I asked. 'Fuzzy. Feels a bit like when I fiddle with Scoobs' ears.'

'Exactly. Isn't it lovely? Its common name is Lambs' Ears.'

He nodded. 'Makes sense. It's pretty.'

We walked on for a few moments as I stroked, rubbed and sniffed various plants. Seb had taken Humph's lead from me, leaving me free to poke about.

'Did you have a garden before?' he asked.

I glanced up at him. 'With my ex?'

He gave a short nod.

'Yes. Just a small one, but I loved it. I'd made it beautiful. Does that sound a bit arrogant?'

'Nope. I'm sure you did. Nothing wrong with acknowledging that.'

'I used to spend time out there every day, even if it was raining. Just a few minutes. It was my happy place. If I'd had a bad day, just being out there amongst all the plants and greenery could lift my spirits so much. They should prescribe gardening on the NHS.'

'There are a few schemes that are doing things like that. Not many at the moment, but we've managed to get a few of our vets into some and, without exception, they've all thrived.'

I smiled up at him. 'That's amazing!'

'Yeah, it's been great. Funding, as always, is the thing, but it's definitely an area I'm looking into more.'

I smiled.

'And in the meantime, we really need to get you a garden. You've been buzzing ever since you stepped in here.'

'It's another of my happy places.'

'Clearly.' He said, giving me that sunshine smile again.

'Lottie!' The owner had now finished serving and came across to say hello. 'How are you, my dear?'

'Fine thanks, George. How are you and Margot?'

'Good! Good! Ramping up for spring.'

'It's good to hear you're busy. I'm sure Mum and Dad will be in here again soon.'

'Oh, they've already been in stocking up on things. You just visiting or can I tempt you into something?'

'Oh George, you know I don't need much tempting, but I've already overfilled my allotted two-paving-slab space with pots at the flat, unfortunately.'

'Aah, never mind. Another time. And what about you, sir?' George looked up at Seb.

'Oh, I'm not much of a gardener, unfortunately.'

'We can soon change that!' George laughed good naturedly.

I glanced at my phone to check the time. 'We'd better be getting back actually. Thanks, George. Love to Margot.'

George waved as he headed back towards the cash desk, where a customer pushing a cart full of produce was just approaching. 'See you soon, Lottie!' he called.

* * *

'It's really nice round here.' Seb glanced around as we made our way back to the house. 'I mean, not just pretty, but there seems to be a real sense of community too. I can see why you like it.'

'Yes. It's like a little pocket of times past, this tiny clump of villages. It feels like people still care about the place and each other. You don't seem to get that a lot now.'

'No. You don't.'

'Do you like where you live?'

'It's all right. Nice enough.'

'Hmm, I can really hear the passion behind that.'

He smirked at my sarcasm.

'I assume your family are close by though?'

Seb cleared his throat a little. 'No. Not especially.'

'Oh.' We walked on a few more steps. 'Where do they live then?'

'About half an hour from here actually.'

'Seriously?'

He nodded.

'Did you live up where you are now with your ex then?'

'Nope. We didn't actually live together. One of those things we'd never really got round to, although obviously we spent a lot of time at each others' places. In the end, that made it better for her. She was able to make a clean break when she needed to. It was one thing I didn't have to be thinking about either. Selling a house so that she could get her equity out, et cetera. It worked out well in the end.'

'So, you had a place then?'

'Yep.'

'Where.'

'Near where my brother lives now.'

'And you sold it?'

'Yep.'

'And moved two hours away?'

'Yep.'

'When?'

'A little while after I came out of hospital.'

'Why?'

'Why what?'

'Why did you sell? Was it memories?'

He shook his head. 'Nope. Nothing like that.' He glanced down at me. 'I guess that makes me sound cold.'

'No. Not really. But I am curious. You don't have to tell me, of course.'

'There's nothing to tell really. I just needed a change.'

'Two hours away from your family. I assume you're not close then.'

'It's not that. My brother and sister-in-law are really good people, and I'm pretty close with them. They've got a couple of kids and I do miss seeing them as much as I might have done had I stayed local.' He gave a shrug and a flicker of sadness momentarily shadowed his face.

'And your dad? Where's he?'

'Same sort of area as my brother.'

As soon as I'd mentioned his dad, Seb's face had hardened, like a visor had dropped into place. I kept silent for a moment, wondering whether to ask any more.

'My dad's not really like yours, Lottie.'

I looked up.

Seb saw the question in my eyes. 'Your parents are easy going. Eager to put people at their ease. I can't remember the last time I felt quite so relaxed with someone I'd literally only just met. I sort of feel like I've known them for ages. They have a real gift of welcoming people, whether they know them or not. It's obviously just how they are.'

'It is.'

'You're very lucky.'

'I am. I know. But just because your dad isn't quite so open as my parents are, I'm sure that doesn't mean he wouldn't like to see you more.'

Seb looked away into the distance. 'It's complicated.'

'Families often are.'

'That's true.' His expression was still shuttered and his body had taken on a tension that it hadn't had all day. I debated whether it was best to just let this go or whether to press on.

'Have you never been close?' I decided to give it a go. He could always change the subject if he wanted to, and, to be honest, I was kind of expecting him to, but something within me made me want to at least try. I hated that he'd suddenly become so tense after the relaxed happiness of earlier.

'We used to be closer.'

I tried to hide my surprise at him actually answering and remained quiet, leaving him to fill the silence if he wanted.

'Until I got injured. Things changed after that.' He let out a sigh and his gaze drifted across the fields to our left as we headed back to the house.

'I can't begin to imagine how difficult it was for you all.'

'Mum was pretty great. Once she got over the initial shock. Dad didn't say much, but he was there. Until Mum died.'

'Seb, I'm so sorry you've had to go through so much.'

He shook his head, the shutters still closed. 'Other people go through much worse.'

'Yes,' I said quietly, 'but we're not talking about other people. We're talking about you.'

He turned, dark eyes looking down at me. 'Yes. We are. Now how did that happen?' The hint of smile on a mouth way too attractive right now gave me hope.

'I have magic powers.'

'Of that, I have no doubt.'

'Will you tell me more?' All or nothing now.

25

Seb bent and gave Scooby a head rub. Humph scooted around my legs to get in on the action and Seb's soft chuckle made me smile as he fussed my own dog too before straightening and beginning to walk on.

I hesitated for a moment and he reached back with his free hand and took mine.

'Keep up,' he teased, as I caught him up and he dropped my hand.

A tractor came chugging up the lane, shattering the bucolic peace. We stood to the side, keeping the dogs behind us, and the driver waved in thanks. Once it had passed, we stepped back out into the lane and continued our walk.

'I told you about Mum. Her heart attack, I mean.'

'You did.'

'I always blamed myself for that. She'd been fine before she got that call to say I'd been injured on deployment.'

'Seb...' I tucked my arm around his. 'It's not your fault. You can't blame yourself for it. She wouldn't want you to, and nobody else does.'

'My dad does.'

I felt the air freeze in my lungs for a moment. 'What do you mean?'

'My dad. He feels the same way I do. About the stress affecting Mum. Having a... detrimental effect.'

My mind fizzed with confusion. 'Are you sure?' I started. 'I mean... he hasn't actually said that.'

'Not in so many words. But I don't...' He stretched his neck from side to side and looked down at me. 'You don't need to hear all this, Lots.'

I squeezed his arm a little. 'I want to. Please tell me.'

His eyes remained on me for a moment, his mind apparently trying to decide which way to step. 'Don't get me wrong. I love my dad. I just wish I could relax with him. I don't blame him for thinking I'm the cause of his wife's death. I already feel that, so it's nothing new.'

'But you don't know that's the case,' I said, softly. I didn't want to contradict him, but that was a heavy burden to carry around, let alone feeling that it was reinforced by your own father.

'When I see my dad, which is usually only when I'm at my brother's, I just feel...' he dipped his head and scratched his stubble, keeping my arm tucked around his as he did so. 'My dad was in the services. And when I see him, I feel like I still am too. I feel like I'm a soldier in his company and that soldier is a disappointment to him.'

'Oh, Seb,' I said, squeezing his arm but not looking up, my heart contracting at his words and the pain he'd done his best to hide. To a lot of people, it probably was hidden. But I'd known Seb a while now, talking to him every day. I knew his normal voice, I knew his voice when he'd discussed difficult situations at work, frustration at not being able to do everything he wanted to for people, and his voice when he spoke about cases, as much as he was able to anyway, that clearly really got to him. The ones that caused him pain. Just as this did. 'I'm sure that's not the case.'

He said nothing but briefly laid his other hand over mine as it curled around his forearm, Scooby's lead loosely sliding up his wrist.

'What does your brother think?'

'Well, he's kind of stuck in the middle, so I try not to bring him into it. We have dinners together and both just try and be civil for the sake of my brother and his family but tend to stay out of each other's way as much as possible. Kids, thankfully, are quite a good distraction.' As soon as he'd started to talk about his brother's family, the tension slid away and the light came back into his eyes as the shutters opened once more.

'You obviously love spending time with them.'

'I really do. I wish I was closer.'

'So, why aren't you? You never really answered me. I mean, I would have thought that you'd want to be closer after... everything.'

He gave an exhale that was part laugh, part exasperation, although I wasn't quite sure if the exasperation was aimed at me or something else.

'Honestly, I think that's exactly why I moved.'

I wrinkled my brow, squinting up at him as the lowering sun shone in my eyes. 'I don't understand.'

'I didn't want to rely on them. I wanted to prove that this wasn't going to change who I was or take away the independence I'd always valued. I'd spent months having to rely on people and it did my head in. They were worried about me, obviously. Wanting to do stuff for me and I couldn't deal with it.'

'But I'm sure that wasn't because they didn't think you could do it yourself. It was because they love you.'

'I know. But in my head, it got all twisted out of shape. I built up this need. This... I don't know... it was something I felt I had to do. I had to put myself out of easy reach. I couldn't rely on them and they wouldn't be able to just pop in and see if I needed anything or check on me.'

'Did it ever occur to you that they would have wanted to do that, whether you'd been injured or not? You'd been away for months already and weren't at home much, even when not deployed. Perhaps they just actually wanted to spend time with you. Because you're you. Not for any other reason.'

'Don't put it like that.'

'Like what?'

'All sensible and reasonable.'

I grinned and laid my head against his bicep for a moment. 'You're not going to like what I'm about to say then.'

'Let me have it.'

'You're kind of annoying.'

'Pardon?'

'You. You're kind of annoying.'

He smiled. 'I see. Any specifics?'

'I'm getting to that. You're determined not to be defined by your injury. That, although you realise it's a part of you, it's not who you are.'

'And that's a bad thing?' His voice was calm.

'God no! Let me finish. It's just that you do all that. Complete all these challenges, make people aware of things and provide education through the charity, making sure as much as possible that people see the person first and the disability second – if at all. But in all your determination to ensure you weren't defined by your injury, by doing what you did, removing yourself from your family and friends, the place you knew, you did that to yourself. Every time you looked around, I can't help thinking there must have been something in your head that said, I'm here because of what happened.'

'See. There you go again.'

'What?'

'Being all wise and, annoyingly, probably correct.'

I squeezed his arm and he returned the gesture, pulling my arm against his body. We walked in companionable silence as we approached the house. Opening the gate and keeping Scooby to heel, Seb waited as Humphrey and I went through.

'You could always move, you know,' I said, as we approached the front door.

'I could.'

'Everyone in the charity works pretty much remotely and I could always book a room for a meeting somewhere if it was required in the future.'

'That's true.'

'You'd be nearer to your brother and be able to see the kids more too.' I didn't mention his dad.

'I would. Of course, this plan of yours does have an element of backfire on your part,' he said, stepping into the cosiness of my parents' house behind me.

'It does?' I asked, frowning.

'It'd also mean I was closer to you.'

'Oh!' I said, unzipping my coat, aware that it had suddenly got quite warm in here.

'There you are!' Mum said, bustling towards us. 'Did you have a nice walk? Is it warm out there? You look a little flushed, love,' she said, placing a soothingly cool hand on my cheek.

'Mmmhmm,' I replied, pretty certain that the flush on my cheeks had only a passing connection with the weather outside and a lot more to do with the man standing beside me.

* * *

Later, having enjoyed a classic Sunday tea of sandwiches, cake and some freshly made sausage rolls, Seb and I began to get ourselves and the dogs ready to make a move. Mum always insisted on sending me home with leftovers and I followed her into the kitchen to help.

'I'll just wrap a bit of this up for Seb. He seemed to enjoy it earlier. Oh, there you are,' she said, glancing up to see him and my dad entering the kitchen. 'I was just saying I'll send you home with some of this cake, if that's all right.'

'Oh, you really don't have to do that.'

'She's worried that if you leave it here, I'll just eat it all,' my dad chuckled.

'You probably would,' Mum chided him with a loving laugh.

'I hate to see good food go to waste.' He winked at us both.

'See?' My mum waved her hand. 'You'll be doing us a favour. It's only a little bit,' she said, placing a massive wedge in some tin foil and neatly sealing it up. 'There's a few sausage rolls in there as well. I made too many really.' She always made too many.

'Thank you.' Seb smiled, having already sensed it was a losing battle trying to protest.

'Anyone in?' Sally's voice drifted in from the front door.

'In here, darling,' Mum called, as she tidied up the rest of the leftovers.

'Hi,' my sister said, greeting my dad and stopping as she suddenly noticed the extra member of the party. 'Hello,' she said, holding out her hand. 'I don't believe we've met. I'm Sally.' I got a pang of envy at how smooth she was. How she dealt with every situation with just the right amount of panache and good manners. If I'd charged in to my parents' kitchen and suddenly noticed the best looking man I had ever met in my life just standing there, I was pretty sure my entrance would not have been anywhere near as dignified or elegant. But then, that was yet another difference between me and Sally.

'Seb Marshall, pleasure to meet you. Lottie's talked about you.'

'Has she?' Sally replied, smiling, as she turned her head slightly towards me, one exquisite brow arching ever so slightly.

'All good,' he smiled, charming her without effort or intention. 'She said you work for an airline.'

'I do. Yes.'

'You off for a few days now, love?' Dad asked.

'Mmm,' Sally nodded, watching Mum packaging up the food.

Mum looked up and frowned. 'You hungry, love? Shall I do you something?'

'No,' Sally stopped her with a hand on her arm. 'I'm fine.'

From the corner of my eye, I saw Mum and Dad exchange a look and I knew why. Sally was normally a bit of a force of nature. She didn't do anything without a purpose. And now she was... almost relaxed. Like a normal person. Which was weird. Of course, there was the possibility that she was still pissed off with me about the whole book club thing but couldn't say anything with company in the house. The more I thought about it, the more I felt I might have struck a bullseye.

Having woken from their after-walk snooze, the two dogs now stretched and, sensing new smells, padded over to investigate. As Scooby trotted happily past his master, following his pal on their mission to investigate the newcomer, Seb called him to heel. Scoobs stopped short of Sally, and looked back, all soulful eyes.

'Don't look at me like that. Come on. Here.' Scooby let out a sigh and trotted back, rewarded for his obedience with a chin rub and a dog treat Seb had left stuffed in a pocket from earlier.

Humphrey, however, being smaller, had taken the shortcut under the table and wound around the chair legs, making it a little more difficult to catch him. And his recall, although pretty good, still wasn't on a par with Scooby's. Blissfully unaware that my sister was not as enamoured with him as the rest of us were, he trotted towards her. I took in the sheen on the fine tights she wore under her short, fitted leather skirt and reckoned I'd be paying for those shortly if I didn't move fast. Knowing my sister, they were unlikely to be three for the price of one at Poundland, and I had no desire to find out their true cost.

Dashing forward, I scooped Humph up just as he was about to rest his little paws on her shin.

'Up we come,' I said to him.

Sally looked at me.

'Sorry. He thinks he's cuter than he is.' I, of course, thought he was beyond cute, but I already knew what my sister thought about him, and dogs in general, from previous experience. Clearly Seb had remembered too.

My sister stepped towards me and, much to my, and my parents', surprise, gave Humphrey a little fuss as he sat contentedly in my arms. 'He is rather sweet.'

I couldn't help the smile that broke on my face. 'Thank you.'

She looked up, meeting my eyes, and my smile. Maybe she wasn't peed off with me after all.

'Are those sandwiches for anyone?' she asked, seeing a few triangles of bread on a plate.

'No, dear. Have them. Do you want to know what's in them so you can enter it into your little app?' My sister had been keeping track of every single thing she ate via an app for years, along with her exercise, sleep and pretty much anything else you could track. Carbs were generally a sworn enemy. I guess today she'd called a temporary ceasefire to hostilities. She'd once tried to get me to do the whole app thing too, but frankly it looked exhausting.

'No, that's all right.'

'Oh... OK. Here you go,' Mum said, putting them on a smaller plate while clearly trying to keep the astonishment out of her voice. 'There's tea in the pot if you want some.'

'Thanks,' Sally said, taking a bite of one sandwich and taking it with her to finish as she poured tea into a bone china mug.

Dad gave me a puzzled, but pleased, look.

OK. Who was this woman and where was my sister?

'I'll go and put these bits in the car,' Seb said, taking the food my mum had piled into two paper bags as he told Scooby to stay. Dad said something about giving him a hand, and, in a move fairly astute for a couple of blokes, it seemed that they had decided their absence might be appropriate for the moment. I looked across at Mum who gave a tiny shrug.

'You all right, Sal?' I started.

'Yes, fine.' She smiled, taking the second sandwich. That was literally the most carbs I'd seen her eat in one go in about three years. Something was up. 'He seems nice.'

'He is.'

'I didn't know you were seeing anyone.' She looked out of the window, down the garden. 'We don't really talk much any more, do we?'

I shrugged. 'I'm not seeing him. We're just friends. And you and I talk plenty. Life's busy.'

'Hmm.'

In my mind, I'd circled back to the book club thing. And also because I didn't really know what else to say. *You're acting really weird* seemed a little blunt, even from me. 'I am sorry about the book club, you know. I hope it hasn't caused you too much trouble rearranging things.'

Sally waved a perfect manicure at me. 'Don't worry about it, Lots. Actually, I've dropped out of it.'

'Oh... really?'

'Yes. It was just getting a bit complicated with my shifts and trying to get to the meetings after a long flight was going to be exhausting.'

'Couldn't they arrange them for when you were off?' I asked, frowning. 'They must have realised you'd be tired after stepping off a long-haul flight.'

Sally curved her hands around the mug of tea. 'Actually, I think they did it on purpose. I'd given them my shift schedule and when they sent me the book club dates, they all clashed.'

'Oh, love.'

Sally gave a one shouldered shrug, then smiled up at us. 'Me dropping out of it wasn't exactly my idea, if I'm honest.'

'What do you mean?' I frowned.

'They kind of uninvited me.'

'Oh Sal. I'm sorry.' My stomach twisted. Not doing stuff because you don't want to is one thing, but I hadn't meant other people to get flak because of it.

'No, Lottie. Don't look like that. It's fine. Actually, you did me a favour.'

'I did?'

'You did.' She reached out and took my hands, curling her long elegant fingers around mine. 'I'm sorry I didn't listen when you tried to tell me before that you felt they weren't very friendly on the times you'd sat in for me.'

'It's all right.'

'No. It's not.' There was a strength in her voice that I hadn't heard in a long time. At least not when it came to something that affected other people. 'I should have listened. You're my sister and I dismissed your comments. I chose to put them above you and assume that it was just you.' She looked up for a moment, away from me. 'Dad, stop hiding in the hall. You're not intruding on anything.'

Dad entered the warm kitchen, followed by Seb, whom Scooby immediately went to greet as though he'd been gone for days. Seb bent down, tactfully making himself as small and unobtrusive as possible, which, bearing in mind his size, was pretty good going.

Sally continued. 'Anyway, when you said about it before, I just thought it was because they were... different to the sort of people you tend to mix with.'

I wasn't sure how to take that, and my confusion obviously showed on my face.

'I don't mean that in a bad way. But they're more reserved. You're used to Jess, who's rather the opposite of reserved. In a good way.'

'OK...'

'So, I just thought it was because you weren't used to them and you like spending time at home on your own. I'm used to mixing with people all the time, so it was bound to be different. But it wasn't that at all and maybe I did know that. Or at least had an idea. But I didn't pay much attention to it. I didn't think I needed to.'

'So, what happened, darling?' Mum asked.

'I got an email a couple of days ago from one of them. I suppose now I look at it, she's rather the ringleader. Honestly, they're a bit like a mean girls clique from school! It was the first I'd heard from them in a while. None of them were returning my messages when I suggested coffee or anything.'

'Just because you couldn't host a book club evening?'

Sally smiled. 'No. Because I couldn't get them the free upgrades they all wanted for a holiday they'd booked over Easter to Bermuda.'

'What?'

'They wanted me to upgrade them to first class.'

'On a holiday you hadn't even been invited on?'

Sally gave an eyebrow shrug. 'Yes. And I don't have that kind of authority anyway. I'm cabin crew for first class, but I can't just pull free upgrades out of my... hat.'

I sniggered. 'You were going to say something else then.'

She smirked. I hadn't seen her do that for years. 'I can't. We have guests.'

'Oh pffft. He's ex-Army. He's heard it all and worse.'

'Good to know for next time.'

'So, they wanted freebies, at one of the busiest times of the year and then cut you out when you couldn't do it for them,' Mum summed it up.

'Yes. That's about it in a nutshell.'

'Well,' Mum said, wrapping a protective arm around her eldest. 'They don't sound like the sort of people you want in your life anyway.'

'No. You're right. I was a bit upset at first, but the more I thought about it, the more it just made me angry that they had treated me like that. That they'd been mean to Lottie when she was doing me a favour, and me forcing her to shut her dog away just because I was worried about them getting a stray dog hair on their designer outfits, and what they'd think of me if they did.'

Things suddenly started making a lot more sense.

'You were right, Lottie. I mean about saying no to things that don't make you happy. They weren't making me happy and, before, I might have bent over backwards to try and win them back, no matter the cost. But I thought about it, and I talked to Oliver and realised that their company didn't make me happy. I was doing it because I thought they were the "right kind of people" for me to mix with. They barely ate anything, so I barely ate anything and I'm not sure that's been the healthiest option I could have chosen.'

'We have worried about you sometimes, darling.'

'I know. And I'm sorry about that. I've been doing a lot of thinking the last few days and I'm going to make some changes. Good changes.'

Mum squeezed her, kissing her on the cheek. 'I'm very glad to hear it.'

'So... Oliver's still on the scene then?' I asked, in what I thought was a casual manner. From the look on my sister's face, I may not quite have nailed it.

'Yes,' she grinned. 'He is. He's on his way down from London this evening and going to spend a couple of days working from my place so that we can spend a bit of time together before I have to fly out again.'

'That'll be nice, love.'

'Yes. Yes, I think it will be.'

If Oliver was supportive of the changes my sister was making in her life, changes that already seemed to be making her happier and healthier, then I was rapidly becoming one of his biggest fans. By the relieved and happy expressions on the faces of my parents, it looked like I might have competition for that title.

26

'How's Jess doing?' Seb asked as we got off the Tube close to the restaurant where we'd arranged to meet her and Harry for dinner.

I shrugged my shoulders. 'She's Jess. She's being all bubbly and normal but, honestly? I'm a bit worried. I've never seen her stunned into silence like she was that night. Tarquin really got to her. I don't know why. Well, I sort of do, but the things he said? Whatever Harry says, it can't make her unhear those words. The damage is done. And I don't know what to do about it.'

'You can't always fix things for people, Lottie. You're there for her, and she knows that. That's probably the best thing you can do for her right now. Harry's crazy about her. Anyone can see that. Even a bloke like me!'

I slanted my eyes at him and he gave a wink. 'I'm pretty sure you're more observant than you pretend.'

'I can neither confirm nor deny that.'

Leaning against the door to the restaurant, I faced him, giving him an exaggerated eye roll in reply. 'Of course, you can't.'

He shrugged.

Jess waved as she saw us enter, and having handed our coats over, we headed across to the table, exchanging hugs.

'How are you?' I asked quietly. I'd spoken to Jess a lot over the past few weeks since the incident, but, like I'd said to Seb, I was certain she hadn't brushed off the comments as well as she claimed to have.

'I'm fine,' she replied, smiling. I still wasn't convinced.

'I'm so glad you could both come,' Harry began, once water and wine had been poured. 'Ideally, I'd have liked to have done this closer to the night in question, but it was important that Seb was able to be here too, and I know coming down is a bit more of a trek for you, so thank you.'

Seb nodded in acceptance.

Harry took a deep breath and let it out slowly. 'Well, as you may have gathered, I basically brought you all here to apologise for Tarquin's behaviour at the party.'

Seb shifted in his seat. 'What he said to Jess was out of order, as was the way he spoke to Lottie. But you didn't have to do all this,' he waved his hand at the high-end restaurant, 'for me as well. I can look after myself. Not that these two can't,' he gave me a little grin. 'But you know what I mean.'

'I appreciate that, Seb. But I felt the need to. I was embarrassed by his behaviour and I have come to think of you, and hope you think of me, as a friend.'

'Without question. But you still don't need to buy me dinner. I'm cheaper than that.' He gave Harry a grin, dissipating his friend's discomfort and leading us all to relax a little more.

Harry returned the smile and lifted the bottle of Cristal from its ice bucket. 'Champagne?'

The meal was delicious and the conversation easy and open with a lot of laughter. It was good to see Jess relaxing and I was happy to see Harry and Seb getting on so well.

Just as we ordered our dessert, a man approached. Late fifties, with a bespoke suit and hand-made Italian shoes, he stopped by our table, laying his hand on Harry's shoulder as he shook his hand, before Harry then introduced him to the rest of us.

'Of course, you already know Jess.'

They exchanged greetings before Harry moved on to me, and then Seb.

'And this is Seb Marshall. It's his charity I'm raising money for with the triathlon next month.'

'Oh yes, I heard you were doing that. A veteran's charity, is that right?'

'Yes, sir.' Seb nodded. You could take the boy out of the army, but you couldn't take the army out of the boy.

'Excellent cause.'

'There's a gala in the summer too, if you fancy buying a ticket. Or a table?' Harry grinned.

The man smiled back good naturedly. 'I'm sure I can fill a table. Send me the details. I'll get my assistant on to it.'

Under the table, I grabbed Seb's hand and squeezed. Harry just sold us a whole table!

'This triathlon?' the man said.

'Yes?'

'Keep in touch about it. Whatever you raise, I'll double it.'

It was hard to shock Seb. He'd seen it all. Done it all. But from the tiny movement I made with my head, I could see his mouth open just the smallest amount. Mine, of course, had almost hit the crisp linen tablecloth. I heard a small squeak and came to the conclusion it must have been me.

Closing my mouth, I gripped Seb's hand even tighter to try and maintain an outward appearance of dignity. Under the table, he placed his other hand on top of mine.

'That's extremely generous of you,' Seb offered.

'Nonsense. It's the least I can do. Our servicemen and women don't get nearly enough assistance through the normal channels.

Much of the time it's down to good people like you to find them the help they need, but none of that comes for free. If I can assist in some small way, it's an honour to do so.'

Some small way... I knew how much Harry had already raised and it was looking pretty damn good. Luckily for the charity, he had a lot of friends with deep pockets, and from what he'd told us, he wasn't done yet. And here was this man offering to double whatever he raised. Plus buy a table at the gala. It might be small to him but it was a huge, huge thing for the charity. Seb pushed his chair back from the table, holding out his hand as he stood.

'Thank you. It's very much appreciated. I look forward to seeing you at the gala.'

'I look forward to seeing you again too,' the man said, laying his hand over Seb's as he shook it. 'It was a pleasure.'

'Blimey!' Jess blurted once he was out of earshot.

'Yeah, he's a good guy.'

'Think he'll actually come through on that, though?' she asked.

'No shadow of a doubt,' Harry confirmed. 'I've known him a long time. He's upfront and says what he means. There are no games with Jacob. I'll send him the details tomorrow and you'll have the confirmation from him shortly after. I guarantee it.'

'Blimey,' Seb echoed.

Harry tilted his head. 'Thankfully, not all of my friends are like Tarquin.'

Encouraged by the wine, I made a steeple with my fingers and rested my chin upon them. 'Can I ask a question?'

'Of course.'

'Why are you friends with him? Tarquin, I mean.'

Harry opened his mouth to reply, but I carried on.

'I mean, I know the whole you've been friends with him since Prep school and all that, but people change. Grow up. Grow apart.'

'Lottie...' Jess flashed a warning. 'I've never wanted to come between Harry and his friends, or family.'

Harry turned, resting his hand over hers and closing around it. 'Jess, darling. Of course you're not. Why would you ever think that you would, or could?'

Jess gave him a look, but Harry seemed genuinely mystified. She shook her head. 'It's fine, Harry. As long as you're happy, I'm happy.'

But Harry was not to be pacified. 'No, clearly there's something more going on here. I need you to tell me.'

'There's nothing. Really,' Jess said, shooting me a look.

'I know what Tarquin said upset you, and I will address that. I've just needed to take my time because I was so bloody angry, and I want to tackle it in the right way. But I'm now getting the feeling there's more to this. Someone else has said something?' He put a hand on her cheek, the gesture tender, nothing but love and concern in his eyes. 'Please, my darling, tell me.'

Jess let out a sigh. 'Oh Harry. We both know I'm not exactly what your friends or family would have planned for. I don't have the background you do, the education, the cut-glass accent, blue blood or white skin. I know none of that matters to you and I love you for that. But we both know it still matters to some people.'

'Yes, I suppose that is true. It does matter to some people – but not the ones that matter.'

Jess gave him a little smile of acceptance and curled her fingers a little more into the hand he was holding.

Harry was still looking at her. 'There's something else going on here, isn't there?'

'No, nothing,' she replied.

Harry looked across the table at me and I swallowed. I knew Jess was still festering about what Tarquin had said, especially about Harry's family, playing on doubts she already had in her mind, exploding them into far bigger ones, but it wasn't my place to say anything. This had to be something between Harry and Jess – as much as I wanted to blurt it all out, I couldn't.

Even without looking, I could feel Jess boring holes in me with her eyes. Reaching out for the water bottle, I busied myself topping up my glass and asking if anyone else wanted some.

'Jess?'

'God, Harry, you're like a dog with a bone!' she laughed, but none of us missed the underlying tension in it, despite her best efforts.

'Yes,' he said softly. 'I can be when it's something important. And this – you – are the most important thing in my life. There's something going on here and I want to know what it is. If we're going to be married, we shouldn't be starting out with secrets.'

'There are no secrets, Harry. But... I have been wondering about things. That perhaps we're rushing things a little. Whether it might be beneficial to everyone if we took a little more time, gave those who need it a bit longer to come to terms with the fact you chose a real wild card to bring into the family.'

'Maybe Lottie and I should go and get some air while you two discuss things,' Seb said, making to push back his chair, but Harry shook his head.

'No, stay. Please.' He looked at me and then back at us both. 'Whatever's going on here, I'm pretty sure Lottie already knows about it already. It just seems to be me that's in the dark.' He paused for a moment, then leant back in his chair. 'I have an announcement. We've all been very interested in Lottie's decision this year to say no to the things she doesn't want and I am going to take a tip from that.'

I felt my stomach churn, the wonderful food of earlier now sitting leaden inside me. Jess' face froze. Under the table, my hands were balled into fists, the short nails I'd managed to grow recently digging uncomfortably into my palms. Suddenly they were warmer as Seb's large hand covered them, and I felt a wave of comfort and support wash through me. I still held my breath.

'It's about time I said no to a few things that I should have done a long time ago.'

Jess' eyes were fixed on the tablecloth in front of her.

'One of those things is maintaining any sort of contact with Tarquin.'

Jess looked up.

'I asked him to leave the party that night after he had insulted not only two of my friends but also the woman I love and plan to spend the rest of my life with. It was inexcusable and I should have not only told him to leave but also that our friendship was over. Just because I've known him forever doesn't mean I have to put up with his behaviour. I don't want someone like that in my life. I want friends I can trust, and whose company I enjoy and who are supportive of me and my life. Not people who want to destroy and poison things.'

'Are you sure?' Jess asked.

Harry interlaced his fingers with hers. 'The last time I was this sure about something I was asking you to marry me, so yes, I'm absolutely positive.'

Their kiss was soft and romantic and I suddenly felt as if I were intruding so averted my eyes to the sparkling chandeliers above us, the intricacy of the ironwork on the stairs and finally my gaze landed on Seb, who was looking at me and grinning.

'What?' I whispered.

He shook his head, but his hand remained on mine, and he gave it the briefest squeeze in reassurance.

Harry, it appeared, wasn't quite done. 'Now, however, I am pretty sure there is something that my lovely fiancée also wants to say no to, but, for the life of me, I can't work out what it is. I only hope that it isn't saying no to marrying me...' Suddenly the confident, positive Harry looked unsure.

Jess' eyes widened at his obvious concern and, without warning, she burst into tears. 'Oh Harry! Of course it's not! I love you! I never thought it was even possible to love someone as deeply as I do you and I can't ever imagine my life without you in it now. I don't want to.'

'So, what is it?' he asked, softly.

Seb slanted his gaze to me and raised an eyebrow. I met his eyes. I had a pretty good idea, but, even though we'd got into the habit of sharing almost everything, this was Jess' secret and not mine to talk about.

Jess rolled her shoulders back, took a huge slug of wine and turned in her seat to face Harry. 'I don't want the small wedding your family have been politely insisting on ever since we got engaged. Despite what Tarquin said, and what some people might think, I only ever plan on doing this once and I want it to be the wedding I've always dreamed of. Not one that someone else thinks is "appropriate".' She made the little shapes in the air with her fingers. 'For whatever reason.'

Sensing she wasn't yet done, Harry remained silent.

Jess took another huge swig and carried on. 'I've seen the pictures of your sister's wedding and it was bloody huge! Even if she was marrying into another old family, it shouldn't make a difference to what we have. I feel like they're insisting on this small wedding because they're ashamed of me. Of your choice. I don't want to be the cause of any more rifts within your circle of friends and certainly not your family, but I don't deserve to be treated like an embarrassment either.'

She let out a breath and downed the rest of her glass. Harry, meanwhile, was looking slightly shell-shocked. After a moment, he came to and reached for his own glass before taking Jess' hands in his.

'I had no idea you felt like this. Why on earth didn't you say something to me sooner?'

'Honestly, I don't know.'

That was the same answer she'd given when I'd asked a similar question of her a few weeks ago.

'Jess, we will have whatever size wedding you want. I consider myself the luckiest man to be standing up there with you, so I've already got everything I want. Now I want you to have everything you want too.'

Without looking, Seb passed over a clean hankie and I mopped up the tears that had sprung to my eyes. It was kind of annoying that he knew they'd be there. And also rather sweet.

'You're right. You were a bit of a surprise to my family. But not in a bad way. My previous girlfriends have all been of rather a similar ilk – but that's what attracted me to you. How different you are to any of them. Your vibrancy and vivaciousness are as attractive to me as...' he gave a cheeky grin, which she returned. 'All of your other delicious qualities. The thought of that dulling because you feel you have to try and please people or fit in in some way makes me vastly unhappy. And if a big wedding is what you want, then that's what we're damn well going to have! In the meantime, I'll speak to my family and find out what this whole small wedding thing is about. It's the first I've heard of it. I mean, they'd mentioned it, but I had assumed that was something that had come from you.'

Jess shook her head.

'Right. Well, as I say, we'll get that sorted, but there is absolutely nothing to worry about on that front. I don't think any of it has been meant as a slight against you, but I'm determined to make sure. And now let me make a toast. To Lottie!'

I sat up, surprised, blinking at the others. 'Me?'

Seb grinned. 'Why not?'

'To Lottie and her Year of Saying No, which is apparently inspiring the rest of us to follow our true wishes. To Lottie!'

Jess and Seb echoed the toast as I sat and turned pink. However, looking at Jess and seeing her relaxed, the tension of the last few weeks having now entirely drained from her body, it was worth it.

27

The next morning, my phone rang with a video call. Seb's face, far too handsome for the time of day, grinned out at me from the profile picture. I was yet to brush my hair and had just shuffled back inside from taking Humphrey out to the communal garden for his morning ablutions. Swiping up, I answered the call.

'Hello,' I said, running a hand over my hair in an attempt to mask the worst of the bedhead.

'Hello you. How'd you sleep after all the excitement of last night?'

I laughed. 'It was a bit dramatic, wasn't it?'

'Yep. One of the more interesting dinners I've been at in a long while.'

Remembering he'd been to dinner with me a few months ago, I raised a brow at him. 'Thanks.'

He gave me a look. 'Dinner with you is always in a league of its own. You know that.'

'Is that so?'

'Uh-huh.'

I made a sniffing motion, turning my head as if to try and track the root of the smell before putting my nose closer to the phone.

'Very funny.'

I grinned. 'What can I do for you anyway? I thought you were at your brother's?'

'I am. We're just about to head off for a trek to tire the dog, and hopefully the kids, out, but I've been requested to ask for your company tomorrow at Sunday lunch.'

'Me?'

'Yes. It seems I may have talked about you a little too much and now they're all itching to meet you.'

'Oh...'

'Don't worry,' he held up a hand. 'I've told them there's no funny business going on.'

'Funny business? Really?'

He frowned and shook his head. 'I don't know how, or why, that particular phrase came out. But you get the idea.'

I got the idea.

'Are you able to come?'

'Yes. If you want me to.'

He smiled, the warmth in it doing funny things to places it shouldn't. 'Of course I want you to.'

'OK.'

'Great. I'll send you the address. It's on the corner and you'll see my car on their drive. About half twelve OK?'

'That sounds lovely, thank you.'

'OK, I'll...' he suddenly swooped off balance and I got a view of the ceiling shortly followed by a cheeky little face.

'Hello!' she said.

'Hello,' I grinned back.

'Are you Uncle Seb's special friend?'

I'd treated myself to a new fluffy dressing gown last Christmas in a festive shade of red. My cheeks now matched it. Before I could answer, there was a bit of scuffling, the phone was righted, and Seb's face appeared once more, this time accompanied by the little girl I assumed was his niece.

He gave a little throat clear. 'I've no idea where she picks these phrases up.'

'Mummy said it,' his niece clarified for us.

'Right. I see. Sounds like I might need to have a word with mummy.' He turned back to the screen. 'I'd better go. See you tomorrow then?'

'Yep. Thanks. Oh! Is there anything I can bring?'

'Just yourself!' I heard a female voice call out.

'I'm beginning to think I'm on a party line here,' Seb said, his voice even but a twinkle of humour shining in his eyes. From behind him, I heard a laugh. 'I'll see you tomorrow.'

'Yep. Have a good walk.'

'Thanks,' he said, giving me a quick wave before the call ended.

* * *

The following day, I pulled up in front of the corner house, just to the left of the drive where Seb's Subaru sat. It was an attractive pale cream Georgian house with large windows and a gravel drive on which was parked an Audi estate and a BMW one series, as well as Seb's car. A large willow tree draped its feather-like leaves in the corner of the front garden and a smart sign showing it to be actually called 'The Corner House' was fastened to one of the stone pillars at the entrance to the driveway.

I got out, picked up the little pot plant I'd dashed to the nursery to get today, as well as the bottle of wine, and crunched up the driveway. As I approached the wide, black, painted door, it opened to reveal Seb laughing as one small child clung to his back and the other clung to his thigh.

'Hi!' I said, stepping in as he shuffled back enough to let me in, his nephew still attached to his leg. He gave it a bit of a shake and the little boy giggled, clinging on tighter. Leaning forward, he gave me a hug as best he could without me headbutting the little girl clinging around his neck. 'You two monkeys want to go and tell your mum our guest is here?'

'OK!' the little boy released his uncle's leg and zoomed off, leaving his sister wriggling on Seb's back.

'Wait for me!' she wailed, as Seb moved to the stairs to enable her to get off safely without dropping to the floor. She slid off, charged down the bottom stairs and raced off in the same direction.

'I'm glad you could make it.'

'Thanks for the invitation.'

'That's all down to my sister-in-law. She started it and my brother was right on it. Like I say, I may have sung your praises a little more than I realised.'

'I'm never going to object to people singing those.'

'Fair enough. One thing though.'

'Oh?'

'My dad's here.' The tension rippled through him as he said it, changing from the relaxed uncle he'd been just moments before. 'Of course, it tends to just be me he has the problem with so...' He let the sentence drift into nothing.

'OK,' I said, determined not to make a big deal out it. 'That's OK. It'll be lovely to meet everyone and put faces to names.'

After a moment he nodded, smiled and led me through to meet his family.

* * *

The meal was a cheerful, chattering affair, full of good food and laughter. Seb sat across from me, and to my right was his dad. Everyone talked with and across each other, relaxed and good naturedly. All with the exception of Seb and his dad. Any exchanges between these two lacked the ease of the others, possessing an almost formal quality to them. When Seb's father spoke to me, however, he was pleasant, relaxed and interested. Seb's explanation about how it only seemed to be his eldest son his dad had the problem with resonated in my head. I'd thought for a moment Seb might have been exaggerating a little, but I hated to admit that it did feel as if he might be right.

'Seb tells us you're into gardening?' his dad said as I finished hoovering up the last of the tangy lemon tart we'd been served for pudding.

'I'm not sure "into gardening" is quite the right description any more as I don't really have a garden to potter about in, but I wish I did.'

'We can be interested in things, even if we don't get to do them. And I'm sure you have plans. You seem like a young lady that makes plans, going by how efficient you've been helping Seb with the charity.' He gave his son a nod across the table, but I noticed he didn't really meet his eyes.

I pretended not to notice, but I had a feeling Seb knew. Smiling, I turned back to his dad. 'You've got me. I have a whole notebook filled with ideas which usually gets added to every time *Gardeners' World* is on.'

'That programme is one of the highlights of my week.'

'Mine too!' I laughed, adding that I had to admit part of the attraction was seeing Monty Don's dogs.

'I'm going up the allotment in a bit. Just a few things to check on. It's only a short walk away if you're interested in coming along?'

'Oh… that sounds lovely, doesn't it, Seb?' I assumed he was invited.

'You go, Lots. It's not really my thing and I said I'd give Jamie a hand with something in a bit.'

I sat for a moment, feeling unbelievably awkward and a little unsure what to do for the best. Thankfully Olivia, Seb's sister-in-law, broke the silence.

'You really should go, Lottie. You'll love it. Grandpops has a lovely space up there and it's in such a peaceful setting too.'

'Are you sure?' I said, looking across to Seb.

'Yep. You'll enjoy it.' With that, he turned his attention to his niece, who was wriggling and giggling, trying to climb up on to his lap.

'Sounds like you have some company then.' I smiled, trying to ignore the feeling in my stomach and hating the pain in Seb's eyes that he did his best not to show.

'Excellent. Can I do anything before we go, Olivia, love?'

'No, no. You two go on. We'll see you in a bit for a nice cup of tea and some cake that Isla helped me make earlier, didn't you, sweetheart?' she said, looking across to her daughter, who was now happily ensconced on her uncle's lap, tucked into the table.

'I did! I did lots of it, didn't I, Mummy?'

'You did.'

'You're going to be a star baker when you get a bit older.' Seb smiled, resting his chin gently on the top of his niece's head.

'What's that, Uncle Seb?'

'You know, when we watch *The Great British Bake Off*, and someone gets a prize for the best thing they've made?'

'Oh, yes. I like the funny man on that.'

'Yeah, sweetheart. Me too.'

'Do you like the funny man, Lottie?'

At this, Seb's brother smirked and gave me a wink. 'Bearing in mind she's hanging around with this one, I'm pretty sure Lottie likes funny men.'

Seb gave Jamie a patient look. 'You're hilarious.'

'I am. It's a talent.'

His brother rolled his eyes, but the laughter was there.

'Right then, shall we go?' his dad asked me.

I nodded, followed him out and a few minutes later we were walking up a small lane to the side of the house that led up to the allotments.

'Seb said you don't live too far away. Do you often walk up here?'

'Sometimes I take the car. It depends what I need to do really, but it's nice to take a walk. Keeps everything moving, you know.'

'As someone who sits at a screen for far too long each day, I know exactly what you mean.'

'It gets me out of the house too, which can be a good thing.'

'I'm sure.'

'Where's your little dog today then?' he asked. He really did have all the data on me it appeared.

'He's over with my parents.'

'You should have brought him. Maybe next time.'

I smiled, unsure as to whether there would be a next time but warmed by the thought that he, at least, felt there would.

'It's handy being so close as I can usually see the grandchildren, even if it's just for a few minutes, or just to drop some veggies off for Olivia.'

'It must be nice to be so close to them. My parents and sister don't live too far from me and I'm always popping in. I have friends, of course, but I think I'd really miss it if I wasn't able to see my family.'

'I'm sure. You sound like you're close with them. That's good.' He nodded, his expression thoughtful. 'It's a shame Seb doesn't live closer. I think he misses seeing his brother and the children. The little ones grow all the time and he's missing out on that. And, of course, Olivia adores him, having adopted him as her own big brother.'

I couldn't help but notice he'd left himself out of all the equations there. 'He has mentioned wishing he could see them more.'

His dad nodded, unlatching a steel bar gate and pushing it open, a loud squeak emanating from its hinges as he did so. The sound apparently acted as some kind of doorbell, alerting a few of the other allotmenteers to the entrance of another of their clan and various hands were waved and greetings called.

'They adore him, those kids. They think he's just wonderful and, of course, his injury is normal to them. They've never known him as anything different. In fact, they love telling people about their uncle with his special leg. It only makes him even better in their eyes.'

'That's lovely.'

'Yes. It's a shame he can't see it.'

Before I could respond, not that I knew what to say, Mr Marshall had stopped in front of a regimentally tidy allotment plot.

'Here we are. Let me introduce you to my plants.'

I smiled, thinking how well this man would get on with my own parents. They'd been great advocates of talking to their plants for years, even though as teenagers Sally and I would both give exaggerated eye rolls and mutter something about how parents could be so embarrassing sometimes. Still, whatever the magic was, it had worked and still did. It was pretty rare for Mum and Dad to have a failure in the garden and when they did, they would have a friendly bicker over who hadn't been chatting to that particular plant, leaving it to feel sad and die off. My parents had always been more free-willed than some, so their technique didn't surprise me. I couldn't help but be a little more surprised at the upright, ex-army man doing it, especially after what Seb had said, and the awkwardness I'd experienced earlier between the two.

'Hello, troops!' he said, stepping into the greenhouse and beckoning me to follow him in. I grinned at the address. It seemed there was always the odd lingering reminder of a life in the services. 'How are we all doing today? This is Lottie, a friend of Seb's. She's come for a visit, so I want you all on your best behaviour.'

'Have you always chatted to your plants?'

He turned, a shy grin on his face. 'Going to report back to Seb that his dad's a bit of a basket case?' He gave me a wink.

'Not at all. My parents chat to theirs all the time, and although I only have a few pots on a paving slab, I'm not going to deny there have been conversations. My neighbours do think I'm a little loopy though. That's probably not helped by me spending an inordinate amount of time in my pyjamas.'

His dad shrugged. 'It's good to be comfortable.'

'I wouldn't go to the shops or anything in them,' I added, taking into account the very particular way this man dressed. Even in casual clothes, he was neat and tidy, creases in the right place, and none where there shouldn't be any.

'No. I don't suppose you would. Each to their own and all that, but it does make me question standards a bit when I read that some do that. Plus, who wants to take all those germs to bed. That's what would bother me the most.'

'Me too. Ugh.' I gave a bit of a shiver at the thought.

'Right, everything looks in order in here. Come outside and I'll show you what I've got growing.'

I stepped out and meandered up and down the rows with Seb's dad, listening as he told me what was in each bed, and when they'd be ready for harvest and sometimes what he planned to do with them. Having been around the plot, we came to a bed full of rose bushes.

'These look like they're doing well,' I said, touching one of the dark green leaves.

'Yes, they seem to like it there. It's a sight for sore eyes when they're all in bloom, and the scent just takes your breath away, especially on a summer's evening when the air is still.'

'Oh, that sounds wonderful!'

'You'll have to come back when they're blooming and see what I mean.'

'I'd love to,' I replied without hesitation, caught up in the excitement of the thought, the heady scent of summer tumbling through my mind.

'In the meantime...' he wandered over to a cold frame within which pots of different shapes and sizes were protected from the rain. Bending down, he lifted one of the glass lid panels, and reached in. Pulling out a plant, he stood and handed it to me. 'For you.'

'Really?'

'Yes. I take cuttings of those roses every year from the border here and the one that's full of them in my garden at home, just in case any of them get a problem. That way I'll always have one to replace it with.' He cleared his throat a little and I realised it was the same habit Seb had when things got close to emotional. 'This was my wife's favourite rose.'

Immediately I understood the need for him to make sure he always had cuttings on the go. 'Are you sure you can spare it?'

He gave a smile. 'Yes, love. Positive. I always overdo it with the cuttings. Just in case.'

'I can understand that. What colour is it?'

'A beautiful sunshine yellow.'

'Oh, that's my favourite colour for flowers too!' I tilted the pot towards me to read the label, bringing it closer to make sure I'd read it properly. In neat, square lettering was the name 'Charlotte'. I looked up at him. The only man in this family I didn't have to look up to was Seb's nephew, it seemed. 'It's called Charlotte?'

The smile was soft, kind and full of a love gone in body but never in mind. 'It is.'

The emotions of Friday night, and now with a smattering of possibly confused ones in between, washed over me and, without thinking, I transferred the pot to one hand and gave Seb's dad a massive hug. When I pulled back, he looked a little startled, albeit pleasantly. 'Thank you so much for this. It's so kind of you.'

'You're very welcome. Seb has always spoken so highly of you, and I know you've done a lot for him and the charity. His mother would have wanted you to have one. She'd probably have had a few words to say about it if I hadn't passed a cutting on to you, in fact, especially knowing you love to grow things.'

'That's a very lovely thing to say.'

He paused for a moment, then nodded softly. 'She'd have liked you very much, I think.'

I swiped at my eyes with the back of my free hand, the other holding the plant pot firmly against my side. 'Oh don't, you'll set me right off. I'm not all stiff upper lip like you and Seb, I'm afraid. I blub at the slightest provocation.'

'That's not a bad thing. Stiff upper lip is useful on some occasions but probably less so than you think.'

He turned back to the cold frame and moved some plants around a little, twisting them so that the light hit them from a different angle, encouraging them to grow evenly.

'Does Seb ever come up here with you?' I asked, hugging my rose cutting.

'No,' he said, the word coming out on a sigh. 'Not really since he was injured. He'd come before, when he was around, and help me do bits and bobs. Of course, there are certain things he can't manage quite so well now and I think because of that he feels...' He stood, and another sigh escaped him. 'I don't know what he feels, Lottie, if I'm honest. I've never expected him to do stuff up here, even before it all happened. This was always my love, not his, but he seemed happy enough to be here and I was glad of the company, just as I would be now.'

I frowned, trying to reconcile this with the awkwardness I'd witnessed earlier and what Seb had said about feeling like a disappointment to his father. Obviously, I had no idea of what was really going on, and it was likely way more complicated, just as Seb had mentioned, but I was beginning to wonder if it couldn't be a lot simpler.

'It just seems like we're very different people these days.'

'Or maybe it's that you're very much alike.'

He rested his hands behind his back for a moment and I got a flash of how he would have looked before he retired, his posture now still and straight as he studied me. 'You're a quiet sort, but I get the feeling you're a little bit like a swan – there's a lot going on that nobody sees.'

I gave a shy smile, aware that he was pretty much right on the money.

'That's what I thought. Come on, let's get you back to the house before I get in trouble with Seb for taking up too much of your time.'

'Where I spend my time isn't really his decision.'

At this he grinned. 'That is true.'

28

We headed out of the allotment, back towards the squeaky gate, me holding on tight to my new plant. The silence was companionable as we listened to the sounds of nature in the trees surrounding the plots. Pulling the gate closed behind us, we set off back down the lane.

'Thanks again for this,' I said, holding my pot out.

'You're very welcome.' Mr Marshall smiled, but there was a sadness behind it. 'I miss my wife every day, but I'm glad she's not here to see how much Seb and I have drifted apart. It would break her heart.'

I glanced across and wondered if it wasn't breaking the hearts of those that were still here.

'Alice was never really cut out to be an army wife. I mean, she adapted and coped, but, given the choice, I know it wouldn't have been her first one. I think Seb, as the oldest, was more aware of that than Jamie. I think he feels I should have been around more for her. Sometimes I feel that maybe I should have left the service and given her and the boys a more settled and stable life.'

I considered this for a moment. 'True, but then you wouldn't have been doing what you wanted and your wife would have known that. From what I've heard about her from Seb and you, I get the feeling that if she knew you weren't doing what you wanted to be doing, it wouldn't have made her happy.'

'Maybe. But perhaps if he hadn't been exposed to that life, Seb wouldn't have ended up going into the army either.'

The consequences of that particular decision were clear but left unsaid.

'Would you mind if I asked you a question?'

'Of course not.'

'It's... a little personal.' I chewed the side of my mouth for a minute. 'Actually, forget I said anything.' I gave him a look under my lashes, embarrassed I had almost got carried away.

His look was even. 'Ask away, Lottie.'

'Are you sure? You don't have to answer if you don't want to.'

He looked across at me.

'OK. I just sort of wondered if you...' I stopped, running through the question in my head. 'If you feel responsible for what happened to Seb.' I rushed on, 'It's just that, from how you were talking, it sounds like you do, and I'm sure he wouldn't want that.'

Mr Marshall remained silent for a few moments and I gave myself a mental kick for not keeping my thoughts to myself. Whether he did or didn't, it was none of my business. I should have just kept my mouth shut. Damn.

'Not directly.' The voice was steady but quiet. I looked up at him, but his gaze was fixed on a point somewhere out on the horizon. 'I didn't plant the IED that blew up his vehicle, but if he'd had a different childhood? Not been exposed to the army life? Maybe he'd have made different choices.' He gave a little shrug, his eyes still on a point in the distance – or perhaps in the past.

'You can't think that way,' I told him, my voice soft. 'Seb made his own decisions. What if you'd been a banker? Or a lawyer?'

He looked at me and screwed up his nose, making me laugh and lightening the moment. But the words I was saying still held weight.

'Hypothetically speaking. That doesn't mean that Seb still wouldn't have become a soldier. And the look on your face just now tells me you were doing exactly the job you were meant to do. Just as Seb was.'

'Perhaps that is true.'

'I'm pretty sure it is. Having met you both, I can't really imagine either of you as anything other than soldiers. Even retired ones.'

'Seb's doing pretty great as a businessman. I mean, from what I hear from Jamie. He doesn't really say a lot about it himself to me.'

I shook my head. 'You're both carrying around all this guilt and all it's doing is making things worse.'

'Seb feels guilty about something?' He stopped walking.

Oh. Crap.

'Umm. No... I just meant... in a general sense.'

'Lottie. I dealt with people in a whole host of situations. Sometimes it was very handy to know if they were telling the truth or not. You get pretty good at working out who's lying and who isn't. And I'm pretty sure that right now, you just told a porker.'

I looked up and saw him see straight through me. Just like his son could. But this wasn't my secret to tell. I'd already said far too much and Seb had told me something in confidence. Not that he'd ever asked me not to say anything, but it had been unspoken – at least I'd taken it that way. I liked this man, sensing that he loved and missed his eldest son very much. Having spoken to both of them, it seemed the chasm between them had been due to circumstances, guilt, pride and a whole host of other reasons that made things complicated when they should be simple. But I couldn't fix this, or even try to, without breaking a trust I wasn't prepared to, even if I thought it could help.

'Understood,' he said simply, gently squeezing me round the shoulders in reassurance and I felt a wave of relief.

* * *

'Look what I got!' I held the pot out to show Seb as he opened the door to us a few minutes later.

He bent his head, reading the tag stood on its side in the earth. 'Charlotte.' He looked across at his dad. 'Is that Mum's rose?'

'A cutting of one of them, yes.'

Seb held out his arm for me to grab on to as I wobbled, trying to steady myself as I took off my boots. 'You'll like it, Lottie. It smells gorgeous. My mum would just sit there on summer evenings sometimes, enjoying the scent on the warm air.' His face had a faraway look on it and I thought back to his dad telling me how he did the same thing up at the allotment, and wished I could tell Seb. But I wasn't sure that was my tale to tell.

'Lottie! Come and bake with us!' Isla grabbed my hand, tugging me in towards the kitchen, forcing me to shove the plant at Seb as I was yanked along. He grabbed it off me, cradling it for a moment as I had done and I suddenly had an overwhelming desire to hold him.

The children had launched into the baking, and moments later I was pretty sure I already had cake mix in my hair from some vigorous stirring by Seb's nephew. His uncle looked over and smiled as the men disappeared into the other room.

'I probably ought to be getting home soon,' I said to Olivia, closing the door of the oven, having put the fairy cakes in to bake.

'Oh no! Stay for tea. Please. It's lovely to have you here. It's so nice to have another woman to talk to.' She gave a little wink before lowering her voice. 'Plus, between you and me, I haven't seen Seb this happy in a long time.'

'Oh, I don't think—'

'I do,' she interrupted. 'I've known that boy a long time and I definitely do.'

'Lottie?' Seb was at the door to the kitchen and right now he didn't look happy at all. I glanced at Olivia and she frowned.

'Yes?'

'Can I have a word with you, please?'

'Umm... of course. Hang on, just let me wash my hands.'

Olivia passed me the towel and we exchanged a confused look before I followed Seb towards the front door. Gesturing me to go through, he followed, checking his key before pulling it closed.

'Enjoy your trip to the allotment?' he said after a few moments.

I pulled a face at him. 'You know I did. I told you that when I came back and showed you the rose. What's going on?'

'Yeah. Thing is, you didn't tell me you'd had a nice little chat with my dad about stuff.'

I didn't care for the thread of sarcasm running through his words, or the tone in which he spoke them.

'What? I was supposed to stay mute the whole time? Is that what you would have preferred?'

'Don't be ridiculous.'

'Well, then what? Clearly you have something to say, so it's probably best if you just said it rather than chasing round the houses.'

'Did you tell my dad that I feel guilty about contributing to my mum's heart problems?'

I stared at him for a moment. The warmth of earlier had been replaced by a steel barrier protecting himself against the world. And me.

'No,' I answered simply, but I could see from the closed look on his face he didn't believe me.

'Really.' He folded his arms across the broad chest. It wasn't a question.

'Yes. Really,' I snapped back, annoyed now.

'So, it's just pure coincidence that in all these years my father has never questioned me about the fact I might be carrying guilt around until five minutes after he's spent time with you?'

'We did have a conversation about guilt, but it was his about certain things—'

'What things?'

'That's not for me to say.'

'Oh, right,' he gave a humourless laugh. 'So, you'll keep confidences for someone you've just met, but not for someone you're supposed to have spent the last few years building a trust with.'

'That's unfair!'

'Is it?'

'Yes!' I yelled back. 'I haven't said anything I'm not supposed to.'

He remained silent.

'Like I said, we were talking about guilt and I did say that it was a shame you were both carrying all this guilt around.'

He gave a shake of his head and I rushed on.

'But that's all I said. Your dad asked what I meant, but I didn't tell him and he understood. I didn't say anything more than that, and even that was kind of an accident. I just thought it was all quite sad and it sort of spilled out.'

'Right. Then, if you have a habit of things just spilling out, it would seem I need to be careful about what I actually tell you in future.'

His words stung and when I looked up, the coldness in his face made my heart contract.

'I've never betrayed your confidence to anyone, Seb, and I didn't today. I've told you everything I said and I'm sorry if that was too much, but I'm not like you. I can't keep everything inside and keep people at a distance, even when it's eating away at you the whole time and just opening up might actually make you feel a whole lot better! But that's your choice, and you're entitled to it. You know what I'm like and you asked me here. So, don't you dare stand there now and look at me like that when I've done nothing wrong.'

'You told him I was carrying guilt around!'

'Everyone carries guilt around, for god's sake! Plus you served in a war zone. It's not exactly unusual!'

'Oh, so he's just put two and two together and come up with four with regards to my mother all by himself then, has he?'

I stopped for a moment. Yes. He had. I knew I hadn't said anything about Seb's guilt being about his mother. Unfortunately, Seb took my hesitation as something other than what it was.

'Right. That's what I thought.'

He turned back to the door, putting the key into the lock. I shoved myself in front of him. Being petite came in handy at times, although I hadn't really thought the manoeuvre through, and we were way closer than I'd planned.

'I haven't finished.'

'I have.'

'Too bad!' I snapped. 'If you're going to accuse me of something, then you can bloody well listen to what I have to say. Don't worry, I'll get out of your way in just a moment.'

Even in his anger, I could see this mildly amused him. Admittedly, if he wanted, he could get me out of the way with one arm but I knew he wouldn't. Besides, it was the principle of the matter.

'Lottie. It's probably best if we just draw a veil over this.'

'No.'

'Yes!' he snapped back, exasperation now showing on his face as he shifted positions. The tension he was radiating probably wasn't helping any of his body to be comfortable. It wasn't doing a lot for mine and mine hadn't been through half of what his had. 'Look. I've never told anyone what I told you and the only reason I told you is because I felt I could trust you.'

'You can!'

'He knows!' he said, flinging his hand out in the direction of the house. 'He's just asked me about it and the only way he can know that is if you told him.'

'I didn't! And it's not. Yes, I said you have guilt, but that was it. What he took away from it was beyond my control.'

'You shouldn't have even said that!'

'Maybe not, but it came out and I can't take it back. The point is, whatever you think, your dad loves you very much and is super proud of you. The fact you two seem to butt heads all the time now obviously really upsets him. Maybe finally talking about things would be good for you both, not to mention the rest of your family.'

Seb tipped his head back for a moment and let out a sigh before looking back down at me. 'Look, Lottie. I know you mean well—'

'Well, that's patronising,' I interjected.

'It wasn't meant to be. It was just a statement of fact. But the rest of the facts are that you've only spent a few hours with my father this afternoon, rather than the lifetime I have. In light of that, you'll forgive me if I say that I think I know my own parent a little better than you do.'

Watching his face, I could see that belief was as immoveable as his body.

'Would you mind letting me back in now so I can collect my things?'

He frowned at me. 'I thought you were staying to tea.'

'I was.'

'So? Everyone's enjoying your company.'

I gave him a look that was a mix of sadness and exasperation. 'Like I said, Seb. I can't pretend things are fine when they're not. And right now they're not. I've been enjoying everyone's company too, but as mine seems unwanted by you at the moment, I think it's best if I leave.'

'That's not what I want.'

'Argh! Seb!' I flung my hands out. 'Honestly, I don't think you know what you want! However it came about, you've just been given the chance to really talk things over with your dad, but by the way you came storming out, I'm guessing you rejected that particular path.'

'I did. So, what else is it that you think I might want?'

A tumble of emotions churned through me as I looked up into that face. Gorgeous, stern, hurt, with just a hint of confusion.

I shook my head. 'Honestly? I don't know. All I know is that I have to leave now.'

He held my gaze for a beat, then reached around me and unlocked the door, pushing it open. I turned and almost stumbled in. Seb's arm caught me before I hit the floor, and righting myself, I pushed him away and headed into the kitchen, doing my best to put on a neutral, if not happy, face.

Everyone was in there. Crap.

29

'Everything OK?' Olivia asked, concern on her face, her eyes shifting to a point behind me which I guessed was Seb.

'Yeah, yeah,' I waved, sticking a smile on my face that felt like it needed a lot more glue. 'Unfortunately, I do have to go though.'

'Oh...'

'Nooooooo!' the children raced round and grabbed onto me. 'You have to stay! You promised.'

Shit. Thanks, Seb.

'I know I said I could, but I... have to go and pick my doggy up.' Great. And now I was lying to children. I was officially a bad person.

'You could get your doggy and come back!' Isla tugged on my arm. 'Please!'

I gritted my teeth to try and stop the tears that were stupidly threatening to form.

'Lottie can come back another time, Isla. She has to go now though, otherwise her doggy will be sad, and we don't want that, do we?' Jamie scooped up his daughter, catching my eye and giving the faintest of smiles which I returned.

'No. No sad doggies.' The little girl rested her head against her father's chest.

'Exactly.'

'Thank you so much for having me!' I said brightly before giving them all a hug goodbye. As I got to Seb's dad, he gave me an extra squeeze.

'I'm sorry,' he whispered.

I pulled back and met his eyes, smiling, and gave the tiniest shake of my head. And with that, I headed out to my car.

Seb followed.

'You don't need to come out. It's getting cooler now. You should go back in.'

'You forgot your plant.' He held it out to me.

'Oh! Oh right, thank you.' I took it from him and went round to the boot, wedging the pot in between a jacket I'd forgotten was in there and some shopping bags, ensuring it couldn't tip over and get damaged.

I walked back to the front and Seb pulled the door open for me. I slid in and tried not to think about how he was the only one whom I hadn't hugged. Or that it was the only time since I'd first met him in person we hadn't hugged goodbye. All of a sudden, it really did feel like goodbye.

'Drive safely.'

I nodded and closed the door after me, turning the key with the other hand as I did so, suddenly wanting to be far away from it all, and him. Hoping that would make it easier. I raised a hand in a half wave but didn't turn to look and pulled away.

I rang Mum on the way home, telling her I'd be swinging by to pick Humphrey up. She asked how it went and I gave her the highlights, leaving out the bit about Seb's and my friendship apparently imploding. I wasn't ready to talk about that just yet.

A short while later, I was back at home, having deferred staying for a cuppa at Mum's with the excuse of having a blinding headache, which was actually true. It had come on in the car and only got worse. So now I was home, in my pyjamas, with my dog. This was where I belonged. This was how things were meant to be. Any thoughts of it being different, of something perhaps developing with Seb and me, allowing myself to become a part of something else, had been well and truly obliterated. That life clearly wasn't for me. I'd spent over seven years living with someone who had never even suggested marriage, or a family, and the dates I'd gone on last year hadn't exactly warmed me to the theme that there might actually be someone out there worth my time. And, more importantly, my heart. And then, despite all attempts not to, I'd ridiculously let myself begin to think far too much about Seb Marshall. Which had probably been the biggest mistake of all.

'What the hell was I even thinking, Humph?' I asked, stroking the little dog's fuzzy body. He was sprawled across me, as though pinning me down so I wouldn't disappear again. But I had absolutely no intention of doing that. 'Maybe I shouldn't have gone up to the allotment with his dad.' I said and smiled as he lifted his head and looked at me for a moment before flopping back down with a sigh. 'Yeah. You're probably right. I did enjoy it. Although maybe if I hadn't chattered on quite so much, I wouldn't have fallen out with Seb now but... I don't know. It felt like his dad had been wanting to get those words out for a long time, but maybe he needed someone separate, not entwined with the family, to be able to talk. Or maybe it's just that I can natter on a bit sometimes when I relax and that can encourage others to do the same.'

Humphrey yawned, emitting a little squeak as he did so.

'Sorry. Am I boring you?'

He made a grumble.

'Either way, I'm glad he talked to me if it's done anything to lighten his load a little. Even if it was at the price of my friendship with Seb. To be honest, if Seb doesn't know I'd never break his, or anyone else's, confidence, then maybe he doesn't know me as well as he thought he did. Or as well I thought he did. So, actually, all of this is a good thing, isn't it? I mean, showing things for what they are?'

Humphrey looked round at me and, I swear to god, if he could talk, he'd have said 'What a crock', but in the light of the fact he couldn't, I decided to take his expression as one of agreement that I was entirely right and I should waste no more time on the matter.

The headache tablets I'd taken earlier didn't seem to be having a massive effect, other than making me feel drowsy. Truth was, I felt exhausted. Denial, apparently, could be incredibly draining.

'Come on, matey. Let's get your ablutions done so I can get to bed and sleep this clanger off.'

Humphrey wriggled a bit, disinclined to move, but I made to get up and he grumbled once in his chatty way before jumping down on to the floor, resting his paws up against my leg and then following me to the door.

I glanced at my phone on the tiny console table that held my keys and other bits and bobs. It had remained silent all evening. Picking it up, I switched it off and put it back on the table before heading out into the dark with my dog.

* * *

The next morning being a Monday I'd normally have had an email waiting for me with Seb's agenda and items that needed doing for the charity, together with a time suggestion for a Skype call to go over any points, but which generally just turned into an excuse to have a natter. This morning, however, there was nothing. I checked my spam folder just to see if anything had got diverted accidentally into there, but, other than the usual dodgy rubbish, there was nothing in there. I emptied it, declining the offers of Russian girls, cures for a 'limp noodle', which at least brought a smile, and promises to get me laid that day. All good offers, I'm sure, but no thank you. Delete.

I pushed away the thought that yesterday might not only have totalled my friendship with Seb but also have put my income at risk. The charity was a big client – my biggest – and if Seb decided to take his business elsewhere that could put a serious dent in things. Still, I pushed my shoulders back, gave them a couple of rolls for good measure and opened my to-do list. If he chose to do that, he had a contract which detailed that three months' notice was needed before he could actually leave. That would give me time to source some more clients and hopefully start building them up. I'd managed before and I'd manage again. It was always bad to rely on just one client anyway and although the charity took up a lot of my time, especially at the moment with the gala coming up, it was why I was always keen to keep up with my other clients and make sure everyone was happy. Right now, that was my main concern. I'd made Seb Marshall pretty unhappy yesterday, but I was going to do everything I could to ensure I kept all my other clients onside. On the plus side, I knew I was good at my job. In fact, I was pretty damn great at my job and Seb knew that. If he did decide to take his business elsewhere, good luck with finding someone as awesome as I was.

Having given myself that mental pep talk, I opened the first email I needed to reply to and began typing.

As it turned out, one of my other clients emailed me shortly after, explaining that they'd brokered an agreement at a breakfast meeting first thing, which was turning into kind of a huge deal and involved a lot of extra work. If I put aside the fact that, once I was made Queen of the World, one of the first things I would ban would be breakfast meetings, I was thrilled for them. They were a fairly new start-up and worked hard. This sounded like it could really be their chance to get noticed and get the recognition they deserved, so I was more than happy to dedicate extra time to them and make sure they had everything they needed going forward.

This, together with my regular client work, plus answering emails and messages from Jess as to what I thought about this dress, or that tiara, or these flowers, was keeping me busy. Now she'd blurted it all out about wanting a big wedding, she and Harry had really started planning. Well, Harry was pretty much just saying she could have whatever she wanted, wanting in part to make up for her going along for months with something she hadn't wanted at all.

'So, they were pretty horrified when they found out what I'd thought,' Jess told me after her and Harry's weekend meeting at his parents' country pad. She'd suggested that he go on his own initially, but Harry had insisted, telling her he wanted her to hear what they had to say so that she knew. That they were a team and they did things together, now and always. Jess had been a little hesitant. Of course, she wanted to know – but a part of her was concerned about what she might find out.

'What was the whole small wedding thing about then?'

'Oh, because when I'd looked at the photos of his sister's wedding, which was bloody massive, I had kind of gone "Blimey, it looks like everyone and his dog was invited!" and so they thought it might be less overwhelming for me if Harry and I had something more subtle.'

'Clearly they need to get to know you better if they think you ever do subtle.'

'I'm going to take that as a compliment.'

'When it comes to you, it's meant as one.'

'Aah, thanks, doll.'

'Pleasure.'

'Anyway, so we sat down and Harry just blurts out what I said at dinner the other night. I mean, I love him, but I could have kicked him! It was mortifying!'

'Sometimes it's best just to pull the plaster off quickly.'

'Yeah, I s'pose. So, there's this long silence, and they're all looking at me and Harry and each other and then his mum burst into tears!'

'No!'

'Yeah! I know! I didn't know what to do. Harry was just sort of stood there. He looked a bit flabbergasted too.'

'So, what happened?'

'Well, then she rushed over to us and just hugged us and said she was so sorry I'd felt like that and how happy they were to be welcoming me into the family.'

'Aww!'

'I know. I didn't know if it was all a bit of fluff to start with. I mean, obviously she doesn't want to upset Harry, but then she started going on about how she's never seen her son so happy or having so much fun, and that I'm like a ray of sunshine beaming into their stuffy old house, I think was how she put it.'

'Oh Jess, that's lovely! I'm so happy it's all got sorted out.'

'Yeah, me too. God, Lots, it was so embarrassing though. When she said that, and she was all teary, I bloody well burst into tears too! I had mascara dripping off my chin! What a flippin' sight!'

'Oh no!'

'I know! Thankfully it just made us all laugh and his mum took me off to the bathroom and helped me clean up and it was really nice. It was kind of this little bonding moment.'

I smiled at the video screen and blew her a kiss. 'I'm really happy for you both, Jess.'

'Me too. And it's all thanks to you.'

'Me?'

'Yeah. If you hadn't been on this "saying no" kick, and not prodded Harry at dinner the other day about stuff, none of it probably would have come out and I'd have had a tiny wedding I didn't want, instead of the absolute fiesta I'm now planning, and would have just harboured resentment against his family for some imagined slight for the next several decades!'

'Well, then it is a good thing.'

'Definitely.'

Jess took a swig of coffee from a mug that told everyone she was the 'World's Best Fiancée' and made a rolling motion with her other hand.

'So, how was your weekend?'

'Yeah, good thanks.'

On the screen Jess squinted at me, peered closer as though that would help and then sat back. 'OK. Something happened. Spill.'

'Nothing happened. I'm fine.'

She checked her watch. 'Shall I call you back when you're ready to cut the poop out?'

I rolled my eyes.

'I've known you since playgroup, girl. And I know when you're hiding something. You may as well tell me.'

'There's nothing to tell.' I wasn't about to rain on Jess' bridal parade with my friendship implosion.

'OK. Last chance. If you don't, I will scour the world to find *the* ugliest, most hideous, most polyester bridesmaid dress I can and post *all* the pictures on *all* social media platforms.' She wagged her finger at me. 'You know I'd do it.'

I wasn't entirely sure she would. But then again, I wasn't entirely sure she wouldn't.

'Honestly. There's nothing much to tell. I kind of had a falling-out with Seb. That's all.'

'That's all?' she repeated. 'That sounds like quite a lot.'

'Not really.'

'Yeah. Really. You two are kind of inseparable.'

'Oh, we are not.'

She gave me a disbelieving 'uh-huh' look.

'But you're fine now, right?'

I wrinkled my nose.

'When was this?' she asked, looking more concerned now.

'Late yesterday afternoon.'

'Have you spoken to him?'

'Nope.'

'Did you try and ring?'

'Nope.'

'Why not?'

'Because he acted like an arse.'

'OK. Fair enough. What happened exactly?'

I gave Jess a potted version.

'Oh.'

'Yeah. Oh.'

'Have you got work to do for him?'

'Yes. I already had some stuff and he sent over an email this afternoon with a few more points on.'

'And?'

'And what did he say about yesterday?'

'Nothing. It was just a generic email, with a couple of other charity bods copied in.'

'Is that normal?'

'Sort of.'

'What does "sort of" mean?'

'It means yes, he usually sends those... but most of the time he'll add in another just to me or will ring me to chat over it too.'

'But he hasn't this time?'

'No.' I shrugged. 'No big deal.'

Jess tilted her head. 'It kind of is though, isn't it? I mean. For you two.'

I gave another shrug. 'Maybe not. Maybe this is just how it is. How it should be. And that's fine. I don't really need someone in my life like that who doesn't think he can trust me so...' I let the sentence drift off and pulled a 'whatever' face to punctuate it and hoped it went some way to covering the sadness I truly felt.

'But... Oh bugger. I've got a call coming in I need to take.'

I waved her off. 'Take it. I need to get on anyway. Also. Love the first dress, not so much the second one.'

'Great minds. OK, talk to you soon. Love you!'

'Love you too,' I said and hung up.

The rest of the week passed in a blur as I helped my start-up company keep on top of everything, as well as making sure all my other clients were happy and content. The only contact I had with Seb was the odd work email, but, other than that, all remained quiet. Thankfully, now Jess was in overdrive with the whole bridal thing, my mind was kept thoroughly occupied.

30

By late Friday afternoon, I was absolutely shattered and ready to call it a day. Checking my to-do-list was up to date, and my inbox was empty, my finger was just hovering over the shutdown key when an email pinged into to my folder, replacing the nice tidy zero counter with a one. I could just leave it until Monday. Oh, who was I kidding? Of course, I couldn't. I opened the application back up.

The email was from Seb. Again, it was copied to several others.

Dear Lottie,

I would like to take this opportunity to thank you, on behalf of the charity, for all the hard work you've put in in order to make the upcoming gala a success.

We've now had confirmation from the last two celebrities you managed to get interested in the cause, and it appears they have been spreading the word about it on their social media.

I've also attached a screenshot from a paper out today of a quote by Prince William about the good work the charity is doing. The same story is in a few different papers apparently, both physical and online, which is great coverage.

Both of these circumstances have led to a massive spike in hits on our website already and we know that they have only come about because of your hard work and determination to go above and beyond the remit of your position in order to ensure the success of the event.

In light of this, I would like to ask you, on behalf of the charity, if you would do us the honour of attending the gala so that you are able to meet the other members of the team and we are able to thank you in person for everything you have done.

Following that was his standard digital signature.

I read the email through again, looking for a hint of personality, but there was none. I pressed reply, thinking how different this situation might have been last week. Deleting my blank email, I went back to the original and hit Reply All instead.

Dear All,

Thank you so much for your email.

I am so pleased to hear that the latest connections have paid off and that, together with the quote we secured, they are already helping to boost the charity's profile even more. That is great to hear.

I'd also like to thank you for your kind invitation to the gala, which I was very honoured to receive. Unfortunately, I will be unable to attend but very much appreciate the thought behind the gesture and, of course, wish you all the very best of luck for its success.

Kind regards,

I finished it off with my own digital signature, pressed send and closed my computer.

'Come on, Humph. Time for a walk.'

For once I wasn't in my pyjamas, which enabled me to go straight out which seemed like the ideal plan right now. Getting out into the countryside with just my dog for company was exactly what I needed. I wasn't going to think about Seb, or the gala, or the impersonal way he'd gone about inviting me. If he'd truly thought I'd accept that, then he really didn't know me at all, but I'd kind of already come to that conclusion. It didn't mean I wasn't sad about the whole thing though. However much I'd tried to pretend I was OK to Jess, and to myself, I wasn't. I was hurt and upset and furious at Seb – but I also felt like I'd lost someone incredibly important from my life and I was still working out how to deal with that. So far this week, general denial and avoidance was working as well as could be expected, but I wasn't entirely sure that was a viable long-term plan.

Seb Marshall had been in my life for the best part of three years and I'd spoken to him most days for the majority of that time. This year we'd grown even closer, and more recently, on the odd occasion when I let the fairies in my brain out of their cage, I'd wondered whether there really could be something more to us.

But there wasn't. And there wouldn't be. Right now, there didn't even appear to be any sort of us and I needed to deal with that.

Getting outside was the best thing I could have done. The evenings were so much lighter now and the branches heavy with blossom. A gentle breeze rippled through the orchard to my right, lifting the scent along and teasing my senses. I reached up, touching a bloom that hung close to the path, feeling its soft petal, grounding myself in the moment. Being mindful of—

'Holy shit!' My phone rang out from my pocket, shattering the peace.

Humphrey looked around at my exclamation and I apologised to him for my language as I wrangled the phone out of a pocket that was a tiny bit too small for it. Having finally managed, I looked at the screen. It was a WhatsApp video call. From Seb. I let it ring off.

Just as I was about to put it back in my pocket, it started up again. I pressed decline. And because I knew Seb and the determination he had when he needed it, I began typing a message.

I'm out. Can't talk

There was no emoji. No kiss. Just facts. Facts I could deal with right now.

OK. Would you be able to call me when you get back?

I looked at the top right of my phone and checked the time. As I did this, I saw the word 'typing' replace 'online' in the top left, just under Seb's name.

I know it's after hours, but I'd really appreciate it

There was a gap and more typing.

Even if I don't really deserve it

I gave a sigh and stuffed my phone back into my pocket. I wasn't sure what to do yet. I couldn't avoid him forever. I enjoyed the work I did for him and the charity and I'd be sorry to lose that – and not just in an economic sense. It felt good to be working with such a great cause and feeling I helped to make a difference.

I gave myself an eye roll and concentrated on getting back to my mindful stroll. Seb Marshall would just have to wait.

* * *

Heading back in, I felt refreshed and that a few of the knots I'd worked into my body throughout the day had begun unfurling. Checking the dog's bowl, I gave it a rinse and put down some clean fresh water, which he immediately set about lapping up, kindly giving the floor area around it a wash for me while he was at it.

I tidied up the kitchen a bit, placing my plate and cup from lunchtime in the slimline dishwasher and pondered over what to do for dinner, settling on some grilled chicken and spicy rice.

Humph stopped drinking and came over to me to see if I was doing anything that might be of interest to him. I felt a drip on my sock and grabbed the towel I had set aside for the dog and bent to smoosh his face with it, laughing as he began the familiar play with it.

'Come on, pooch. Let's get this over with.'

Humphrey gave me a quizzical look before trotting after me as I made my way to the sofa and sat down, then he hopped up and got comfy on my lap by circling a few times and plopping down with an effort that belied his size. I moved him off my bladder and picked up my phone.

Opening the app, I went to calls and saw the two unanswered ones from Seb. Pressing on one of these, I took a deep breath and pressed the little video camera button. He answered on the second ring.

'Hey.'

'Hello.'

Bugger. I was hoping he might have got less attractive in the past week. He hadn't.

'Good walk?' he asked.

'Yep, not bad.' The conversation already felt strained and awkward in a way it never had before.

'Right. Good. Great.'

'Yep,' I said again.

Seb looked at me for a moment then let out a sigh. 'I hate this.'

'What?'

He made a motion with his hand. 'This. Us.'

I frowned.

'The weirdness.'

'Is it weird?' I asked, in a voice that was so weird it didn't even sound like mine. But I wasn't about to admit that.

Seb tilted his head. 'You know it is, Lots.'

I gave a maybe yes, maybe no, head wobble and stayed silent.

'You turned down the gala invitation.'

'Yes. Thanks, but I'm busy that night.'

'You never mentioned it before.'

'You never asked.'

Seb thought that over and, by the look on his face, realised that was probably true. 'Are you really though?'

'Yes.'

He ran a hand over his dark crop and looked at the screen. It felt like he was looking straight through me and seeing the very empty space on my calendar for that particular day. I did my best not to blush and give myself away. He didn't say anything for a moment, but I was pretty sure he knew it was a lie.

'Everything I put in the email was true. You've done so much for the charity, and even more for this gala. I know it's going to be successful and a lot of that is down to you going above and beyond.'

I shrugged. 'It's a good cause.'

'So come.'

'I told you I'm—'

'Busy. Yes. Right.'

This was going nowhere and frankly just making me feel worse. I glanced over to the clock before turning back. 'I'd better get on with some dinner.'

'I'm sorry,' he said before I'd quite finished. 'About last weekend. I'm so sorry, Lottie. I should never have let you go like that.'

'You didn't *let* me go anywhere. I chose to leave,' I said, throwing one leg over the saddle of my high horse.

Seb gave me a look. 'You know what I mean.'

I dismounted but couldn't quite shake off the haughty demeanour. 'It was fine,' I said, attempting to sound like it hadn't bothered me in the slightest. Again, I wasn't sure I was pulling it off. A glance at the screen would suggest I definitely wasn't, but I continued on anyway. 'I'd probably overstayed my welcome anyway, so it was a good time to leave your family in peace.'

'You hadn't overstayed your welcome in the slightest – I'm not sure you could ever do that in my family's eyes. They're kind of your biggest fans right now. And that includes my dad, who's never exactly been the ebullient type when it comes to praise. But that's just his way.'

My ears perked up. Was Seb actually defending his father?

'Well, I very much enjoyed meeting them too. And, if you speak to him, please thank your dad again for the rose. I'm taking it over to my parents' place this weekend to pot it up so I can sneak it in onto my paving slabs outside.'

'I'll do that.'

'Thanks. Well, I'd better get on.'

'Lottie?'

'Hmm?'

'I want to apologise.'

'Yes. Well, you did. Kind of.'

'I want to do it a lot better than "kind of". If you'll let me.' He shook his head. 'I wish I wasn't so bloody far away. Doing it on here is the worst. It doesn't feel right.'

I shrugged.

'Fine. Right. OK. I am truly sorry about Sunday. I completely overreacted, and I don't know why. I guess I do know why, but it still doesn't excuse how I treated you.'

'So, what was the reason?'

'For me acting like a complete arse? I think that was how my brother phrased it at least?'

'I like your brother.' I couldn't help but smile.

'The feeling's mutual.'

'So?'

'I guess... I guess I'm just not used to it.'

'Used to what?'

'Being talked about like that.'

'I wasn't talking about you. Your dad was talking about you and I was listening. It felt like he had things he needed to say, and I was happy to listen. It's not like we were talking about you behind your back for any nefarious reason, Seb. He's just hurting. More than you know, I think. Just like you are.'

'I think you're right.'

I shook my head impatiently. 'I already know I am. It's just you two that are too stubborn to admit it.'

'I can be stubborn about a lot of things. That's helped me in the past in certain situations. But it's probably not helpful in every circumstance.' He dragged a hand across his jaw, dark with a five o'clock shadow. 'God, I'm making a right mess of this. Look, Lottie. I should never have let you leave like that last week. I accused you of something and then didn't let you explain properly, and even when you tried, I didn't listen. That was a mistake, and one I've spent the past week regretting, wondering if my pig-headedness has broken the friendship I value most in my life.' He paused. 'Has it?'

I took a deep breath and let it out slowly, running my hand down Humphrey's soft fur as he snoozed comfortably, unaware of the emotions tumbling through his owner right now. 'Honestly? I don't know.'

I saw my answer register on Seb's face and tried not to let the pain in his eyes affect me. I hated seeing that hurt but he'd caused me pain too and I couldn't forget that.

'All I really did was listen to your dad. I got the impression from him, and from things you've said, that he doesn't talk about feelings a lot. Kind of like someone else... but that's all I did. I did make the comment about how you both seem to be carrying guilt around, but I never – *would never* – have said any more than that. Even that came out by accident.'

'I know that now.'

'That's not really the point though, is it?' Now I'd started, I didn't seem able to stop. 'The point is that you didn't believe me. You just automatically assumed I'd broken your trust, when that's the one thing I'd never do. And then you made me feel like everything was my fault. Punishing me by ignoring me. Sending group emails instead of talking to me as you normally would and just being so cold and distant. Making everything so different from how we've been.'

'Lottie, I know and—'

'I made a mistake with you.' I interrupted.

'What mistake?' he asked, his eyes full of concern beneath the dark brows, now drawn together.

'Letting the lines between business and friendship blur. That was wrong of me and I won't—'

'Don't say it, Lottie. Please. I know I was in the wrong and I'm sorry. You have no idea how sorry I am. But I'm asking for your forgiveness. I know I don't necessarily deserve it, but I need it. I need you in my life, Lottie. I didn't realise just how much until all this happened.'

31

Seb sat back on the sofa and let a steady breath out, his eyes never leaving the screen in front of him. 'I built up a barrier around myself after everything happened. I'd always been pretty open before then, but it changed me, and I know I shouldn't be surprised at that, but I thought once I got back on my feet again, no pun intended, I'd kind of get the old me back. And I did. To an extent. To all intents and purposes, I was friendly and open, but I never really let anyone in again properly. Not in the way I had before. My brother and Olivia persevered, but when you keep shutting people out, eventually they stop knocking at the door, and you can't blame them.

'And I ended up doing it with my dad. I was so caught up with my own grief when Mum died, so busy swimming in this sea of guilt I'd created, that I never really acknowledged his. He'd needed me and, in a way, he'd needed me to need him. Not in a do everything for me kind of way, but... it's hard to explain.'

'I think I know what you mean,' I said, quietly, wondering how he'd come to all these conclusions.

'I'd shut him out, along with everyone else, and having just lost the love of his life, he didn't really know to deal with me too. So, neither of us did anything. We stayed polite as much as possible. Civil. I'd made it easier to keep that distance, having put a literal one in place by moving away, but, deep down, that wasn't what either of us wanted. It took me a while to admit that. I thought I was fine. That I didn't need us to be close any more, and this chasm just got bigger and bigger until eventually neither of us had any idea how to bridge it.' Scooby's head suddenly filled the frame, a big eye peered at me before disappearing to lay on Seb's lap. Judging by the 'oof' sound he let out, the lab hadn't done it in the most delicate of manners.

Seb wriggled a bit, getting comfy around the dog. 'I'm still learning, Lottie. I know that's no excuse. But I'm not used to being as open with people as I am with you and I guess it just took me by surprise. I still don't know how you got behind the defences. I'm normally really careful, but with you it feels like I just left the door open for you to stroll right in to my life... and my heart.'

I watched him, my heart pounding as his words swirled around my brain, and I tried to work out exactly what it was that he was saying.

'I can't tell you how many times I've picked the phone up this week and started to call you. How many emails I've begun and deleted. How many messages I've done the same with.'

'But instead you chose to send impersonal, group emails?' I raised a brow.

He closed his eyes slowly before opening them again. 'I know it sounds stupid, but I felt that at least I was in some sort of communication with you that way. Twisted logic, I'm sure, but it felt like if we still had that connection, it meant I hadn't lost you entirely.'

'It made it worse, Seb.'

His shoulders slumped, the normally upright bearing he held, even when relaxed, was abandoned. 'I don't know how to apologise enough. I know I hurt you. I saw it in your face when I accused you of overstepping the line with my dad and I saw it when you were getting in the car. All I wanted to do was pull you to me and wrap you in the biggest hug I could.'

'So, why didn't you?' I asked, unable to keep the tremor out of my voice as my mind went back to that moment, the squeeze of my heart as real now as it had been then. 'Why let me drive off thinking you believed the worst of me? The look you gave me? I don't think I've ever seen one so cold and you were the last person I thought would ever do that.'

'I didn't because I was stupid, and stubborn and confused. And maybe a little bit scared.'

My eyebrows shot up at this. 'You? Scared?'

The faintest shadow of humour teased his lips and he gave a little brow raise of his own in acknowledgement. 'God, I wish I lived closer. I'd much rather do this in person. At least it'd give you a chance to take a swing at me, which is kind of what you looked like you wanted to do when I answered the call.'

'I'm going to neither confirm nor deny that.' He smiled at the reply. 'And stop changing the subject. What were you scared of?'

He took a deep breath then let it out slowly before he spoke. 'How well you fit in my life.' He sat forward and I heard the dog groaning in protest at having an apparently comfy position disturbed. 'Lots, you're the best thing that's ever happened to me. Meeting you, spending time with you, and getting to know you more and more has opened my eyes to a world I'd forgotten even existed. I acted like an idiot. A complete and utter idiot, and I can't even begin to tell you how sorry I am, but you have to know how much you mean to me and tell me what I can do to make it up to you. To make this right.'

I wished for once that I was like my sister with her cool, collected personality instead of my slightly more erratic one which meant I was, at the moment, pretending there weren't tears shining in my eyes and the odd one tipping out onto my cheek. I resolutely ignored it, hoping that if I didn't draw attention to it, Seb might not notice.

The video quality always varied on these things and, with a bit of luck, his end might be on the fuzzy side today.

'Do you need to get a tissue?'

Bugger.

'Nope. I'm fine.'

He drew a hand across his mouth. 'I never want to make you cry, Lottie.'

'Too late!' I tried to laugh it off, but it only half worked. His face looked as grim as ever.

'I'm sorry I didn't call you. I wanted to talk to you the moment your tail lights disappeared, but it's taken me a week to build up the courage to do it. I guess half of me was worried you'd tell me I'd messed up badly enough for you not to want to talk to me, outside of work at least, ever again.'

'It took you a week to find the courage to do that?'

'I know...' he raised his free hand in a single-sided shrug.

'No... I mean. After everything you've done. Things you've seen. Been through? I don't think courage is something you're lacking in, Seb.'

He gave a wan smile. 'Maybe that gives you an idea of just how worried I've been then.'

I shook my head and saw his Adam's apple bob.

'This isn't going to be good, is it?'

'You did mess up. Big time. You didn't trust me and that was really hurtful.'

He nodded but said nothing, which I was glad of. He could only say sorry so much, and I already knew he meant it.

'But, if we're lucky, we learn from our mistakes. I'm pretty sure we'll both learn something from this one.'

The smile that broke on his face was like a sunbeam bursting through the clouds after a storm. 'Does that mean I haven't screwed this up completely?'

'It means you had a bloody good go but didn't quite manage it. This time.'

He put a hand on his chest. 'I swear to god, Lottie. There will not be a next time.'

'See that there isn't, soldier,' I teased.

He flicked his eyebrows up. 'Yes, ma'am.'

'But I don't understand. You've always seemed to cope so well.'

'And I have. And until you showed up, I didn't even realise there had been anything missing from my life. I'd turned things around, regained my life and my drive, and I thought I had everything. But your friendship showed I was wrong. Getting to know you, sharing so much with you – it's brought something that I hadn't even realised I was missing. But when you took it away... when I sent you away, it was like all the colour and warmth drained away too. I've had a week of nothing but grey and I never want to go back to it.'

I didn't know what to say. But then Seb smiled and I could see no words were needed.

'I want to make it up to you. Is there any way I can see you this weekend?'

'Seb, there's nothing to make up. Really. We've talked it over now and we've both agreed you acted like an arse and you've apologised. It's done.' I gave a little shrug and smiled as additional confirmation.

He grinned. 'That is true, but I'd still love to see you. Maybe catch that hug I let you leave without last week.'

'Well, tomorrow I'm heading off to a garden show with my parents, but I guess Sunday might be an option.'

'Which garden show?'

I told him.

'That's great! I'm going to that too.'

'You are?' I said, surprise evident in my voice.

'Yeah,' he gave a small, lopsided smile. 'With my dad.'

'Oh... right.' The surprises kept on coming.

'Maybe we could all meet up?' he suggested.

'That sounds a brilliant idea. I'm sure my parents will get on really well with your dad, and obviously they still think you're wonderful.'

He pulled a face. 'Even after this week?'

'Luckily for you, I've been kind of swamped and didn't get a chance to call them and whinge.'

He gave an exaggerated mop of his brow.

'I'll message them in a minute. I'm sure they'll be thrilled to meet him.' I stood and wandered out to the kitchen to flick the kettle on, taking my phone with me. 'I have to say, I'm a little surprised to hear you're going with your dad,' I said, dropping a teabag in one of my largest mugs and pulling the milk out of the fridge ready. 'Although it's a good surprise.'

'Thanks. I'm pretty happy about it too. I'll tell you all about it tomorrow.' Seb smiled and the happiness radiated out of him. There was a relaxation there when he spoke about his dad now that certainly hadn't been there before, and I was intrigued to hear more. 'Sounds good.'

32

The following morning, Mum, Dad, me and Humphrey all piled out of the car at the show and made our way to the area I'd arranged to meet up with Seb and his dad. Humphrey sensed them first, suddenly tugging at his lead. I looked up to see Seb give a command to Scooby, who was now standing beside his master, his feet dancing on the spot as his tail whizzed back and forth in a blur. Once upon them, we let the dogs say hello as Seb stepped forward and wrapped his arms around me in a huge hug, his head down by my shoulder and the softest whispered sorry drifted into my ear. His hug tightened and I reciprocated momentarily, acknowledging and forgiving. His eyes lingered for a moment as he pulled away, his hand brushing mine as he then quickly introduced his dad to my parents and they immediately began chatting.

I gave his dad a hug and told him how pleased I was to see him. He replied in kind and although unspoken, I could see something had changed between him and Seb. Not just by the fact they were here together but the atmosphere between them, their body language, their manner – everything was different and far more relaxed.

'Hello,' Seb said quietly, turning away from our parents, who had already begun to wander towards the first stalls, talking and laughing.

'Hi,' I smiled up.

'I'm so glad you could come today.'

'Likewise. I have to say it was kind of unexpected when you said what your plans were.'

'I can see that. If you'd asked me a week ago if I thought this is what I'd be doing with my weekend, I'd have thought you'd been on the smarties.'

'So?' I asked, looking up at him as we wandered slowly along the first row, stopping occasionally for me to look at a plant and for Seb to nod with the encouragement of someone who has no clue what they're looking at but is still happy to be there. It was wonderful. 'What happened?'

He blew out a breath. 'Well, once you left last weekend, I was not exactly the most popular person in that house.' He glanced down. 'My dad wouldn't even look at me. Jamie's always been the quieter one and has pretty much kept out of things between me and my dad. He and Olivia have always made sure we're both included in family stuff, but the problems between me and Dad, as far as he was concerned, were between us and he, quite rightly, didn't want to get involved. But once I came back inside from seeing you off, the tension was pretty high and he'd had enough.'

'What happened?' I asked, stroking the leaves of a chocolate variety of herb and holding my hand up for Seb to catch the scent.

'Ooh, nice. What would you use that for?'

'Literally no idea. I'd probably just plant it and give it a sniff each day.'

'Sounds as good a reason as any.' With that, he handed over some money to the stallholder, pointing at the plant as he did so.

The female stallholder gave him a wide smile and returned his change.

'Seb. You don't need to do that!'

He shrugged, shoving his wallet back in the inner pocket of the light jacket he wore. 'I wanted to.'

'You don't have to make anything up to me.'

'I know. It's not for that.'

'What is it for then?'

'You.'

'For?'

'Does there have to be a reason?'

He had me there.

'I guess not.' I ran my fingers through the fringy leaves again, releasing the scent and then allowing Scooby and Humph to see what I'd bought, just so that they could be sure it wasn't food for them. After a few sniffs, they were satisfied on this point and we all moved on. 'So, Jamie?'

'Right, yes. So, baby brother basically frogmarched me and our dad down to their summer house, away from the kids, and told us that it was about time we both said whatever it was that we needed to as all of this had gone on for way too long, and he and Olivia were sick of it.'

'Oh. Gosh!'

'Yeah, I know. I think Dad and I suddenly realised that we hadn't really considered the impact our... whatever it was... was having on other people. We both just sort of thought so long as we weren't arguing, it was all OK. Looking back now, I can see it must have been a bit of a trial for Jamie and Olivia, walking about on eggshells, trying to keep both of us happy. It wasn't fair on them. He was right.'

'So, you talked?'

'Not immediately,' Seb said, raising his hand in a wave to his dad, who had turned from further up the aisle to see where we were. He smiled and waved in return before turning back to what seemed like an enjoyably in-depth conversation about something or other with my own dad. 'Firstly, we both just stood there and stubbornly insisted that there was absolutely nothing wrong and nothing to talk about.'

'Aah.'

'Yeah... that didn't exactly go down well. I can probably count on one hand the amount of times I've seen my brother lose his temper. I mean, like really lose it, but he'd had it up to here by then and he just let us have it and said something about being glad that Mum wasn't there to see us both acting the way we were.'

'You know, your dad said something very similar when we went up to the allotment. That it would have made her sad to see you two at odds.'

'He was right. They both were. Of course, because of my hang-up that was kind of the wrong thing to say. Or maybe the right thing, depending on how you look at it.'

'I'm thinking the fact that you're here today means it was probably the right thing.'

He smiled, nodding in acceptance. 'So, Jamie says that about Mum and it just flicks a switch and I yell something about how it's nice to know that he blames me for Mum's death too.' He shook his head. 'Poor Jamie. He looked so shocked and hurt and I watched all the colour drain out of my dad's face. My brother asked me what I meant and, the next thing I know, everything was tumbling out. Everything I'd kept inside for so long. All that I told you and more – much more – came out. Stuff I didn't even realise I was holding on to. It all just...' he spread his hands, 'got blurted out.'

He glanced around. Despite his size, Seb was softly spoken, but it was a personal conversation, and the confession had been hard fought. His expression now was one of relief but tinged with surprise, as though he still couldn't quite believe he'd opened himself up as much as he clearly had.

'I thought I'd dealt with a lot of this stuff, and I had really, in a lot of ways. But there was still that guilt as to how it had impacted my family. How I'd felt guilty for getting injured and causing my family trauma. Poor Olivia was pregnant at the time and the stress I put her and Jamie under was something I'd completely buried.'

I tucked my arm through Seb's, suddenly wanting to show my support in any way I could.

'I hadn't realised I was still carrying around some survivors' guilt. I'm not sure that will ever leave me, even though I've had counselling and all the rest. It's a part of me, just as everything I've experienced is. But I'd never told my family that. I'd never told my dad – probably one of the few people on the "outside" who would understand. Someone who'd been there and could relate. But I never gave him the chance. I shut those memories away from them all until Sunday, when it all came out.'

I squeezed his arm, not wanting to interrupt but wanting him to know I was listening. That I was there for him too.

Seb let out a long breath between his teeth. 'That day, my mate wasn't supposed to be driving. I always drove. There was no reason, but it was just the way it was. I don't know why that day was different, but my mate called me out on it and said he wanted to drive for once. It was one of those moments that seem insignificant at the time but minutes later can change your whole life, and the lives of those around you.'

'You wouldn't have seen the IED either though.' I said, softly.

'No. They bury those suckers pretty well. And that area was supposed to be clear. It's still unknown as to whether it was one that was missed or if more had been put in place since the previous sweep. Either way...' he left the sentence unfinished. The reality was that it didn't matter why it was there, just that it had been. And they'd hit it. 'But the driver's side took the most impact.' He shook his head. 'Billy wasn't supposed to be driving. That was my job.'

'No,' I said, trying to push back the tears that were raw in my throat. 'You already said there was no reason why you always drove. It was just one of those things. It wasn't your job to drive. Just as it wasn't his. Someone has to drive and, that day, he chose to.'

'I shouldn't have let him.'

'Did you outrank him?'

'Yes.'

'Were you that bothered about driving? Or about him not driving?'

'No. On any other day, it wouldn't even have registered.'

'Exactly.'

'But he had a wife, Lottie.' His voice was soft and I let him lead me to the side, to a grassy hill that, if we turned our backs on the show, let us look out over the North Downs, green and verdant, rolling across the vista.

I nodded and the tears had now pushed their way up. One dropped down on to my cheek. I removed my arm from Seb's in order to brush it away, but he turned as I did so and his brow wrinkled. He was back in the present, his face full of concern.

'Oh, Lottie, please don't cry,' his hand was at my face, gently cupping my chin as the other thumb brushed the tear from my skin. Scooby sat looking up at us, the lead slack on his master's arm. Humphrey sat and leant against his pal. 'I didn't mean to upset you. God, that's the last thing I want to do. I shouldn't have said anything.'

'No, you should!' I said, catching his hand. 'I want you to. I always want you to be able to talk to me. About anything. At any time. Promise you will?' I gripped his wrist, but he remained silent. 'Promise me!' I said, a little more desperate.

'I can't bear to see you cry.'

'Well, it's going to happen sometimes, but that doesn't mean I'm not strong enough to hear it. Now, carry on.' I nodded at him. 'Please.'

'Do you want to sit for a moment?' he asked.

'That's a good idea.' We'd long since lost our parents in the midst of the show, but I think Mum had already expected that to happen.

Seb eased himself down and I sat next to him, the dogs around us, our backs to the show and the new leaves of an ancient oak shading us from the strengthening spring sun. He looked down at me, and then gently wrapped an arm around me, and I leant into him, feeling his strength and his vulnerability. There was more too, but things were emotional enough right now and I wasn't about to give myself any more to think about, so I pushed that away.

'I am sorry about your friend.' I shook my head. 'That sounds so trite. I don't know what else to say though.'

'It's not. And I know. There isn't much to say. I went to see his widow and sorry was all I could say then too.'

'She didn't blame you though.'

'No. She didn't. She was angry still, obviously, and grieving. But she told me he was doing the only thing he'd ever wanted to do and she'd known the risks when she'd married him. She's a strong woman.'

I swallowed, not sure I would have been able to find the strength that this woman had. 'But you still blamed yourself?'

'I just kept turning over why I hadn't insisted I drive that day? Then he'd still be here.'

'Do you know that for sure?' I asked. 'I mean, if you'd hit that device slightly differently, it might have just taken you both. Isn't that possible?'

Seb looked out across the sweeping view, but I had a feeling his mind was somewhere far less beautiful. 'I suppose that's possible, yes.'

'But you're still here,' I said, my voice wobbling more than I had planned. 'I know you wish that your friend was too, but none of it was your fault. The "if onlys" can take us in circles, but generally they don't take us anywhere good.'

He rested his head on mine but remained silent.

'I'm so glad you're still here,' I whispered and he dropped a kiss on the top of my head.

We stayed like that for a few more minutes as we both collected our thoughts and memories.

'So, what happened next? I mean, last Sunday? Once you'd got on your roll.'

Seb shifted position and Scooby laid his dark head across his owner's thigh. 'Jamie asked me what I meant about him blaming me too, and I told him. Them. All about how I felt that the worry of me being deployed each time had affected Mum's health, and then getting injured... That's a parent's worst nightmare, isn't it? I guess it doesn't matter how old your kid is. Being told something has happened to them? I just...' he shrugged. 'I just felt that all of that contributed to Mum's heart condition and ultimately the attack. My brother and I have always been close and he and Mum – they were so alike. Peas in a pod, my dad always said. And then she was gone. And I had to look at this little brother I adored and know that I contributed to him losing someone he was so close to. Who meant the world to him. And then, of course, there was Dad.'

He shook his head slowly and smiled. 'I'd let loose this absolute torrent of confession and anger and guilt and he was just looking at me. He'd taken a seat by this time and was just looking at me, no colour in his face. His expression was... the only word I can think of is "shattered". I'd seen it before on the faces of men and women who've seen things you would never wish to. And I'd seen it once on Dad too. When the surgeon came out from the Emergency Department theatre where they'd rushed Mum. Dad knew. We all knew. But I guess they still have to say something. On Sunday, I just looked at Dad and told him what I'd truly felt. That I'd stood there that day and watched the light go out in his eyes. People think he's this tough old soldier, that nothing bothers him, but, god, he adored my mum. He would have done anything for her.'

I thought back to what his dad had said about considering quitting the army life for his wife and boys and knew that Seb was right.

'I told him I felt responsible for putting that light out and I didn't know what to do about it. How to handle having been instrumental in taking the woman he adored from his life. Preventing Jamie's kids from ever really knowing their grandmother. I didn't know how to make up for that. Jamie and Olivia kept me close and the kids helped, but I'd shoved this wedge between me and Dad and neither of us knew how to remove it.'

'What happened then?'

Seb let out a little huff of air that was sort of a laugh. 'I just sort of flopped into a chair. Turns out emotional downloads can be pretty exhausting.'

'They can.'

'I felt a bit stunned, to be honest. By the look of the other two, I wasn't the only one. And then Dad got up, came over and crouched down in front of me. I sat up a bit and he took my face in his hands and looked at me. Really looked at me so that I was focused back on him. And then he just said "No."'

'No?' I asked, brushing away more tears with the back of my hand. Seb pulled a pack of tissues from his pocket and handed it over to me without comment. 'Thanks. No what?'

'Just no,' he said, turning to me, a smile now thankfully having replaced the haunted look of earlier. Brushing a stray lock of hair back from my face, he caught a tear that had diverted and left a damp trail down my temple. 'It seems that you and your year of saying no are quite influential. First your sister, then Harry, then Jess and now, of all people, my father.'

'I don't understand.'

'He told me how much he liked you first of all, and that whatever I'd thought you'd done, you hadn't so that was up to me to fix, if you'd let me. But that was for another day. Then he said he needed to say something and I needed to listen. He said about remembering me mentioning you were having this year of saying no, and now it was my turn to say no.'

33

I sat, waiting, watching. The dogs had dozed off and the noise and chatter of the show seemed distant as I concentrated on Seb.

He swallowed and began again. 'He told me it was time to say no, but it had to be for more than a year. It was for ever. That I was to say no to all those thoughts of guilt – that, no, I wasn't responsible for my mother's death, or my friend's. Both those things had happened, but I didn't cause them, and it was time to stop blaming myself.'

'Oh, Seb. And did you listen?'

He nodded. 'I need to thank you.'

'Me?'

'Yes.'

'I'm not sure I did anything.'

'You did. Whatever you said, which I know now wasn't what I thought, it got him thinking. And it got him talking. He's not always been a big one for that, especially since Mum. He loves Olivia to bits, but he's never opened up like he seems to have done to you.'

'Olivia already has a lot on her plate with two small children. I expect he probably thinks she has enough to do without listening to him, although I have a feeling she'd be more than happy to.'

'I think you're right. But you seem to have the magic touch.'

'I don't know about that. But maybe magic can happen when you're chatting to plants.'

Seb laughed suddenly, rolling his eyes. 'Oh god, don't tell me you talk to the damn things too!'

I slapped my hand across his mouth, watching as his eyes widened and then filled with laughter. 'There's thousands of plants here! You'll hurt their feelings!' I whispered.

Gently, he removed my hand, keeping hold of it within his own. 'Hurt their feelings.'

'Yes,' I said, with a definitive air.

'Right.' He pulled a face. 'My dad wasn't growing anything dodgy up there, was he? You didn't partake in a bit of the old...' He made a cigarette puffing motion with his free hand and rolled his eyes up.

I batted him on the arm. 'No, he isn't and no we did not.'

'I'm beginning to wonder. My dad talking like I can't remember about some pretty personal stuff and both of you having conversations with plants. You've got to admit, it's kind of weird.'

'It's not weird. Talking is good.'

'You're right.' I didn't mean that. Poor choice of words. And yes, it is good. And I'm not sure either of us will ever be able to thank you enough.'

'Oh shush,' I said, looking away. 'I didn't do anything.'

He caught my chin and I turned back to face him. 'Yeah,' he said. 'You did. Whether you intended to or not. Later, Dad said he was kind of surprised to find himself chattering away to you. I told him I could totally relate. That you have a way about you that makes everyone just spill the beans.'

We sat in silence for a few moments, just absorbing the peace and beauty of the surroundings.

'My bum's gone to sleep,' I said, eventually.

'I'm pretty sure I can help with that, if you need assistance.'

'I most certainly don't need assistance, thank you very much!' I laughed as I stood and jiggled about for a few moments, trying to wake things up.

Seb pushed himself up and once more gained the height advantage. At our feet, the dogs stretched and Seb took the leads from me so that he could walk them over to the base of the tree for them to tinkle. When he returned, I'd stopped jiggling and everything was more or less back to normal.

'Better?' he asked, holding out his arm for me to take again, both the leads hanging loosely over his other wrist, with Scoobs and Humphrey waiting patiently.

'Much.'

'Shame,' he winked and we moved off, my phone ringing just as we did.

'Hi, Mum,' I answered.

'Hello, love? You two all right?'

'Yes, thanks. Where are you?'

'We're over in one of the refreshment tents, near the centre of the show, and we just wondered if you wanted to join us? No pressure,' she added, casually.

I grinned and gave Seb a little eye roll. 'Want to go and meet the parentals for a coffee?'

'And cake! Tell him there's cake. Lots of it!' I heard Seb's dad add, laughter in his voice, and felt a rush of happiness warm my veins.

'Apparently there's cake, your dad says.'

'Then we should definitely do that.'

'We're on our way.'

'Lovely. There's a stall to the left of it selling copper ornaments, including a huge giraffe. It's hard to miss. We'll save you some seats.'

'OK, see you in a minute.' I disconnected and stuck the phone back in my pocket. 'It sounds like your dad is having a good time. I hope so anyway.'

'He will be.'

We walked on.

'There's something else I need to say.' Seb's voice was soft.

I looked up.

'I don't ever want to go another week without talking to you.'

I rested my head on his arm as we walked along, the gesture and closeness hopefully conveying my feelings more than any words could. 'It was kind of weird.' I said after a few moments.

He stopped and I pinged gently back against him. 'It was more than weird for me. It was... awful. Empty.'

'You knew where I was,' I said, quietly. 'And it was you that didn't show up to our normal Skype meeting on Monday. When that happened, I just guessed you were still angry and didn't want to talk to me.'

'I should have messaged you to explain about that. After everything with Jamie and Dad, I was kind of exhausted and they didn't want me to drive home. I'm not sure I could have done, to be honest. We went back to the house and talked some more and I ended up staying over. I guess it took it out of me even more than I thought as when I woke up the next morning it was nearly 11 a.m. and I hadn't heard a thing. When there's two small children in the house, that's saying something.'

'That's true.'

'Like I said, I should have just rung you then and there, but once I replayed my actions of the day before, I kept faltering, knowing I'd acted like a complete dick and just couldn't think why you'd even want to hear from me. So, I convinced myself it would be better for me to leave it a bit, let things settle.'

'I can understand, but, from where I stood, it just felt like you didn't want to talk to me.'

He placed his free hand gently on my other arm and looked at me, intently, honestly. I could see the flecks of gold in his dark eyes. 'I don't think there's ever been a point since we met that I haven't wanted to talk to you, as probably evidenced by the fact I kept you up talking until about 2 a.m. when you came to stay.'

'It was fun though.'

He grinned and my treacherous tummy did a couple of flips and flops. 'It was. But, seriously, I mean it. I guess I've always known it, but this week has proved something to me.' He was close now, one hand at my waist, the other gently pushing an overlong chunk of fringe from my temple. 'I cannot ever imagine a time when I would ever not want to talk to you, see you.' He moved again, his face close to mine. 'Be with you.'

'Seb...'

He stepped back as my phone rang.

I let it ring off, wanting him back, wanting that closeness, knowing those lips had been about to press mine, that body, hard with muscle, moving closer to mine. Admittedly, the middle of a plant show hadn't been where my fantasies had ever taken place. But he was bloody gorgeous and, although last year had been full of disappointments on the dating front, I wasn't quite on the verge of taking a vow of celibacy just yet. And...

OK, I was reading this right, wasn't I? I glanced up. He smiled at me in a way that could melt chocolate and I gave it right back. Yep. I was right. I'd said no once before, but I was suddenly thankful Seb had a streak of persistence. Unfortunately, he wasn't the only one.

'Yes, Mum!' I answered as the phone began to ring again. 'We're coming.' I had a bone to pick with my mum later.

Seb was still close to me, but amusement now replaced the heat that had filled his eyes moments before. 'I'm guessing we need to get a shifty on.'

'I think so.'

'OK, one more thing though.'

'Yes?' I asked, looking back up at him, feeling sparks shoot throughout my body. Now I'd let those floodgates open, I wasn't sure there was much I could do to hold them back.

Seb took my hand, enclosing it within his own. 'Would you do me the honour of coming to the gala? I know you said no before, and that you're busy, but if there's any chance of you being able to rearrange the—'

'I'm not busy.'

He smirked. 'Lottie Wentworth. Did you fib?'

'Yes. Because you were being an arsehole. That means it's all right for me to fib.'

'Fair enough. And so, where do we stand on that answer now?'

'I just told you I'm not busy,' I said, looking up through my lashes.

His answer was a broad smile as he tightened his hold on my hand and led the four of us towards the refreshment tent. Sneaking another glance at the deliciously hot man beside me, a long, cool drink might not be such a bad idea.

34

The last couple of weeks had passed in a blur as I tried to keep up with my regular clients, provide extra assistance for the start-up as they teetered on the cusp of something amazing, plus help the charity get every last little thing into place in order for this gala to be as successful as we all hoped it would.

Seb and I hadn't really had a chance to catch up properly on much outside of the gala, let alone get together to see what the next step might be following our moment at the show. But now it was here and, although we'd taken a chance on an open-air venue, it had been worth it. The warmth of the early summer day had become a balmy summer evening, and somewhere beyond the mass of light pollution was a plethora of twinkling stars, pinned on a twilight blue sky.

Harry and Jess had booked tickets for the event and kindly also provided both Seb and I with a room each at a local luxury hotel at a much-discounted corporate rate.

With a bit of luck, you'll only be using one of the rooms.

Jess followed this with a winky face when she messaged me the details from Harry.

I sent her a rolly eyes one back, which she thought hilarious and swapped it for an aubergine. I didn't have an answer for that.

I'd originally planned to meet Seb early, but a last minute crisis with another of my clients before a big meeting meant I'd had to catch a later train, arranging instead to meet Seb, as well as Jess and Harry, at the actual event.

'I don't have a ticket!' I flapped slightly when I called Seb to tell him I had to change our plans. I'd gone over the security arrangements with Seb myself. Obviously he had plenty of contacts in that area, so I wasn't worried, but he'd been keen to ensure I was up to date on every aspect, in case I needed anything.

'You don't need one.' Calm as ever in comparison, I could hear his smile down the phone.

'I do! We made that a big point. That tickets must be presented!'

'Lottie. You're effectively part of the charity. Your name is on the list. You'll be fine. Don't worry.'

'Oh. Oh, it is?'

'Of course.'

'Oh. Right. Good. That's good then.'

'You OK?'

'Am I OK going to the biggest social event I've ever been to in my life, and not knowing hardly anyone? Yep. Fine. Dandy. Perfectamundo.'

'Now you're beginning to worry me. Is that even a word?'

'Of course. No, I'm fine. Honest.'

'Just let me know as soon as you get there and I'll come and meet you anyway, OK?'

'You don't have to do that.'

'I want to.'

'OK. But I mean if you get caught up talking to someone—'

'Then I'll have to make my excuses and tell them there's a very hot date waiting for me. Believe me. They'll understand.'

I felt my cheeks colour with pleasure a little at his words. 'Not if it's one of the women who was planning on bidding on that date with you.' I said, laughing.

I heard the sigh of relief he let out. 'Thank god for Harry and his generosity. To be honest, I think an all-expenses-paid luxury weekend at his Paris apartment is going to raise us a lot more money than pizza with some old soldier.'

'You're not old. And anyway, I know which I'd rather have.'

'Paris?'

'Obviously.'

He laughed, the sound rippling through me and twisting into my stomach to mix with the excitement and nerves already lodged there.

'Right. I'd better go. I'll call you when I get there.'

* * *

'If you just want to wait here, Miss Wentworth, Mr Marshall will be with you shortly.'

'Thanks,' I said and grabbed the skirt of my dress, making sure I didn't end up base over apex before the night had even started. Unlike Jess, I wasn't used to such high heels, although I did love them. They were accessorising a full length ball gown – another new experience for me and also assisted by Jess who'd basically gone and chosen it for me from a very swanky boutique. She would have even tried it on, had we been similar sizes, but I'd at least managed to do that bit, and she'd then worked her magic in getting the small alterations needed completed in time for the gala. The end result was definitely a different look for someone who spent approximately 70 per cent of her life in pyjamas. I'd snapped a pic at home for Mum and sent it to her. She'd then called me, crying, to say how beautiful I looked and I'd had to cut the call short before she set me off and ruined the make-up I'd paid a fortune to have done in between trying to get everything else done today.

A shrill scream pierced the air and two of the security guards turned, bodies tensed. Slightly embarrassed, I gave them a little wave, pointed to Jess, made a little 'what can you do' face and got swept into Jess' arms.

'Oh my god!!!!' she screamed. I could practically see all the exclamation marks dancing around our heads. 'You look bloody amazing!'

'Umm, thanks. You look gorgeous, of course. As always!' I turned her round and admired the tiny sparkling Swarvoski crystals in the back of her hair as they sent darts of light out like little fireflies each time she moved. 'Your hair looks beautiful.'

'Do you like it?' she swished a bit more. 'I'm sort of trying it out for the wedding. I was thinking if I had this like under the veil, then I...' She drifted off when she realised my attention had also drifted off.

Harry stepped forward, said hello and kissed me on the cheek and I think said something about how lovely I looked, which I nodded at, trying to focus and not be entirely rude despite the fact I was no longer really listening.

'We'll catch up with you in a bit,' he said, taking Jess' hand and leading her away. She turned and widened her eyes, as she gestured with her head before blowing me a kiss with a huge grin on her face.

* * *

Seb stepped forward and I tried to remember the last time I had ever seen someone look this good. In full black tie with a perfectly fitted suit – this was definitely not an off-the-peg job – he looked better than even I could have imagined, which was saying something. I surreptitiously checked that my jaw hadn't physically dropped as much as it had mentally. This was the first time I'd seen Seb in anything other than casual clothes and, well, let's just say he definitely made it work. Judging by some of the looks I now saw being directed his way, I wasn't the only one to think so. Right, so now I just needed to be as calm and smooth and classy as those other women.

'Is that real?' I asked, poking at his bow tie.

Shit. Did I really just say that? Lottie! What happened to calm, smooth and classy?

Seb's laugh rang out as he hugged me to him. Standing back, he took my hands, his smile still wide. 'You look breathtaking.'

I opened my mouth. Closed it, thought about trying again and gave up.

He frowned a moment. 'Everything OK?'

I nodded this time. It was easier. 'I've just never been called breathtaking before. It sounds like something...' I reached up and touched my hair, suddenly nervous, 'out of a fairy story.'

Seb caught my hand back. 'Right now, you look like something out of a fairy story.'

'So long as it's not the evil queen, I guess we're good.'

Oh, for the love of god, Lottie, shut up.

Seb grinned. 'Most definitely *not* the evil queen. I was kind of going for the beautiful princess thing, but I'm sensing it's not gone as smoothly as I'd hoped for.'

'No, it has. I mean, it's lovely. You're lovely. What you said was lovely, I'm just a bit nervous all of a sudden and seem to have lost the ability to take a compliment. Or, you know, act like a normal person.' I was horribly aware I was now babbling and quickly clamped my mouth shut.

Seb gave me a lazy, unbelievably sexy, smile. 'Normal is very overrated.'

I returned the smile. 'That is true.'

He pulled me to him. 'You look stunning. Really.'

I felt the blush rise and hoped it didn't contrast too much with the emerald green of the corseted satin gown. I flapped a bit to move some air around. It didn't really work, but I had noticed Seb's eyes drift.

If we're being honest, I wasn't exactly overendowed in the 'upper echelon' department, so I was as surprised as anyone when I'd tried this dress on. Whatever sorcery went into the construction, it seemed to involve finding a whole lot more cleavage than I started out with. Hence, I wasn't used to having it on display.

'Umm... eyes up, soldier!'

Seb's head snapped up. 'Sorry.' And he did actually have the dignity to blush, so, for a moment, we were a matching pair.

'This is what happens when I leave Jess in charge of finding a dress for me.'

'Remind me to thank Jess later. Several times.' He gave me the cheekiest of grins and I bumped my arm against him. 'Come on, I want you to meet some people.'

'Sebastian, darling!' A woman whose age it was impossible to guess, thanks, I imagined, to access to a decent plastic surgeon, approached us in a cloud of expensive, and very heady, perfume.

'Lady Gardner, how lovely to see you. Thanks so much for coming and supporting us tonight.'

'Absolutely no question! Although, you naughty thing, changing that auction lot has rather caused a few tantrums in our house.'

Seb frowned. 'Which auction lot?'

Glancing at the younger woman with her, and the way she'd been looking at Seb, I had a pretty good idea.

'The date with you, you silly boy. Petunia here had already demanded we bid on it.'

'Mother!' Petunia snapped in horror.

Lady Gardner waved her away. 'She's been looking forward to it for ages! Obviously, her father would have kept bidding until she won. You know what he's like when it comes to her.'

'Mother. Be quiet!'

I gave her a sympathetic smile but received only a glare for my trouble so I left her to it. I guessed the fact that Seb was still holding my hand hadn't exactly won me any favours in her eyes, but at least I'd tried.

'That was really just a bit of a joke a couple of the staff started. It wasn't really ever going to be a proper... thing.' Seb hesitated, stumbling over whether to describe himself as an auction lot.

'Oh. Really? That is a shame. Genevieve Carstairs certainly didn't seem to know that. She's been telling everyone she planned on winning that bid, whatever the price.' Lady Gardner seemed to suddenly notice me. And the fact Seb was attached to me. 'But I see why things may have changed now. Never mind,' she smiled, 'Maybe next time.'

Ummmm...

Seb squeezed my hand as though he could he hear my brain turning that sentence over.

'Mother. Can we go now?'

Lady Gardner rolled her eyes. 'Lovely to see you, Sebastian. And nice to meet you...'

She hadn't actually met me. Poor Seb had barely had a chance to introduce me, so it was hardly surprising she didn't know my name.

'Lottie,' I filled in for her.

'Lottie. Lovely. Well, good luck tonight! It's looking marvellous.'

'Thank you. I hope you enjoy yourselves.' Seb included both the women in this. Lady Gardner beamed. Petunia gave him an awkward smile that still did nothing to hide the lust. Her eyes dragged to me, and the smile disappeared completely, turning cold.

'Maybe next time, Seb,' she repeated her mother's phrase before stalking off on long, Bambi-like legs without an ounce of cellulite.

'Her mother didn't mean that. She's just kind of a bit ditsy.'

'Petunia definitely meant it,' I said. 'Money buys everything but taste and manners.'

He gave me an apologetic look. 'I don't know what her problem is.'

I looked at him for a moment before realising he was actually serious. 'Oh my god. Seb. You're kind of adorable.'

He gave me a look. 'And now I sound like a puppy.'

'That's good. I love puppies.'

He grinned and gave me a squeeze.

'Her problem is that she fancies the arse off you and had plans to seduce you via that auction lot. And then it all went to pot. Although I think she's still planning for it to be on the cards at some point.'

'Then she's in for another disappointment. Also, I don't think I've ever been seduced in my life.'

I rolled my eyes. 'Yeah right.'

'What?'

'Of course you have. You probably just think it was all you. But I can pretty much guarantee, some of those dates? You weren't in control at all.'

'Well. Whether that's true or not. And I'm erring on the side of "not in a million years", there is no way I'm interested in Lady Petunia Gardner.'

'She's obviously rich.'

'And?'

'I don't know. She's pretty. And she doesn't have cellulite. That's kind of all I have to go on right now.'

He shook his head and gave me a look that sent a bolt of electricity firing out in every direction. I tried to get some more air in, but this bloody dress seemed to be doing its utmost to prevent that. All that happened was I suddenly became a heroine in an old Barbara Cartland novel, complete with heaving bosom!

'OK, you really need to stop doing whatever it is you're doing, or I'm going to have to go and sit down for a bit.'

'I'm not doing anything!' I protested. 'It's this flippin' dress! It's got a will of its own.'

His eyes were suddenly heavy-lidded and he leaned into me, moving us back a little behind one of the fairy-light wrapped trees. 'I know we've been planning this for months, and you've worked so hard on it, but right now I'd happily leave to get you alone.' He rested a hand at my waist and I felt the warmth of it through the fine fabric of my dress, his touch setting off a fizzing and tantalising warmth that began in my stomach and radiated in every direction.

'I know you've turned me down once this year, so I probably shouldn't even be thinking this, let alone saying it.' He ran a hand back over his hair, freshly cropped for the event. 'But, honestly, none of those feelings have gone away and seeing you standing there tonight...' he swallowed, then smiled. 'You took my breath away, Lottie. I don't know what else to say. I was floored. And if I'm wrecking everything by telling you all this, I'm sorry and I'll do my best to fix it again. But I just can't not tell you how beautiful you are.'

Neither of us said anything for a moment. I opened my mouth to say something, then closed it again. Seb shifted his weight.

'And now you can tell me "no" again.' He smiled, a hint of resignation showing in the dark eyes.

I looked up at him. 'Do you think we could do that?'

His brow wrinkled. 'What?'

'You get me alone somewhere?' I was going for teasingly sexy, but all that happened was a bloody great grin.

Seb studied me for a moment, before his smile matched mine. Then he gave a groan and dropped his head to my shoulder, closer to him now with the help of the five inch heels.

'No.' He ground the word out. 'Unfortunately.'

'Damn.'

'My thoughts exactly. Except a little stronger.'

'Double damn?'

He moved, his breath tickling my bare neck. 'Something like that.' Seb pushed himself back and pulled a face.

'You all right?'

'Mmmhmm,' he replied, shifting again.

'Oh... oh. I see.'

'That's kind of what I was hoping to avoid.'

I giggled.

'It's not funny,' he said, with a massive grin on his face.

'Then why are you smiling?'

'Because I'm thinking about getting you alone.'

'Then you'd better stop doing that or you're going to be stuck behind this tree all evening.'

'So long as you're with me, I can think of worse places to be.'

'Seb.' I leant my head on his arm for a moment. 'You really need to be out there schmoozing.'

'I know.' He let out a sigh. 'I know, I know.' He cleared his throat, gave one more shuffle, looked at the heavens for a few moments and then back at me. 'OK. We'll pick this back up later.'

'Sounds like a plan.'

* * *

The evening passed in a whirl of introductions, expensive champagne and delicious food. The auction did even better than we'd hoped for, even without the delectable Seb as a prize, a fact that Petunia was still miffed about, judging by her expression, but I'd lost sympathy on that particular front. Saying no to bothering about rude, spoilt brats was one of the easier tasks of the year, it turned out. I glanced back at the object of her desire, who was laughing with Harry about something. Saying no to Seb Marshall was not going to be an easy task. Luckily. I didn't want to. He was now most definitely on my Yes list.

As the night wore on, the dance floor began to fill. Jess and I had already had a few goes at shaking our things out there. Then the band segued in to a slower melody and Harry appeared on the floor to sweep Jess into a romantic embrace. I smiled as I walked away, watching the love shining out of both their faces. And then I stopped suddenly as I bounced off something. Or rather someone. His arm came out to steady me.

'Oops!' I said, as Seb's arm rested at my waist. 'I was just coming to sit with you.'

'And I was just coming to dance with you. If you'll allow me the pleasure.'

Oh lord, Seb. Don't say things like that when I've had several champagnes and you're looking like you do right now...

'Oh! Yes.'

'I'm no Mario, but I can shuffle around with the best of them to a slow song.'

'You don't have to,' I said, slightly concerned. I know he hated me, or anyone, fussing about him, but it had been a long day and he'd been on his feet a lot already.

He looked at me for a moment. 'It's nothing to do with my leg. I'm just shit at dancing. Always was.'

I grinned and gave him a little push in the chest. 'I think I'll be the judge of that. I bet you've got a killer shuffle.'

'Don't say I didn't warn you,' he said, as we reached a space on the dance floor.

'I wouldn't dream of it,' I replied, enjoying the feel of his body close to mine, his arms around me, the smell of him and the tantalising feel of his breath on my ear when he dipped his head to speak to me over the music. I wanted the night to both last forever and be over in equal measure and, as Seb gently tangled the fingers of one hand in my hair, I felt everything slide into place. I was where I was supposed to be. With the man I was supposed to be with. The years I'd thought I wasted weren't wasted. They were just a path I had to tread to get me to where I was supposed to be. Here. With Major Seb Marshall.

* * *

'We can get away soon,' Seb laid a hand on my cheek. 'You look shattered. Why don't I get you a taxi now and you can head back to the hotel?'

'No, I'm fine. Really. I'll just wait until you're ready to go too.' I was in little doubt that the only thing that would be happening tonight now was both of us collapsing on the bed. Possibly still fully clothed, but it would still be nice to do that together.

'Seb?'

I saw his face register the voice before he even turned. For just a moment, emotion filled his eyes and then, just as quickly, it was gone. In its place was... nothing. The unreadable face that I'd not seen in a long time was back.

He turned in the direction of the voice, and I followed.

'Hello, Seb.' The woman hesitated for a moment, then stepped forward, placing a kiss on his cheek. Mid-thirties, elegant, and strikingly beautiful, with long dark hair that bounced in soft curls down one side, the sheen of it reflecting the soft lighting around us.

'Hello, Maria. I didn't realise you were coming tonight. I... I would have come and seen you earlier.'

I glanced at him as subtly as I could. There was something going on here that I didn't understand, but what I did know is that, whoever this woman was, her being here wasn't something he'd expected.

'You had a lot of people to meet and greet,' she smiled softly at him, and he nodded. 'It looks like it's gone very well.'

He nodded. 'Yes. I hope so. I'm sorry,' he said, turning to the man with her, 'we haven't been introduced. Seb Marshall.'

'Mark Bishop.' Older than the woman, but just as attractive, they made a perfect couple.

'Pleased to meet you.'

They shook hands.

'Mark Bishop,' Seb repeated before looking back at him. 'Bishop Investment Holdings?'

The man nodded. 'Yes.'

'Then I believe I owe you a large thank you. Your recent donation was incredibly generous.'

'It's a good cause.'

'Well, it's very much appreciated, sir. Thank you.'

He nodded again, graciously and without ceremony.

Seb turned to me. 'Maria, Mark, this is Lottie.'

We all shook hands and smiled and I suddenly felt entirely out of place.

'Well, we should probably leave you in peace.' Maria smiled at us both, and Mark held out his arm for her to take. As she did so, the light caught and flashed on something. An exquisitely cut diamond the size of my thumbnail set atop a platinum band on the third finger of her left hand. Seb's eyes settled on it for a moment longer than mine before he raised them to her.

'It looks like congratulations are in order.'

She glanced down, suddenly realising what he'd meant. 'Oh,' she looked flustered for a moment, clenching her fist and opening it again. 'Yes. Mark proposed last summer. We're... we're getting married next month.'

Seb smiled. 'That's wonderful, Maria. Congratulations,' he nodded to Mark, who returned the smile. 'You've got a special woman there. But I guess you already know that.'

'I certainly do.'

'It was great to see you, Seb. You look really well.'

'Yep. Doing good. Thanks.'

'I'm really pleased. Look after yourself.' She leant and placed a gentle kiss briefly on his cheek.

He gave a sharp nod and watched as they turned and walked away.

'Seb?' I prompted him after a few moments. The couple had gone, but his eyes were still fixed on the distance, his mind somewhere else.

'Hmm?' he turned back to me and, for a second, it was almost as though he was surprised to see me there, and I saw the wash of sadness across his face.

'Someone you know?' I asked. Clearly it was, but I didn't really know what else to say, and Seb didn't appear to be about to offer any explanation.

'Err... yes. Yes, that was...' he cleared his throat. 'That was Maria.'

I'd kind of gathered that much. I was more interested as to who Maria actually was and why her presence had had such an impact on Seb.

I waited. Nothing.

'And Maria is?'

'My ex.' He looked at me and clarified, 'My ex-fiancée.'

35

Suddenly everything fell into place. He'd mentioned before that none of his relationships since had been particularly long lasting, and his ex from the health spa had said something about them just not having chemistry. Carla was gorgeous and so was Seb and although I knew that wasn't exactly a prerequisite for a happy match, I also knew that it was hard to get chemistry to bubble when one of you keeps a lid on things.

I still didn't know whether Maria had walked away from Seb, or whether he'd pushed her away, but from the look on his face now, it was a situation he regretted. And now she was due to marry a man she appeared very happy with.

I reached out to him but he was still distracted. The closeness of earlier, the attention, the lustful impatience... it had all gone.

'You seem a little distracted. Shall I leave you to it?'

'Huh? No, no. It's fine.' He turned briefly as he heard his name being called before turning back to face me, glancing at his watch as he did so. 'It's getting late so feel free to go if you want. I've got some things I still need to tie up here.'

'Ooh, that sounds promising,' Lady Genevieve Carstairs purred as she approached, wrapping her hands around one of Seb's biceps.

He turned his head towards her briefly, the smile automatic and distracted. Not that she seemed to notice.

I shifted my weight, suddenly feeling like a third wheel. All the promise of earlier had dissolved into nothing. Even the celebratory fireworks had left trails of smoke across the twilight, but looking at Seb now, there was no trail of the feelings he'd professed just a short time ago. Seeing his ex had changed something, but with Lady Carstairs entwining herself around him, there wasn't even an opportunity to ask him about it. To try to find out what had changed in those moments. And whether it was irreversible.

'Oh!' Genevieve widened her eyes and glanced between us. 'Oh gosh, I haven't interrupted anything, have I?'

I hoped for her sake she didn't have any acting aspirations because she was bloody awful at it.

I did my best to keep my features immobile, even though I was inwardly screaming, Yes!

'No.' Seb shook his head and I swallowed hard.

Lady Carstairs smiled and slid her arm to his waist. 'Oh, I am glad. I hate to have to steal him away, but I'm still waiting for the dance Seb promised me as consolation for taking himself out of the auction.' She gave a tinkly laugh, although I wasn't sure at what. 'You are a naughty man. And after I'd promised all that money too.'

Seb said nothing, his gaze drifting over to the exit. Maria was slipping into an expensive looking coat, assisted by her fiancé.

'It's a good job you've got other ways of persuading me to part with my money.' Her voice had dropped an octave as she gazed up at him.

Seb frowned for a moment, then cleared his throat. I felt my face burning as emotions hurtled around inside me.

'I should leave you to it,' I said.

Seb focused back on me, paused for a moment, then gave a short nod. 'Shall I call you a cab?'

I shook my head. 'No. Don't worry. I'll sort myself out.' I reached into my clutch for my phone and went to press Jess' contact. I didn't know if her and Harry had left yet, but I was hoping not.

'Lottie?' Seb asked.

'Yes?' I glanced up from the phone.

'Is everything OK?'

'Perfect. But you're right. I'm tired and should get home. I mean... back to the hotel.'

I dialled and Jess picked up almost instantly. I turned slightly and asked her where she was.

Two minutes later, Harry and Jess found us and we said our goodbyes. Jess gave me an enquiring look at Genevieve Carstairs' possessive arm around Seb's waist. I returned it with a tiny shake of my head and she surreptitiously gave my hand a gentle squeeze.

'Bye, Seb.' I gave him a peck on the cheek and he made no show of being surprised, or of having expected anything more. In a way, that made my decision easier. Or harder, depending on the way you looked at it.

'Is everything all right between you two?' Jess asked, a question I knew was full of as much restraint as Jess possessed.

'There is no "us two",' I stated as I clambered into the back of the black cab.

Harry handed Jess in and followed, giving the driver the instructions as he did so.

Jess gave me a surprised look. 'That's not how it looked earlier. Especially not on the dance floor.'

'Looks can be deceiving then, I guess. There's nothing.'

'I wouldn't worry about Ginnie,' Harry ventured. 'She's a terrible flirt but nothing ever comes of it.'

Having already been through three husbands, two of whom had started out as someone else's husband, if Jess' previous information was to be believed, I was disinclined to agree with this well-intentioned statement. It was common knowledge she had set her sights on Seb and if marriage vows were no obstacle to her, then whatever fledgling thing Seb and I had momentarily possessed certainly wasn't. Especially when Seb himself wasn't prepared to stand up for it.

I knew something was off with him. That seeing his ex had sparked something. Something I didn't understand. Hadn't been given the chance to understand. But I was still hurt. Hurt and angry with myself for not sticking to the decision I'd made earlier in the year. I'd said no to him once before and that's what I should have stuck with.

'Lots? You all right?' Jess took my hand.

'Yep,' I said, taking it back. Right now, Jess' concern was making me feel a little wobbly and I was already doing my best to hold it together.

'But I thought—'

'I did too, Jess, but I guess I was wrong.'

'What's going on?' she asked.

I leant my head back against the seat of the cab and watched the neon signs of London flash past. 'Can we not talk about it right now, Jess?' I looked over at her. 'Please?'

She reached across and took my hand again and this time I let her. 'Of course. But you know where I am if you want me.'

I nodded and then turned back to the window, wanting the night to be over. Wanting to be out of this stupid bloody dress and wanting to be home, with my dog, knowing that at least I could trust him not to break my heart. Unlike Major Seb Marshall.

* * *

The gala had been a huge success and, in the weeks following it, the charity had been attracting more attention and more investors. Seb was run off his feet and I was doing everything I could to help with the new plans he had for the charity. A part of me had hoped that when I spoke to him again, once he'd got over the initial shock of seeing his ex, he'd get back to his normal self. But the bigger part of me knew that wasn't going to happen, and the past few weeks had proved me right.

I knew I hadn't imagined things at the garden show, or at the gala. The way he'd looked at me, the words he'd spoken, the way he'd held me. But I, it seemed, like all the other women he'd dated since he'd got back on the scene, had been nothing more than a distraction. It was why his other liaisons never lasted that long. Seb might have opened his heart to his family now regarding the guilt he'd been carrying, but he seemed incapable of opening his heart to anything more than a few dates with women. Maria had captured his heart. He'd asked her to marry him and then, when everything turned upside down, she'd left. Or been sent away. It didn't really matter which, because she'd still taken his heart with her. Which was really inconvenient, because I'd spent the last several months trying not to give mine to him, and the moment I did, he hadn't even noticed.

We'd talked, but he was definitely more distracted than before and, while I knew he suddenly had a lot more on his plate thanks to the success of the gala, he was also more withdrawn. From saying he wanted to be with me, now he barely rang and had made no suggestion to meet up. Jess had tentatively mentioned she'd seen a picture in the society pages of Seb accompanying Genevieve Carstairs to some function or other, but I'd quickly changed the subject and Jess, thankfully, hadn't pursued it. Perhaps Seb's habit of keeping his real feelings at a distance from any romantic partner worked for Lady Carstairs. From the way she'd been looking at Seb that night of the gala – and pretty much everything I'd heard about her with regards to him– feelings were not the thought foremost in her mind. And if he was now accompanying her on social engagements, I guess that arrangement worked for him too. But even without a wealthy heiress in the way, I knew that wasn't an arrangement that would work for me. I was all or nothing. I gave my all and I wanted 'all' back. Maybe it was selfish to ask that much, but I wasn't prepared to be with anyone now who wasn't prepared to give that to me. So I focused on my work, keeping myself busy with my other clients and doing everything I needed to with the charity. But thoughts of Seb still stubbornly pushed themselves into my brain. It was time to stick to my original year plan. It was time to say no. Again.

Dealing with Seb as a client no longer brought me joy. It brought me pain and heartache and a sense of feeling idiotic that I'd let my silly little crush turn into something far deeper. The one thing I'd resolutely told myself I definitely wouldn't do. Luckily his latest email had given me the opportunity to resolve things once and for all.

Dear Lottie,
Got an important meeting with a new sponsor next Monday. I know it's short notice, but it'd be great if you could come. I'd really appreciate your input. I realise this is a bit beyond what virtual assistants get involved with, but I'd be appreciative.
Let me know.
Thanks

Once again it was signed with his digital signature. Nothing more personal. I had a sense of déjà vu and kicked myself. Was I really going to keep going round in circles with this bloke? No, was the simple answer to that.

Dear Seb,
Thanks for your email. I was just about to contact you.
Unfortunately, I won't be able to attend this meeting. My current workload

is such that taking extra time out like this just isn't possible and, as you say, this is really beyond the scope of my duties as a virtual PA.

This leads me on to the point that I was going to discuss with you. As the charity has grown, and now with the extra attention brought about by the gala, it would seem that this is the perfect time to be considering a dedicated PA. I have done everything I can really but am unable to keep allotting the extra time it needs and do not want to risk giving my other clients less than 100 per cent of my attention.

In the circumstances, I am having to cull my client list and am now writing to give you three months' notice, as per our contract. This should give you ample time to source potential applicants and interview them.

Until then, I will continue with my work for you, but this will be restricted to a virtual basis, as was the original agreement.

I wish you all the best with the meeting on Monday and know that you will be able to handle things brilliantly.

Kind regards

My own digital signature ended the message and I pressed send before I could second guess anything.

Ten minutes later, my phone rang. I ignored it and thankfully it fell into silence. After three more missed calls, all from Seb, I switched both my computer and phone off and took Humphrey out for a walk. It hadn't been the ideal way to end a working week, but I knew it was the right thing to do.

'We both know that, don't we?' I asked the dog as we meandered along. He looked round at me, tipped his head to one side and then, deciding the conversation wasn't actually that interesting, continued to snuffle and trot along, leaving me to my thoughts.

* * *

A knock on my door on Saturday evening had Humphrey scooting off my lap and running to and from the door, just in case I hadn't noticed this interruption to my quiet night in. I ignored it for a bit. My parents and Jess both let me know when they were coming over, as did Sally, on the odd occasion she came round, which, since her transformation into 'much more chilled' Sally, was now more regular, and more often than not, accompanied by Oliver, who I'd really grown to like and who seemed to be very supportive of my sister. As I hadn't ordered anything either, there was no reason for anyone to be knocking at my door. Generally when that happened, it soon stopped and I heard the noise move further down the hall and greetings exchanged. The numbers had fallen off several of the doors ages ago and despite repeated requests, the maintenance company still hadn't got around to putting them back on.

This time, however, the knocking continued. I shooshed Humphrey, scooping him up on my way through the hallway and moved the peephole cover aside.

Crap. I dropped it back into place and stood back. Now what?

I unlocked the door and pulled it open.

'Hi.'

'Hello,' I said, forcing a cool, collected note into my voice. I wasn't sure if it worked, but I was sure as hell going to try.

'Am I interrupting anything?' Seb asked.

Bearing in mind I was in my pyjamas, that was pretty unlikely. 'Not a lot. You're a bit out of your way.' I concentrated on keeping my tone casual.

'I came to see you.'

'Oh.'

Seb shifted his weight. 'I wasn't really sure if that would be OK. I didn't want you to feel I was stalking you or something.'

I rolled my eyes. 'That's a bit dramatic.'

He shrugged. 'You never know how people are going to react sometimes. Anyway. Just so you know, I spoke to Jess and she told me to "get my well-toned arse over to see you asap", I believe were her words.'

'That does sound like something Jess would say.' I was slightly miffed that she hadn't prewarned me, but then there was every chance I would have taken that opportunity to suddenly find a need to vacate my flat for a while. We'd known each other so long, she would have sussed that within seconds. Also, I'd sent her a quick message yesterday saying that I needed a bit of an unplug over the weekend so not to worry if I didn't reply to any messages, so even if she had tried, I wouldn't have seen it anyway. Obviously, the upshot of all that was that I now had a six foot three hunk of gorgeousness standing in my doorway, something for which I had been completely unprepared. Argh! Did he have to be so bloody good looking and smell so damn good! I was doing my best here and the universe was so really not helping. 'I'm sorry about the meeting. I just can't lose that time, I'm afraid.'

'Lottie, I'm not here about the meeting. Right now, I couldn't care less about that damn meeting. I'm here about you. I care about you.'

'Oh. Right. Well, I'm fine. As you can see.'

He gave me a patient look which I ignored.

I leant out, giving the corridor a cursory look. 'No date with Lady Carstairs tonight then?'

He frowned. 'No. Of course not.'

I rolled my eyes.

'What was that for?'

A family walked past behind him and the two children gave us both curious stares. I didn't really know my neighbours. I'd always wanted to live somewhere that had a warm, neighbourly feel to it. This flat wasn't it, but lately I was realising there were a few things I wanted that may not ever come true. One of them was now standing in front of me, which was a little inconvenient as I was in the throes of doing my best to get over him.

Seb glanced at the family in his peripheral vision. 'May I come in? Or if you don't want me in your home, perhaps we could go somewhere a little more private than this hallway.'

I stood back and indicated for him to come in, which he did.

Closing the door behind him and turning back to me, he repeated the question.

'Please don't treat me like I'm an idiot, Seb.'

'I'm not.'

'Jess saw the photo of you together at some fancy do.' I shrugged, trying to put as much disinterest into it as possible. Not the easiest when it feels like your shoulders have suddenly become welded to your ears with tension.

'I met her at the function in order to be introduced to some more possible supporters of the charity.'

'Right.'

He shifted his weight, tension radiating from him. 'It's true, Lottie. I don't know why you'd think otherwise?'

'Oh, for god's sake. Seb, I'm not stupid! It was hardly a secret that she'd set her sights on you and people like that get what they want.'

'Well, she didn't get me!'

'Really?' I said, unconvinced.

'Yes. Really,' he snapped. 'Where the hell has all this come from?'

'Seriously?' I threw my hands up. 'Maybe it's come from the fact that one minute at the gala you couldn't get enough of me and the next moment, your ex walks up and suddenly it's like I barely exist! And, to top it all, Lady Bloody Carstairs comes up and starts wrapping herself around you and you just stand there, lapping it up!'

'I was not lapping it up!'

Maybe he had a point. In truth, he'd just stood there, looking like his mind was somewhere else entirely. But my point was that he hadn't made any effort to disentangle himself from her.

I said nothing, even though all the words were bubbling and racing in my head. *Just tell him to leave, Lottie. You've made your decision. Stick to it this time.*

For a moment, we just stood there, staring at each other, each trying to decide the next move.

'Would you like a drink?' Good manners elbowed their way to the fore.

Inner me slapped a hand to her forehead.

'I don't want to put you out.'

God, I hated this formality. Why did things have to get complicated? *Because you opened your heart to him, Lottie, that's why*, I snapped back at myself.

'You're not. I'm making tea. Have one or don't. It's all the same to me.' I tried to sound nonchalant, but even I knew I hadn't pulled that one off.

'Lottie, you deserve an explanation.'

I walked towards the kitchen, leaving him to follow if he wanted, which apparently he did.

'I don't know what you mean.' I glanced at him and, by the look on his face, he was fully expecting my nose to grow. Just as I was.

'I'm pretty sure you do. Like I said before, you're a terrible liar.'

'And yet you seem to be a pretty damn good one,' I said, throwing a teabag into the pot with such force, I was surprised it didn't bounce straight back out again.

'I never lied to you.'

'And there you go again!' I snapped, splashing hot water into the pot.

'Maybe you should do that when you're a little less angry.' Seb's brow rippled with concern. 'You're going to burn yourself if you're not careful.'

I slammed the kettle down. 'You do not get to tell me what I should and shouldn't do.'

'I wasn't trying to. It was just a suggestion to try and keep you safe.'

'Well, I don't need any of your suggestions either. I'm quite capable of looking after myself, thanks very much.'

He dragged a hand across his face. 'I didn't mean to imply you weren't. I just don't want to see you hurt.'

'It's a bit bloody late for that then, isn't it, Seb? Maybe you should have thought about that before you decided to pretend I actually meant something to you.'

He threw his hands up. 'You do mean something to me!'

I held up a hand. 'Don't. I'm not into the few dates, quick shag and see you later kind of relationship, Seb, and you knew that. It might be old-fashioned, but that's me. I spent years in a relationship that went nowhere and, for all I know, I might have wasted my best chance at having a family. But I knew you were a threat because I liked you. I mean, really liked you and then, for a few stupid hours, you made me believe that you felt the same. But, of course, you didn't. You never let women in, properly. You play with them, and that might work for some, but it doesn't for me, and if you'd known me at all, you'd have known that. So, doing what you did is something I'd have not thought you capable of before. I guess I was mistaken.'

'I don't play with anyone!' he replied, his voice calm but anger flashing in his eyes, 'And I resent that accusation. I've never used anyone, and I never would.'

I gave him a look.

'I wouldn't. And, to quote you, if you knew me at all, you would also know that.'

I did. Deep down, I knew that. Whatever I thought of Seb, I knew respect for others was something he held as a non-negotiable aspect of his personality.

I turned away.

'Lottie.'

'Why are you here, Seb?' I asked, my voice quiet.

'To see you.'

'Why?'

'I think you know why.'

I shook my head, furious with myself at the tears that burned in my eyes. 'A few weeks ago I thought I did, but then everything changed. I don't even blame you. But that doesn't mean I can't just shrug it off like you can.'

'You think I can shrug you off?'

'Yes. I do. You did a pretty good job of it on the night of the gala and every day since. So yes. I absolutely do.'

He stepped forward, closing the distance between us. 'I could never shrug you off. I know you probably don't believe me, but you've been on my mind this entire time.'

'You're right. I don't believe you.'

'What can I do to change that?'

My kitchen was tiny at the best of times, but with Seb's bulk filling it, it suddenly became claustrophobic. I pushed past him and headed out into the living room. Humphrey was still snuggling against Seb's legs. Traitor. I plopped down on the sofa and left them to it.

'Men,' I muttered.

Two minutes later, Seb appeared with a cup of tea, made just the way I like it, which he put down in front of me, and Humphrey, whom he placed next to me on the sofa. Humph immediately clambered over and found a comfy spot on my lap.

'Oh, now you're interested?' I grumbled at him, stroking his fur. 'Thank you for the tea.'

'You're welcome.' Seb looked at the space next to me. 'May I sit?'

I shrugged in a 'whatever' manner and he took it as a yes.

'I'm sorry I've hurt you. Especially after I promised I'd never do that again, and I know that having screwed up once, I probably don't even deserve another chance, but I've come here to ask if there was any way you could find it in your heart to forgive me.'

I shook my head. 'I don't think so, Seb. I'm sorry.'

He nodded. 'I understand,' he said, a crack in his voice. 'And I won't take up your time any longer than I have to. But, if you would give me a few minutes, I think you deserve an explanation. Once I've told you, I'll leave you in peace, and will, as you suggest, advertise for a PA so that you don't have to deal with me any more.'

I looked round at him. 'Does it matter now?' I asked, softly.

'It does to me. And I think it does to you too.'

I shook my head. 'I already know, Seb. I saw your face when you saw her. I don't really think you were planning on using me. I don't know why I said that. But I understand, and I know you're hurting too. It's bound to be a shock when the woman you love tells you she's getting married. As far as you're concerned, it's you that should be marrying her. Finding out, especially like that, can't have been easy, and I'm sorry for that. Whatever did or didn't happen between us, I wouldn't wish hurt on you. You've been through enough.'

'I don't need your pity, Lottie.' His words were soft. There was no accusation, just a statement.

'I'm not pitying you, Seb. I've never pitied you. I've admired you, liked you, loved you. But I've never pitied you.'

He reached out and took my hand. 'I'm not in love with Maria, Lottie. Yes, seeing her took me by surprise, and when she said she was getting married, it threw me back into my memories. We were supposed to get married shortly after I finished my tour, after all. When I got injured, we postponed the wedding. And then we postponed it again. I think both of us knew it wasn't going to work. I'd changed and Maria was struggling with coming to terms with the fact that the life she had planned out for us now was going to be a lot different. I tried to tell her that it didn't have to alter and that I was determined it wouldn't. I refused to acknowledge a lot to start with and my anger, stubbornness, pain and everything else that comes with it started taking its toll on our relationship.'

'That's understandable. It can't have been easy on either of you.'

'No. I don't think I realised how hard it was on her until I started the charity. As you know, we do our best to support the family as well as the service personnel. Listening to some of the partners' stories, I guess it gave me a new perspective on what it must have been like for Maria. I'd felt angry with her for a long time, but I was able to let that go and have more empathy for her situation. But I hadn't seen her since the day she left until I saw her at the gala. I'm surprised she was there, but her fiancé is a great supporter and it wouldn't surprise me if that's been influenced by Maria. Seeing her set off a whole slew of emotions, you're right. But you're wrong if you think it's because I'm still in love with her. I just got thrown back into some memories and I didn't want to drag you into that.'

'You should have given me the choice.'

He brushed his thumb across the back of my hand and I tried to ignore the feelings his touch ignited within me. 'I should,' he answered, simply. 'But I was scared. I'd lost a woman I loved once already and I was scared that if I invited you in, I might lose you too.' He shifted on the sofa, closing the gap. Humphrey shuffled around, stretching himself so that his bum was on my leg and his head on Seb's thigh. 'I can't lose you, Lottie. I thought I'd felt pain before, but when I got your email, I knew I'd blown it. I thought I was trying to protect you, but I wasn't. I was trying to protect myself.'

'I think you think I'm more easily scared than I am.'

He gave a rueful smile. 'Funny. I've been spending a fair bit of time with my dad the last few weeks, talking stuff over and he said exactly the same thing. It seems everyone is wiser on this than me. And maybe braver than me too.'

'I don't know about that.'

'I do. If I'd have had the guts I thought I did, I'd have asked you out the moment you were free, like I wanted to, instead of just faffing around and giving myself excuses not to.'

I frowned at him. 'I don't understand.'

Seb carefully moved the dog out of the way before standing and gently pulling me up with him. His warm, strong hands, with their hint of roughness. cupped my face. 'Lottie, I've been nuts about you since the moment I met you. Frankly, the fact you were already with someone was a huge pain in the arse. I knew I was in trouble with you, but as soon as we spoke, I didn't want to let go. I thought if I could have a friendship with this amazing woman, it was the next best thing.'

I frowned again. 'So, when I split with Tom? I mean, you never even hinted you might be interested.'

'I was about to. I didn't want to be a rebound, so I waited for a bit. But I waited too long, because the next thing I knew you were on this crazy path of saying yes to everything. Including dates you didn't want to go on.'

'And you think I'd have done that to you?' I laid my hands over his, still cradling my face.

He gave a shrug, smiling. 'I literally had no idea. I had no clue if you'd ever consider me. I was kind of the opposite to your ex by the sounds of things and maybe hipster arty sorts were more your type. That's definitely not me.'

I laughed then. 'No, I think we can agree that's definitely not your niche.'

'I just didn't want you to be saying yes to me because of some pledge. I wanted you to say yes to me for one reason. Because you truly wanted to.'

'I would have.'

He ran a hand back over my hair, following it down my back until it stopped at my waist and pulled me closer. 'I was a fool not to ask you.'

'So,' I said, 'once my year of saying yes was done, why not ask me then? Assuming you hadn't given up on the idea by then.'

'I never gave up. But just as I was about to ask, you told me you were planning to say no to stuff. Honestly, I could have cried. And I don't really do that.' He pulled a face. 'I had no idea if you liked me and I thought if I asked you out, and you said no, then it was just going to make things so awkward and I'd lose a friend, and the best assistant in the world.'

'I'm not sure which one worried you the most, going by that.'

He grinned and I felt the fireworks fizz and pop throughout my body.

'So, what happened?'

He pulled me as close as he could. 'In the end, I couldn't wait. And I knew we had chemistry. I began to allow myself to believe that you might actually be interested in me. But then you said no and I was worried I'd wrecked everything, but I had to ask and at least I had my answer. I thought once I had that, I'd be able to put things behind me and move on. Just be the friend you wanted me to be. But I couldn't. I couldn't help it. I was already far too deep in love with you to put it behind me and when you said what you did at the gala...' His Adam's apple bobbed as he searched for words. 'I couldn't believe my luck. I couldn't believe that you might actually feel the same... or at least something like it.'

'Shall I tell you a secret?'

He gave a disturbingly sexy flick of his eyebrows.

'I've had a crush on you since you first became my client.'

Seb looked genuinely shocked. 'Seriously?'

I gave him a shrug. 'You're kind of hot.'

His laugh rumbled through me as he wrapped his arms around me and pressed me close into his body. 'Does that mean I'm forgiven?

'Like I said, you're kind of hot. Luckily for you.'

'OK,' he said, looking down into my face. 'So, what we're saying here is that if we'd both just talked to each other a bit more, we might have saved ourselves a bit of heartache.'

'Or possibly a lot?'

He pulled me close and kissed the top of my head. 'So, how about this? We make a deal that, from now on we talk to each other. About everything.'

'Everything.'

'We have a deal then?' he asked.

'We do. Would you like to seal it with a handshake?'

A smile slid on to his face. 'It's a start, but I'm pretty sure we can think of some far more fun ways to seal this deal.'

I slid my arms around his neck, raising on to my tiptoes as his lips pressed down on to mine. I smiled into him as his arms scooped down and wrapped around my backside, lifting me up so that my legs were wrapped around his waist and my fingers felt the muscles in his neck as he kissed me. His lips moved as one hand brushed my hair back and he followed it down with his soft warm mouth.

'How are you feeling about that year of saying no now?' he asked, his voice low and thick.

'Like I said before, there are always exceptions to the rule.'

EPILOGUE

A year later, I looked across the large, secluded garden of the home Seb and I had bought together in Tinkerton. It was a work in progress, but I loved every moment of making that progress.

We'd had some help, of course, from Mum and Dad who often had a spare plant or two to drop off for me and advice, if I wanted it. Seb's dad was now also a regular visitor, always eager to hear about the latest plans we had for the garden. It was lovely to see him and Seb take a gentle walk around the garden, or just sit together under the sail shade, chatting over things, especially when I thought back to how difficult things had been between them a year ago.

The original bond they'd shared had now been repaired and was, if anything, far stronger. Thanks to his dad, Seb had managed to get a couple of allotment plots for the charity to use and the gardening therapy Seb had wanted to expand upon was now happening. Mr Marshall, along with several other of his allotmenteer pals were volunteering on the scheme, offering advice, assistance and sometimes just companionship as the previously bare plots began to grow and bloom under the care of the veterans.

I loved that this house and its large garden allowed us both to be closer to our families. Jamie, Olivia and the children were often here for Sunday roast but still nothing beat my mum's, and as Seb's dad was now such firm friends with my own parents, the circle of love had spread to include everyone and more often than not, both our families were all around the same dinner table at one house or another every Sunday. I couldn't have been happier, especially as this now included Sally when she could make it.

Our hunch that Oliver might last longer than my sister's usual relationships did had been correct, and she was currently sporting a rock on her left hand that would have paid for a professional make over of my entire garden. But the best thing was that Sally now seemed so much more comfortable with who she was. She would always strive to be the best she could be – that was just her way. But now she seemed happy with who she actually was. When her and Oliver had become engaged a few months ago, Sally had cut her hours and although she still travelled, she now also had time for a life with Oliver. The compromise seemed to be suiting both of them enormously – although none of us had ever worked out exactly what it was that Oliver did in the City.

Jess and Harry's wedding was indeed the fiesta she had always wanted, and more. His family were, quite rightly, bonkers about her. As Harry's mum had said, Jess had swept into their stuffy routines and brought with her an energy and joy that they hadn't realised they'd needed – or even wanted – until she arrived and now they couldn't imagine life without her. Jess was, of course, thrilled to be the centre of this adoration and I couldn't have been happier for them both.

And then there was us. I shaded my eyes and looked across the garden, watching the most gorgeous, sexy and honourable man I'd ever met manhandle a large fern into the area I'd designated for it. Even my fiancé was coming around to the possibility that he might be more green fingered than he first thought, and I smiled as he stood back from the large plant we'd just brought back from the nursery.

'Which way do you want it to face?' he called.

'Turn it to your left a bit.'

He followed the instruction.

'Oops! I meant right.'

Seb grinned and moved it back.

'There. That's perfect.'

He left the plant and walked back over to where I was stood in the shade in one of several seating areas I'd created. Flopping down into one of the chairs, he pulled me onto his lap. Scooby and Humph followed and lay at his feet. 'Jamie and Dad will be here in about an hour. I'll get them to give me a hand getting that in.'

'Thank you.'

'You're welcome.' He tilted his head at me. 'You sure you're not taking on too much with all this? We can always find somewhere else.'

I leant forward and kissed him softly, before shaking my head. 'No. I love this garden and it's going to be the perfect setting for our reception. I know it's not finished – but then gardens are never finished. They just evolve. I like that idea, and it seems a perfect metaphor for a wedding reception, and love, don't you think?'

He brushed my hair back with one large hand and rested his thumb and forefinger at my chin. 'What I think is that in two weeks I get to call you my wife and that makes me happier than I ever could have imagined. I also think I was a complete idiot to wait so long to ask you out, meaning I missed out on having all this much earlier.'

I rested my forehead against his. 'Good things come to those who wait.'

'And what about those who can't wait?' he said, with a wicked grin, his eyes darkening as he pulled me closer.

'Well, sometimes good things come to them too...'

ACKNOWLEDGMENTS

As always, thank you to James – your continual support and belief in me and my writing mean so much, ironically, more than I could ever put into words. Thank you for your enthusiasm and pride in me and my writing and for always being my cheerleader.

A huge thank you to the amazing team at Boldwood Books, including Amanda, Nia and Megan. Special thanks go to Sarah Ritherdon, my editor, for helping me make Seb and Lottie's story the best it could be. Thanks also to the copy editor, Jade Craddock, and proof reader, Rose Fox, who both did brilliant jobs tidying up the oopsies.

Thanks to Rachel Burton, Rachel Dove, and Victoria Cooke for the sanity saving chats. You're all brilliant!

Thank you also to the lovely Lucy Knott whose support and love for my books, along with her wholehearted kindness is a much treasured gift.

A big thanks to Darren Underwood for the jelly baby info, and also for sending me my own stock of emergency jelly babies during edits.

I'd also like to send a big thank you to the bloggers who help spread the word about my books. Your time, reviews and support are always so appreciated.

And last, but not least, thank you to everyone who has ever read and loved one of my books. As a committed bookworm myself, I know there is so much choice out there so when I hear that a book has brightened your day, or kept you up reading at night, I feel absolutely thrilled and honoured that you chose one of mine with which to spend that time. Hearing that you enjoyed it, and connected with the characters, truly fills my heart. Thank you.

MORE FROM MAXINE MORREY

We hope you enjoyed reading *My Year of Saying No*. If you did, please leave a review.

If you'd like to gift a copy, this book is also available as an ebook, digital audio download and audiobook CD.

Sign up to Maxine Morrey's mailing list for news, competitions and updates on future books.

http://bit.ly/MaxineMorreyNewsletter

If you'd like to read more from Maxine Morrey, *#No Filter* is available to buy now.

ABOUT THE AUTHOR

Maxine Morrey is a bestselling romantic comedy author with eight books to her name including *#No Filter* and the top ten hit *The Christmas Project*. She lives in West Sussex.

Visit Maxine's website: www.scribblermaxi.co.uk

Follow Maxine on social media:

- facebook.com/MaxineMorreyAuthor
- twitter.com/Scribbler_Maxi
- instagram.com/Scribbler_Maxi
- bookbub.com/authors/maxine-morrey

ABOUT BOLDWOOD BOOKS

Boldwood Books is a fiction publishing company seeking out the best stories from around the world.

Find out more at www.boldwoodbooks.com

Sign up to the Book and Tonic newsletter for news, offers and competitions from Boldwood Books!

http://www.bit.ly/bookandtonic

We'd love to hear from you, follow us on social media:

facebook.com/BookandTonic
twitter.com/BoldwoodBooks
instagram.com/BookandTonic